ESSENTIAL
PROBABILITY
PRACTICE WORKBOOK
WITH ANSWERS

CHRIS MCMULLEN, PH.D.

Essential Probability Practice Workbook with Answers
A Self-Teaching Guide
Chris McMullen, Ph.D.

Copyright © 2024 Chris McMullen, Ph.D.

www.improveyourmathfluency.com
www.monkeyphysicsblog.wordpress.com
www.chrismcmullen.com

Cover design by Melissa Stevens

www.theillustratedauthor.net

Zishka Publishing
ISBN: 978-1-941691-62-5

Mathematics > Probability

Contents

Introduction

This book is designed to help students learn fundamental probability concepts and to offer practice applying the concepts to solve a variety of classic probability problems. Topics include:

- Working through a variety of problems that involve finding **permutations** or **combinations**, including permutations with repeated elements.
- Counting the total number of **handshakes** when groups of people shake hands with one another.
- Making **histograms** to display the possible outcomes for a selection.
- Rolling N-sided **dice**, beginning with fair dice and then considering special dice that are not fair.
- Using probability to determine **odds**.
- Grabbing socks from a drawer, including the distinction between the case where all of the socks are selected at once and the case where each sock is **placed back** in the drawer before the next sock is selected.
- Drawing multiple **cards** from a deck.
- Determining the probabilities for **seating arrangements** at a round table.
- **Coloring** regions, with or without restrictions.
- Counting possibilities in the context of **shapes** and **grids**.
- Solving **classic** probability problems, like the **birthday** problem.
- Fundamental concepts like **conditional probability**.
- Finding the **expected value** and **variance**.
- Basic **data analysis**.
- Probability distributions like the **binomial** and **Poisson** distributions.

1 Permutations

Probability problems generally involve a set of elements. If you flip a coin in the air, the set of outcomes has two elements: heads or tails. A standard deck of cards is a set consisting of 52 elements, such as the ace of spades or the nine of clubs. A six-sided die is a set consisting of six elements: the numbers 1 thru 6.

A particular order of the elements is called a **permutation**. For example, consider the set consisting of three colors: blue (B), green (G), and red (R). This set has six possible permutations: BGR, BRG, GBR, GRB, RBG, and RGB. Note that the order of the elements is important for a permutation. For example, BGR is different from BRG. (In Chapter 2, we will explore combinations and see how they are different from permutations.) It is helpful to learn how to count things like permutations (and combinations) before we begin calculating probabilities.

When a set has a sufficiently small number of elements, it is easy to list the different possible permutations and count them, but when a set has a large number of elements, the number of permutations can be very large. For example, a set of three distinct colors has six permutations (see the previous paragraph), where as a set of twelve distinct colors has 479,001,600 permutations. Fortunately, there are formulas for calculating permutations, so it isn't necessary to list and count them.

The formulas for permutations involve a mathematical operation called a **factorial**. A factorial is indicated by an exclamation mark (!) and means to multiply successively smaller numbers until you reach the number one. For example, 3! is read as "three factorial" and means to multiply 3 by 2 and 1, such that $3! = 3(2)(1) = 6$. Similarly, 4! equals $4! = 4(3)(2)(1) = 24$. Of course, the factorial of one is $1! = 1$, but it may seem surprising that the factorial of zero equals one (it's not zero): $0! = 1$.

There are different permutation formulas for different cases. It depends on whether or not there are any repeated elements, and if you are permuting the full set or just a subset. You can also make permutations by selecting elements from two (or more) different sets. We numbered these common cases below for easy reference.

Case 1. The simplest kind of permutation is when all of the elements of a set are **different** and you want to find the permutations of the **full set**. If the set has N elements, the full set has $N!$ permutations. For example, consider the set of four digits that includes 3, 5, 6, and 8. Since there are 4 elements, in this example $N = 4$. There are $4! = 4(3)(2)(1) = 24$ permutations of the full set: 3568, 3586, 3658, 3685, 3856, 3865, 5368, 5386, 5638, 5683, 5836, 5863, 6358, 6385, 6538, 6583, 6835, 6853, 8356, 8365, 8536, 8563, 8635, and 8653.

Case 2. When finding the permutations of the **full set**, if any elements are **repeated**, divide by a factorial for the repeated elements. For example, the word ELEMENT has one L, one M, one N, one T, and three E's. To find the number of permutations for the full set of these letters, first find $7! = 7(6)(5)(4)(3)(2)(1) = 5040$ (since the word ELEMENT has 7 letters) and then divide by $3! = 3(2)(1) = 6$ to get $\frac{7!}{3!} = \frac{5040}{6} = 840$. The reason for dividing by 3! is to avoid overcounting, since if any two E's are swapped you get the same permutation (and 3! is the total number of permutations of three E's). For example, if the first and last E's are swapped in MELTENE, you still get the same permutation MELTENE (whereas if the M and N are swapped, you get a different permutation, NELTEME); we will explore this idea further in Example 2. As another example, consider the word DIVIDE, which has one E, one V, two D's, and two I's. To find the number of permutations of the full set of these letters, first find $6! = 6(5)(4)(3)(2)(1) = 720$ (since the word DIVIDE has 6 letters) and then divide by $2! = 2(1) = 2$ twice (once for the two D's and once more for the two I's) to get $\frac{6!}{2!2!} = \frac{720}{2(2)} = \frac{720}{4} = 180$.

Case 3. When all of the elements of a set are **different** and you want to find the permutation of a **subset**, divide by a factorial for the number of elements that are excluded from the subset. Specifically, if the full set has N elements and the subset has r elements (where $r \leq N$), the number of ways to permute the elements from the full set into the subset is $\frac{N!}{(N-r)!}$. For example, suppose that a bag contains nine balls where each ball has a different color, and a person will grab three balls from the bag at random (without replacement). To find the number of permutations of three balls selected from the bag of nine balls, divide 9! by 6! (since $9 - 3 = 6$) to get $\frac{9!}{(9-3)!} = \frac{9!}{6!} =$ $9(8)(7) = 504$. (Note that 9! equals $9(8)(7)(6!)$, such that $\frac{9!}{6!}$ equals 9 times 8 times 7. If necessary, try writing 9! and 6! out longhand to see why.) Note: In this permutation problem, the order in which the balls are grabbed matters. For example, if you grab a red ball, blue ball, and green ball in that order, it is different from when you grab a blue ball, then a green ball, and then a red ball. If you don't care in which order the balls are selected, that is referred to as a combination (not a permutation), as discussed in Chapter 2.

Case 4. When finding the permutations of a **subset**, if any elements are **repeated**, the repeated elements make the problem more challenging. You can't just divide by a factorial for the repeated elements (it turns out to be more complicated than Case 2). Instead, you will need to reason out the answer, as shown in Examples 6-8. For example, the number 81,258 has one 1, one 2, one 5, and two 8's. To make three-digit permutations using digits from the number 81,258, first imagine that there is only one 1, one 2, one 5, and one 8, and use the Case 3 formula with $N = 4$ (instead of 5) and $r = 3$ to get $\frac{4!}{(4-3)!} = \frac{4!}{1!} = 24$, and then count how many permutations allow two 8's (these are 188, 288, 588, 818, 828, 858, 881, 882, and 885) to obtain the final answer of $24 + 9 = 33$. The permutations are 125, 128, 152, 158, 182, 185, 188, 215, 218, 251, 258, 281, 285, 288, 512, 518, 521, 528, 581, 582, 588, 812, 815, 818, 821, 825, 828, 851, 852, 858, 881, 882, and 885. (Note: It would be incorrect to use Case 3 with $N = 5$ and $r = 3$ to get $\frac{5!}{(5-3)!} = \frac{5!}{2!} = \frac{120}{2} = 60$ and then divide by 2! for the two 8's to get $\frac{60}{2} = 30$. This doesn't agree with the correct answer of 33 because in this case, unlike Case 2, dividing by 2! doesn't properly correct for overcounting. In Case 2, every repeated element is used in every full permutation, not in Case 4, which is why dividing by 2! doesn't work. For example, 188 has two 8's, while 128 has one 8.)

Case 5. Suppose that one set has N_1 elements and **another set** has N_2 elements, where every element is **different**, and that you wish to make permutations using r_1 elements from the first set **followed by** r_2 elements from the second set (where $r_1 \leq N_1$ and

$r_2 \leq N_2$). In this case, there are $\dfrac{N_1!\,N_2!}{(N_1-r_1)!(N_2-r_2)!}$ permutations. For example, suppose that one set consists of the letters A, B, C, and D, and a second set consists of the digits 1, 3, 5, 7, and 9. To find the number of 5-character permutations that begin with two letters from the first set and end with three digits from the second set, let $N_1 = 4$, $r_1 = 2$, $N_2 = 5$, and $r_2 = 3$ to get $\dfrac{4!5!}{(4-2)!(5-3)!} = \dfrac{(24)(120)}{2!2!} = \dfrac{(24)(120)}{(2)(2)} = 12(60) = 720$. Examples of possible permutations include BC159 and AD793. Note that the first two characters must be letters and the last three characters must be digits in this example.

Case 6. When making permutations using r_1 elements from a set of N_1 elements **followed by** r_2 elements from **another set** of N_2 elements, if any elements are **repeated**, work out the answer for each subset separately (using Case 3 or 4, as appropriate) and then multiply the answers. For example, consider using two letters from the word POWER followed by two digits from the number 747. First use Case 3 for POWER with $N_1 = 5$ and $r_1 = 2$ to get $\dfrac{5!}{(5-2)!} = \dfrac{5!}{3!} = 5(4) = 20$. Next use Case 4 for 747, for which it is easy to see that there are 3 permutations: 47, 74, and 77. Multiply these results to get the final answer: $(20)(3) = 60$. Examples of possible permutations include EO74, WR77, and RP47.

Case 7. Sometimes, permutation problems give additional **conditions** or **restrictions**. When this happens, begin with the appropriate case from Cases 1-6, and reason out how the condition or restriction affects the answer. (It may help to first work through a simpler example on scratch paper using simpler numbers.) As an example, consider the set of four digits 9, 8, 1, and 5. Suppose that we wish to know how many permutations of this full set are odd numbers. First find the total number of permutations (Case 1) to get $4! = 4(3)(2)(1) = 24$. One-fourth of these numbers end with 9, one-fourth of these numbers end with 8, one-fourth of these numbers end with 1, and one-fourth of these numbers end with 5. Thus, the number of permutations that are odd numbers equals $\dfrac{3}{4}(24) = 18$. It's easy to see that this is correct by listing them: 1589, 1859, 1895, 1985, 5189, 5819, 5891, 5981, 8159, 8195, 8519, 8591, 8915, 8951, 9185, 9581, 9815, and 9851. (The ones that are even are 1598, 1958, 5198, 5918, 9158, and 9518. You can verify that 18 are odd and 6 are even.)

Example 1. How many four-letter permutations of the word MATH are there?

Since no letters are repeated in the word MATH and since we are using all four letters, use the Case 1 formula: $4! = 4(3)(2)(1) = 24$. The answer is small enough to list the different permutations: AHMT, AHTM, AMHT, AMTH, ATHM, ATMH, HAMT, HATM, HMAT, HMTA, HTAM, HTMA, MAHT, MATH, MHAT, MHTA, MTAH, MTHA, TAHM, TAMH, THAM, THMA, TMAH, and TMHA.

Example 2. How many four-letter permutations of the word NINE are there?

Since the letter N is repeated and since we are using all four letters, use the Case 2 formula: $\frac{4!}{2!} = \frac{4(3)(2)(1)}{2(1)} = 4(3) = 12$. (Note: If we label the two N's as N_1 and N_2, as if they were different, we would get 24 permutations: EIN_1N_2, EIN_2N_1, EN_1IN_2, EN_2IN_1, EN_1N_2I, EN_2N_1I, IEN_1N_2, IEN_2N_1, IN_1EN_2, IN_2EN_1, IN_1N_2E, IN_2N_1E, N_1EIN_2, N_2EIN_1, N_1EN_2I, N_2EN_1I, N_1IEN_2, N_2IEN_1, N_1IN_2E, N_2IN_1E, N_1N_2EI, N_2N_1EI, N_1N_2IE, and N_2N_1IE. However, since the two N's are really identical, any permutation where N_1 and N_2 are swapped is really the same; for example, EIN_1N_2 and EIN_2N_1 are the same: EINN. Since there are 2! permutations of two N's, we divide 24 by 2! to get the answer of 12.) The 12 permutations include: EINN, ENIN, ENNI, IENN, INEN, INNE, NEIN, NENI, NIEN, NINE, NNEI, and NNIE.

Example 3. How many four-digit permutations of the number 3733 are there?

Since the digit 3 is repeated in the number 3733 and since we are using all four digits, use the Case 2 formula: $\frac{4!}{3!} = \frac{4(3)(2)(1)}{3(2)(1)} = 4$. The answer is small enough to list the different permutations: 3337, 3373, 3733, and 7333. (Note: If the number had four different digits like 2749, the answer would have been 24 like Example 1. Since there are 3! permutations of three 3's, we divide 24 by 3! to get the answer of 4. If we listed the three 3's as 3_1, 3_2, and 3_3, as if they were different, we would see 24 permutations, similar to what we did in the note for Example 2. Since all of the 3's are really identical, only 4 of those 24 permutations would actually be unique.)

Example 4. How many 13-letter permutations of the word INFINITESIMAL are there?

The word INFINITESIMAL has one A, one E, one F, one L, one M, one S, one T, two N's, and four I's (with a total of 13 letters). Since there are repeated letters and since we are using all 13 digits, use the Case 2 formula (dividing by 4! for the four I's and by 2! for the two N's): $\frac{13!}{4!2!} = \frac{6,227,020,800}{24(2)} = 129,729,600$.

Note: Many scientific calculators have a factorial function. If there isn't a button or a 2nd button feature for it, try looking for the probability or statistics functions. You might also try asking Google how to use the factorial function on your calculator's model, or read the owner's manual, or visit the calculator company's website.

Example 5. A bag contains five balls. The balls have the following colors: blue, green, orange, red, and yellow. How many permutations are there for selecting two balls from the bag (without replacement)?

Since we are selecting a subset and since there are no repeated colors, use the Case 3 formula with $N = 5$ and $r = 2$: $\frac{5!}{(5-2)!} = \frac{5!}{3!} = \frac{5(4)(3)(2)(1)}{3(2)(1)} = 5(4) = 20$. The answer is small enough to list the different permutations: BG, BO, BR, BY, GB, GO, GR, GY, OB, OG, OR, OY, RB, RG, RO, RY, YB, YG, YO, and YR. (Since these are permutations, order matters, such that BG is different from GB. If we didn't care about order, we would find a combination instead of a permutation, as discussed in Chapter 2.)

Example 6. How many three-digit permutations can be formed using the digits from the number 42,445?

Since we are selecting a subset and since the digit 4 is repeated, this is Case 4. Recall that Case 4 doesn't have a single formula, but requires reasoning. We will begin by ignoring the repeated digit, and assuming that the only digits are one 2, one 4, and one 5. Use the Case 1 formula to find that there are $3! = 3(2)(1) = 6$ permutations of 2, 4, and 5: 245, 254, 425, 452, 524, and 542. Now consider the cases where the 4 is repeated. There are 6 permutations with two 4's: 244, 424, 442, 445, 454, and 544. There is also 1 permutation with three 4's: 444. The total number of permutations is $6 + 6 + 1 = 13$. The final answer is 13. The permutations are 244, 245, 254, 424, 425, 442, 444, 445, 452, 454, 524, 542, and 544. (Note that it would be incorrect to use the Case 3 formula with $N = 5$ and $r = 3$ and then to divide by 3! for the three 4's. Try it, and then try to understand why it doesn't work. Why does dividing by 3! work in Example 3, but not in Example 6? Think about it.)

Example 7. How many four-letter permutations can be formed using the letters from the word RADICAL?

Since we are selecting a subset and since the letter A is repeated, this is Case 4. Recall that Case 4 doesn't have a single formula, but requires reasoning. We will begin by ignoring the repeated letter, and assuming that the only letters are one A, one C, one D, one I, one L, and one R. Use the Case 3 formula with $N = 6$ (since there are 6 letters if we don't count the second A) and $r = 4$ to find that there are $\frac{6!}{(6-4)!} = \frac{720}{2!} = \frac{720}{2} = 360$ permutations of 4 of the letters in RADICL (where we have thus far excluded the second A). Now consider the cases where the A is repeated. We could have permutations of the form AAxy, AxAy, AxyA, xAAy, xAyA, or xyAA, where the x is either C, D, I, L, or R (but not A) and the y can be any of these letters provided that it differs from x. The first structure includes AACD, AACI, AACL, AACR, AADC, AADI, AADL, AADR, AAIC, AAID, AAIL, AAIR, AALC, AALD, AALI, AALR, AARC, AARD, AARI, and AARL. There are 20 permutations for each of the 6 structures, which means that there are $20(6) = 120$ permutations with two A's. The final answer is thus $360 + 120 = 480$ permutations.

Example 8. How many three-digit permutations can be formed using the digits from the number 122,333?

Since we are selecting a subset and since the digits 2 and 3 are repeated, this is Case 4. Recall that Case 4 doesn't have a single formula, but requires reasoning. We will organize our solution into parts as follows:

- When there are no repeated digits, the Case 1 formula gives $3! = 3(2)(1) = 6$ permutations: 123, 132, 213, 231, 312, and 321.
- When there are two 2's, there are 6 permutations: 122, 212, 221, 223, 232, and 322.
- When there are two 3's, there are 6 permutations: 133, 233, 313, 323, 331, and 332.
- (There can't be both two 2's and two 3's in a three-digit permutation.)
- When there are three 3's, there is 1 permutation: 333. (Note that there can't be three 2's because 122,333 only has two 2's.)

Add these up to see that there are a total of $6 + 6 + 6 + 1 = 19$ permutations.

Example 9. How many three-character permutations have one of the letters in SUM followed by two of the digits in 7146?

Since we are selecting from two different sets and no elements are repeated, use the Case 5 formula with $N_1 = 3$ (for the letters S, U, and M), $r_1 = 1$, $N_2 = 4$ (for the digits 7, 1, 4, and 6), and $r_2 = 2$: $\frac{3!4!}{(3-1)!(4-2)!} = \frac{3!4!}{2!2!} = \frac{6(24)}{2(2)} = 36$. The permutations are M14, M16, M17, M41, M46, M47, M61, M64, M67, M71, M74, M76, S14, S16, S17, S41, S46, S47, S61, S64, S67, S71, S74, S76, U14, U16, U17, U41, U46, U47, U61, U64, U67, U71, U74, and U76. Note how the Case 5 formula requires characters from one set to go first and characters from the other set to go last. If you want to allow things like 1M7 or 64S in this example, that would make it Case 7 instead of Case 5 (where you would have to reason out how many additional permutations are possible by putting the letter in the middle or end instead of the beginning; see if you can figure out why the answer to this example would be 108 instead of 36 if the instructions didn't specify that the letter had to come before the digits).

Example 10. How many four-character permutations have two of the letters in AXIS followed by two of the digits in 12,233?

Since we are selecting from two different sets and the digits are repeated in the second set, this is Case 6. We may treat the two sets separately. Selecting two letters from AXIS corresponds to Case 3 with $N_1 = 4$ and $r_1 = 2$. The Case 3 formula gives $\frac{4!}{(4-2)!} = \frac{4!}{2!} = 4(3) = 12$ permutations for the letters. Selecting two digits from 12,233 corresponds to Case 4. Since there are just three unique digits, it is easy to list the permutations for the digits: 12, 13, 21, 22, 23, 31, 32, and 33. Multiply the 12 permutations for the letters by the 8 permutations for the digits to get the final answer: $(12)(8) = 96$. Each allowed permutation for the letters may be followed by each allowed permutation for the digits. Examples of allowed permutations include AI22, IS13, and XS32.

Example 11. How many two-digit permutations greater than 60 can be formed using the digits from the number 7462?

Since this question includes a condition ("greater than 60"), it is Case 7. First ignore the condition and use Case 3 (because we are forming a subset and no digits are repeated): $\frac{4!}{(4-2)!} = \frac{4!}{2!} = \frac{24}{2} = 12$. Now consider how the condition affects the answer. In order for a permutation to be greater than 60, it must begin with a 6 or a 7. One-half of the answers begin with a 6 or a 7 (and the other half begin with a 2 or a 4), so the final answer is $\frac{12}{2} = 6$. The permutations are 62, 64, 67, 72, 74, and 76.

Example 12. How many five-digit permutations greater than 50,000 can be formed using the digits from the number 45,494?

Since this question includes a condition ("greater than 50,000"), it is Case 7. In contrast to Example 11, this time if you use Case 2 (since we are using the full set and the 4 is repeated) to get $\frac{5!}{3!} = \frac{120}{6} = 20$, it won't be as easy as dividing by two because, with the repeated digit, it doesn't turn out that one-half of the permutations are greater than 50. So we'll attack this example from a different angle. If the permutation begins with a 5, there will be $\frac{4!}{3!} = 4$ permutations of the remaining four digits (4, 4, 4, and 9), according to Case 2. There are similarly 4 permutations that begin with a 9. The final answer is $4 + 4 = 8$. The permutations are 54,449, 54,494, 54,944, 59,444, 94,445, 94,454, 94,544, and 95,444.

Example 13. How many five-letter permutations of the word LIMIT begin with an I or a T?

Since this question includes a condition ("begin with an I or a T"), it is Case 7. If a permutation begins with an I, the remaining letters will be I, L, M, and T. There are $4! = 4(3)(2)(1) = 24$ permutations of these letters. If a permutation begins with a T, the remaining letters will be I, I, L, and M. There are $\frac{4!}{2!} = 4(3) = 12$ permutations of these letters (we used the Case 2 formula because the I is repeated). Our final answer is $24 + 12 = 36$. The permutations are IILMT, IILTM, IIMLT, IIMTL, IITLM, IITML, ILIMT, ILITM, ILMIT, ILMTI, ILTIM, ILTMI, IMILT, IMITL, IMLIT, IMLTI, IMTIL, IMTLI, ITILM, ITIML, ITLIM, ITLMI, ITMIL, ITMLI, MIILT, MIITL, MILIT, MILTI, MITIL, MITLI, MLIIT, MLITI, MLTII, MTIIL, MTILI, and MTLII.

Chapter 1 Problems

Directions: For each word or number below, determine the number of permutations of the full set of letters or digits.

(1) ARC

(2) ROOT

(3) SQUARE

(4) 225

(5) 61,374

(6) 88,787

(7) INFINITY

(8) SEVENTEEN

(9) ISOSCELES

(10) 194,419

(11) 8,228,288

(12) 11,535,813

Directions: The number in brackets [ ] indicates that a subset is to be formed. For example, "8172 [3]" means to make 3-digit subsets. For each word or number below, determine the number of permutations of the letters or digits into the indicated subset.

(13) HELIX [2]   (14) FACTOR [4]   (15) QUADRANT [3]

(16) 8172 [3]   (17) 59,455 [2]   (18) 736,149 [5]

(19) VENN [3]   (20) UNION [2]   (21) ELLIPSE [4]

(22) 7747 [2]   (23) 24,226 [3]   (24) 114,499 [3]

Directions: For these problems, the permutations begin with the indicated number of letters and are followed by the indicated number of digits. For example, "CUBE [2], 5491 [3]" means to use 2 letters followed by 3 digits (like CU915 or BE491). For each case below, determine the number of such permutations.

(25) CUBE [2], 5491 [3]

(26) AREA [3], 345 [2]

(27) PRISM [3], 818 [2]

(28) ORIGIN [4], 72,156 [3]

(29) MATRIX [1], 93,699 [3]

(30) DEGREE [3], 602 [2]

(31) FRACTAL [4], 5000 [2]

(32) ABSCISSA [7], 2244 [3]

Directions: For each word or number below, determine the number of permutations of the indicated number of letters or digits that satisfy the given condition. For example, "276 [2], even" means to make 2-digit subsets that are even numbers.

(33) 276 [2], even

(34) 3582 [4], greater than 5000

(35) COMPLEX [4], end with a vowel

(36) SERIES [4], 2 consecutive E's

(37) 90,480 [5], don't begin with 0

(38) 63,965 [3], evenly divisible by 6

(39) PERCENT [5], begin and end with E

(40) SPIRAL [4], 2 consecutive vowels

2 Combinations

A particular subset of elements is called a **combination**, regardless of the order. The distinction between a combination and a permutation is that **order doesn't matter** for a combination. For example, consider a bag containing one blue ball, one green ball, one red ball, and one yellow ball. If a person grabs three of the balls at once, there are 4 possible combinations: BGR, BGY, BRY, and GRY. (In contrast, there are 24 possible permutations: BGR, BGY, BRG, BRY, BYG, BYR, GBR, GBY, GRB, GRY, GYB, GYR, RBG, RBY, RGB, RGY, RYB, RYG, YBG, YBR, YGB, YGR, YRB, and YRG.) Changing the order of the elements doesn't result in a different combination. For example, BGR, BRG, GBR, GRB, RBG, and RGB are all the **same** combination (but these are 6 different permutations).

The formulas for combinations involve the "N choose r" formula. The notation $\binom{N}{r}$, which is read as "N choose r," represents the number of ways to choose a subset of r elements from a set of N distinct elements when the order is not important.

$$\binom{N}{r} = \frac{N!}{r!\,(N-r)!}$$

For example, if a person grabs three balls at once out of a bag containing four balls, there are $\binom{4}{3} = \frac{4!}{3!(4-3)!} = \frac{4!}{3!1!} = 4$ possible combinations (listed in the first paragraph).

Combination problems can be reasoned by applying the above formula. Following are a variety of common cases for combinations.

Case 1. The simplest kind of combination is when a set has N **distinct** elements and you choose r elements from the set (without repeating the same element). In this case, the number of combinations is $\binom{N}{r} = \frac{N!}{r!(N-r)!}$. For example, the number of 3-digit combinations of digits from the number 83,562 is $\binom{5}{3} = \frac{5!}{3!(5-3)!} = \frac{5!}{3!2!} = \frac{5(4)}{2} = 10$. The combinations include 235, 236, 238, 256, 258, 268, 356, 358, 368, and 568. (Note, for example, that 235 and 253 are the same combination; unlike permutations, changing the order of the digits doesn't result in a different combination.)

Case 2. If a set of elements has N distinct elements and you are choosing r elements such that you allow the same element to be **repeated without limit**, the combination formula is $\binom{N + r - 1}{r}$. For example, consider the number 83,562 that we used to illustrate Case 1. Suppose that we allow each digit to be repeated without limit. This means that we may use more than one 8 even though only one 8 appears in the given number. In this case, there are $\binom{5 + 3 - 1}{3}$ ways to choose 3 digits, which equates to $\binom{7}{3} = \frac{7!}{3!(7-3)!} = \frac{7!}{3!4!} = \frac{7(6)(5)}{6} = 35$. The permutations include 222, 223, 225, 226, 228, 233, 235, 236, 238, 255, 256, 258, 266, 268, 288, 333, 335, 336, 338, 355, 356, 358, 366, 368, 388, 555, 556, 558, 566, 568, 588, 666, 668, 688, and 888. (Since order doesn't matter for a combination, 236 is the same as 263, 326, 362, 623, or 632, for example.)

Case 3. If you are choosing elements and you allow the elements to be **repeated**, but **only as many times as they appear** in the given set (unlike Case 2, where elements may be repeated without limit), you will need to reason out the answer. For example, consider the number 83,565, where the digit 5 is repeated. To find the number of combinations of 3 digits out of one 3, one 6, one 8, and two 5's, first ignore the extra 5 and choose 3 digits out of 8356 to get $\binom{4}{3} = \frac{4!}{3!(4-3)!} = \frac{4!}{3!1!} = 4$. These combinations include 356, 358, 368, and 568. Now find the combinations that use the second 5: 355, 556, and 558. All together, there are $4 + 3 = 7$ combinations.

Case 4. If you choose r_1 elements from one set and if you also choose r_2 elements from a **second set**, where all of the elements are **distinct**, to find the total number of combinations, multiply the answers for each subset. For example, suppose that there are 7 girls and 5 boys in a class. To make a team consisting of 2 girls and 2 boys, first use the Case 1 combination formula to find the number of ways to choose 2 girls from 7 girls and to choose 2 boys from 7 boys. This gives $\binom{7}{2} = \frac{7!}{2!(7-2)!} = \frac{7!}{2!5!} = \frac{7(6)}{2} = 21$ ways to choose 2 girls and $\binom{5}{2} = \frac{5!}{2!(5-2)!} = \frac{5!}{2!3!} = \frac{5(4)}{2} = 10$ ways to choose 2 boys. The final answer is $\binom{7}{2}\binom{5}{2} = (21)(10) = 210$. (Note that the answer would be different if you form a team of 4 students without adding the restriction that 2 be girls and 2 be boys.)

Case 5. If a set of N **distinct** elements is to be divided into **subsets** (where every element of the original set is to be placed into one of the subsets), divide $N!$ by factorials for the sizes the subsets. Such subsets are called **partitions**. For example, suppose that a class of 6 students is to be divided into three groups, where one group has 1 student, one group has 2 students, and one group has 3 students. Since every student will be in one of the groups, the answer is $\frac{6!}{1!2!3!} = \frac{720}{(1)(2)(6)} = 60$.

Case 6. Suppose that two **successive choices** are made. That is, suppose that there is a set of N **distinct** elements. First, r elements are chosen from the set. Next, k elements are chosen from the remaining $N - r$ elements. The number of combinations for these two successive choices is $\binom{N}{r}\binom{N-r}{k} = \frac{N!}{r!(N-r)!}\frac{(N-r)!}{k!(N-r-k)!} = \frac{N!}{r!k!(N-r-k)!}$. For example, suppose that a bowl contains 7 mints, a boy selects 2 of the mints, and a girl selects 3 of the mints. When the boy selects 2 mints, there are 7 to choose from, so there are $\binom{7}{2} = \frac{7!}{2!(7-2)!} = \frac{7!}{2!5!} = \frac{7(6)}{2} = 21$ combinations for the boy. There are $7 - 2 = 5$ mints left after the boy selects 2 mints. When the girl selects 3 mints, there are 5 to choose from, so there are $\binom{5}{3} = \frac{5!}{3!(5-3)!} = \frac{5!}{3!2!} = \frac{5(4)}{2} = 10$ combinations for the girl. The total number of combinations is $(21)(10) = 210$. This agrees with the formula $\binom{N}{r}\binom{N-r}{k}$, where $N = 7, r = 2$, and $k = 3$: $\binom{7}{2}\binom{7-2}{3} = \binom{7}{2}\binom{5}{3} = \frac{7!}{2!5!}\frac{5!}{3!2!} = \frac{7!}{2!3!2!} = \frac{5040}{24} = 210$.

Case 7. If a combination problem gives an additional **condition** or **restriction**, you will need to reason out how this affects the answer. As an example, suppose that a person would like to invite Ana, Bob, Cal, Dee, Ely, and Fey to a banquet, but can only choose 4 of these people. Without any restrictions, the number of combinations would be $\binom{6}{4} = \frac{6!}{4!(6-4)!} = \frac{6!}{4!2!} = \frac{6(5)}{2} = 15$. Using the first letters of their names, these would be: ABCD, ABCE, ABCF, ABDE, ABDF, ABEF, ACDE, ACDF, ACEF, ADEF, BCDE, BCDF, BCEF, BDEF, and CDEF. If the person insists upon choosing Ana and Bob, this restriction changes the answer. In this case, the person is really just choosing 2 friends out of 4 (Cal, Dee, Ely, and Fey): $\binom{4}{2} = \frac{4!}{2!(4-2)!} = \frac{4!}{2!2!} = \frac{24}{(2)(2)} = 6$. The combinations include: ABCD, ABCE, ABCF, ABDE, ABDF, and ABEF. (These are the combinations that include Ana and Bob.)

Following are a few additional remarks regarding the combination formulas.

- $\binom{N}{N-r}$ is the same as $\binom{N}{r}$ because $\binom{N}{N-r} = \frac{N!}{(N-r)!r!}$ equals $\binom{N}{r} = \frac{N!}{r!(N-r)!}$. Note that $N - (N - r) = N - N + r = r$ (distributing the minus sign). As an example, compare $\binom{7}{7-2} = \binom{7}{5} = \frac{7!}{5!(7-5)!} = \frac{7!}{5!2!}$ with $\binom{7}{2} = \frac{7!}{2!(7-2)!} = \frac{7!}{2!5!}$.

- The special cases $\binom{N}{0}$ and $\binom{N}{N}$ both equal 1. For example, $\binom{N}{0} = \frac{N!}{0!N!} = 1$. (It helps to remember the rule that $0! = 1$.)

- To better understand the partition rule (Case 5), imagine that 11 books are to be divided among a boy, his father, and his mother, with the father receiving 6 books, the mother receiving 3 books, and the boy receiving 2 books. Choosing 6 books, for the father we get $\binom{11}{6} = \frac{11!}{6!(11-6)!} = \frac{11!}{6!5!}$. Choosing 3 books from the remaining 5 books (since $11 - 6 = 5$), for the mother we get $\binom{5}{3} = \frac{5!}{3!(5-3)!} = \frac{5!}{3!2!}$. Choosing 2 books from the remaining 2 books (since $5 - 3 = 2$), for the boy we get $\binom{2}{2} = \frac{2!}{2!(2-2)!} = \frac{2!}{2!0!} = \frac{2}{(2)(1)} = 1$. Multiply the three answers to get $\left(\frac{11!}{6!5!}\right)\left(\frac{5!}{3!2!}\right)(1) = \frac{11!}{6!3!2!}$, which agrees with the rule for Case 5. (Note how the 5! cancels out. Such cancellation is basically why the partition rule works.)

Example 1. How many three-letter combinations of the word FOUR are there? Since there are no repeated letters, this is Case 1: $\binom{4}{3} = \frac{4!}{3!(4-3)!} = \frac{4!}{3!1!} = \frac{24}{(6)(1)} = 4$. The combinations include: FOR, FOU, ORU, and FRU. (Note, for example, that FOR and OFR are the same combination.)

Example 2. How many two-letter combinations can be made using an unlimited number of F's, O's, U's, and R's? Since each letter may be repeated without limits, this is Case 2: $\binom{4 + 2 - 1}{2} = \binom{5}{2} = \frac{5!}{2!(5-2)!} = \frac{5!}{2!3!} = \frac{120}{(2)(6)} = 10$. The combinations include: FF, FO, FR, FU, OO, OR, OU, RR, RU, and UU. (Note, for example, that FO and OF are the same combination.)

Example 3. How many three-letter combinations of the word INVERSE are there? Since the E is repeated, but we are not allowing unlimited repetition, this is Case 3. First ignore the second E, and choose 3 letters out of the 6 letters E, I, N, R, S, and V to get $\binom{6}{3} = \frac{6!}{3!(6-3)!} = \frac{6!}{3!3!} = \frac{720}{(6)(6)} = 20$. These combinations include: EIN, EIR, EIS, EIV, ENR, ENS, ENV, ERS, ERV, ESV, INR, INS, INV, IRS, IRV, ISV, NRS, NRV, NSV, and RSV. Now list the combinations that involve two E's: EEI, EEN, EER, EES, and EEV. The final answer is $20 + 5 = 25$.

Example 4. A bag contains 9 green balls and 6 red balls. (A) If 5 balls are selected, how many combinations are there? (B) If 3 green balls and 2 red balls are selected, how many combinations are there?

(A) Use the Case 1 formula to choose 5 balls from $9 + 6 = 15$ balls: $\binom{15}{5} = \frac{15!}{5!(15-5)!} = \frac{15!}{5!10!} = \frac{(15)(14)(13)(12)(11)}{(5)(4)(3)(2)(1)} = 3003$. (Note: Two balls are distinct even if they have the same color. For one, they have different locations. For another, if you examine them with a magnifying glass, you can distinguish them through minor imperfections.)

(B) This is Case 4. Choose 3 out of 9 green balls to get $\binom{9}{3} = \frac{9!}{3!(9-3)!} = \frac{9!}{3!6!} = \frac{(9)(8)(7)}{(3)(2)(1)} = 84$ and choose 2 out of 6 red balls to get $\binom{6}{2} = \frac{6!}{2!(6-2)!} = \frac{6!}{2!4!} = \frac{(6)(5)}{(2)(1)} = 15$. Multiply these numbers to get the final answer: $(84)(15) = 1260$.

Example 5. A bag contains 15 balls. (A) If 10 balls are selected, how many combinations are there? (B) If a boy selects 4 balls and then a girl selects 6 balls, how many combinations are there?

(A) Use the Case 1 formula to choose 10 balls from 15 balls: $\binom{15}{10} = \frac{15!}{10!(15-10)!} = \frac{15!}{10!5!} = \frac{(15)(14)(13)(12)(11)}{(5)(4)(3)(2)(1)} = 3003$. Note: It's same answer as Part A of Example 4; $\binom{15}{10}$ is equal to $\binom{15}{5}$ because $5 = 15 - 10$.

(B) This is Case 6 because successive choices are made. Basically, this is different from Part A because now the 10 balls are divided into two groups (4 for the boy and 6 for the girl). Use the Case 6 formula: $\binom{15}{4}\binom{15-4}{6} = \binom{15}{4}\binom{11}{6} = \frac{15!}{4!11!}\frac{11!}{6!5!} = \frac{15!}{4!6!5!} =$

630,630. The answer is greater than in Part A because there are many ways to divide the 3003 combinations from Part A into two parts (4 for the boy and 6 for the girl).

Example 6. A bag contains 10 balls. Lacy selects 5 balls, Suzy selects 3 balls, and Tony selects 2 balls. How many combinations are there?

Since the balls are divided into groups and since every ball is put in a group, this is Case 5. Use the partition rule: $\frac{10!}{5!3!2!} = \frac{(10)(9)(8)(7)(6)}{(6)(2)} = 2520$.

Example 7. A team of 4 people is to be selected from 7 applicants. (A) How many combinations are there? (B) How many combinations are there where one of the team members serves as a team captain?

(A) Use the Case 1 formula to choose 4 people from 7 applicants: $\binom{7}{4} = \frac{7!}{4!(7-4)!} = \frac{7!}{4!3!} = \frac{(7)(6)(5)}{(3)(2)(1)} = 35$.

(B) This question adds a condition, which makes this Case 7. One way to solve this problem is to treat it as Case 6 with two successive choices. First choose 1 captain from 7 applicants to get $\binom{7}{1} = \frac{7!}{1!(7-1)!} = \frac{7!}{1!6!} = 7$, then choose 3 additional team members from the remaining 6 applicants to get $\binom{6}{3} = \frac{6!}{3!(6-3)!} = \frac{6!}{3!3!} = \frac{(6)(5)(4)}{(3)(2)(1)} = 20$, and then multiply these together: $(7)(20) = 140$. An alternative way to solve this problem is first form groups of 4 people as in Part A to get 35 and then multiply by the 4 ways that each group can have a team captain: $(35)(4) = 140$. (Note: This sort of condition is not a "restriction" in the sense that it results in "additional" combinations. For every combination in Part A, there are 4 ways to choose a team captain.)

Example 8. How many two-digit combinations of the number 265,483 do not involve any odd digits?

Since this question includes a condition (no odd digits), it is Case 7. Simply ignore the odd digits and use the Case 1 formula to form 2-digit combinations from the 4 even digits (2, 4, 6, and 8): $\binom{4}{2} = \frac{4!}{2!(4-2)!} = \frac{4!}{2!2!} = \frac{24}{(2)(2)} = 6$. The combinations include: 24, 26, 28, 46, 48, and 68. (Note, for example, that 24 and 42 are the same combination.)

Chapter 2 Problems

Directions: For each word or number below, determine the number of combinations of the letters or digits. The number in brackets [ ] indicates the size of the subset. For example, "9061 [2]" means to make 2-digit subsets. If the symbol ∞ also appears in brackets, this means each letter or digit may be repeated without limit.

(1) MEDIAN [2]   (2) GRAVITY [5]   (3) CALCULUS [3]

(4) 9061 [2]   (5) 45,207,163 [4]   (6) 8,920,574 [3, ∞]

(7) BINARY [4, ∞]   (8) ISOSCELES [3]   (9) GRADIENT [5, ∞]

(10) 625,255 [3]   (11) 146,493,404 [4]   (12) 8,937,246,015 [7, ∞]

Directions: Determine the number of combinations of the letters or digits. The numbers in brackets [ ] indicate the sizes of the subsets. For example, "PIE [2], CHART [3]" means to make 2-letter subsets of PIE and 3-letter subsets of CHART. As another example, "17,925,863 [4,2]" means to make successive subsets of 4 digits and 2 digits.

(13) PIE [2], CHART [3]

(14) 17,925,863 [4, 2]

(15) SPHERICAL [4, 3, 2]

(16) 6,037,192 [5], 548 [2]

(17) FIVE [2], THOUSAND [6]

(18) DOMAIN [1], 9250 [2], 417,836 [4]

(19) FRACTAL [4], 5000 [2]

(20) 9,563,802,714 [4, 4, 2]

Directions: Determine the number of combinations for selecting the indicated number of balls. The numbers in brackets [ ] indicate the sizes of the subsets. For example, "9 blue [6], 7 green [5]" means to choose 6 out of 9 blue balls and 5 out of 7 green balls, while "11 balls [6, 3]" means to first choose 6 balls out of 11 and then choose 3 of the remaining balls. Some problems also include a condition. For example, "8 blue, 4 red [2], same color" means to choose 2 balls that are both blue or 2 balls that are both red.

(21) 12 balls [4]

(22) 11 balls [6, 3]

(23) 9 blue [6], 7 green [5]

(24) 8 blue [4], 11 green [5], 9 red [6]

(25) 24 balls [8, 6, 4]

(26) 20 balls [12, 5, 3]

(27) 8 blue, 4 red [2], same color

(28) 9 blue, 8 green, 7 red [3], same color

Directions: For each problem below, determine the number of combinations that satisfy the given condition. For example, "16 people [4], with one captain" means to make teams of 4 people where one person on the team serves as the team captain.

(29) 361,049 [3], exactly one odd digit

(30) LONGITUDE [6], at least 2 vowels

(31) 16 people [4], with one captain

(32) PROBLEM [5], include both B and E

(33) 5 blue, 6 green, 4 red [4],
2 of one color + 2 of a different color

(34) LOGARITHM [3],
either has all vowels or all consonants

(35) 6 blue, 9 green, 5 red [5],
no more than 2 may be red

(36) DECIMAL, 768 [5],
more letters than digits

3 Counting Problems

In this chapter, we will explore a variety of counting problems that arise in probability questions, including some that don't involve permutations or combinations.

A simple, yet important, case involves counting **sequential numbers**. For example, if you read pages 4-11, how many pages will you read? It surprises many students that the answer is NOT seven. If you begin reading at the top of page 4 and finish reading at the bottom of page 11, you will read pages 4, 5, 6, 7, 8, 9, 10, and 11. If you count, you will see that there are 8 pages (not 7). If you subtracted 4 from 11 to get 7, you almost had the right answer, but not quite. After subtracting 4 from 11 to get 7, you then **need to add 1 for the first page**: $11 - 4 + 1 = 8$. To better understand why you have to add one after subtracting, compare the two similar cases that follow.

- If you have 4 apples and would like to have a total of 11 apples, you need to buy $11 - 4 = 7$ apples. In this case, you already have 4 apples to begin with, so you don't need to add one.
- If you read pages 4-11, when you start reading, you haven't yet read page 4. The subtraction $11 - 4 = 7$ tells you how many pages you need to read once you finish reading page 4, so you need to add 1 for page 4 itself: $11 - 4 + 1 = 8$.

With **sequential numbers**, you need to **add one** after subtracting if you are **counting both of the endpoints** (like the second bullet point above, where neither page 4 nor page 11 has been read yet). However, if you are only counting one of the endpoints (like the first bullet point above, where you already have apple number 4), don't add one after subtracting. Following are a couple of examples:

- If you read pages 83 thru 147 in a book, add one after subtracting because both endpoints (pages 83 and 147) are counted: $147 - 83 + 1 = 65$.
- If you have \$63 and want to have a total of \$100, don't add one because you don't need to earn the 63rd dollar (since you already have it): $\$100 - \$63 = \$37$.

The same concept may be applied when working with **multiples**. For example, if you count by 5's starting at 120 and finishing at 200. How many multiples of 5 are there?

The trick is to divide each number by 5 (and then add 1 after subtracting because we are counting both of the endpoints): $\frac{200}{5} - \frac{120}{5} + 1 = 40 - 24 + 1 = 17$.

Another important issue with counting problems in probability is deciding whether to add or multiply two numbers. You may have already encountered this issue in the previous chapters. For example, suppose that a bag contains 4 blue balls and 3 green balls. To find the number of ways to select 2 balls of the same color, we add: $\binom{4}{2} + \binom{3}{2} = \frac{4!}{2!2!} + \frac{3!}{2!1!} = 6 + 3 = 9$. (This is Case 7 in Chapter 2.) In contrast, to find the number of ways to first select 2 balls from a bag of 4 blue balls and then select 2 balls from a bag of 3 green balls, we multiply: $\binom{4}{2}\binom{3}{2} = \frac{4!}{2!2!}\frac{3!}{2!1!} = (6)(3) = 18$. (This is Case 4 in Chapter 2.) When is it correct to add and when is it correct to multiply? Use the sum and product rules that follow to determine this.

According to the **product rule** (or **multiplication principle**) of combinatorics, if there are M ways that one event can occur and there are N ways that a second event can occur, if the two events are **independent** then there are $M \times N$ ways that the **combination** of the two events can occur. For example, when selecting 2 balls from a bag of 4 blue balls and then selecting 2 balls from a bag of 3 green balls, since both events occur in combination, we multiply: $\binom{4}{2}\binom{3}{2} = \frac{4!}{2!2!}\frac{3!}{2!1!} = (6)(3) = 18$. (For the product rule, it is important for the two events to be **independent**. If one event is selecting a dress and another event is selecting shoes, if the shoes will be selected so that they match the color of the dress, then this is an example where the events are NOT independent.)

According to the **sum rule** (or **addition principle**), if there are M ways that one event can occur and N ways that a second event can occur, if the two events **won't both occur together** then there are $M + N$ ways to choose **one** of the events. For example, when selecting 2 balls from a bag containing 4 blue balls and 3 green balls, to find the number of ways that the 2 balls can be the same color, we add because either one event occurs or the other (two balls can be blue or two balls can be green, but at most one of these events can occur): $\binom{4}{2} + \binom{3}{2} = \frac{4!}{2!2!} + \frac{3!}{2!1!} = 6 + 3 = 9$.

For the **product rule**, one event **and** a second event **both** occur in combination. (It isn't a choice of one or the other.) For the **sum rule**, either one event **or** a second event occurs. (The two events won't both occur together.) Compare the two examples below.

- A purse comes in orange, pink, red, and yellow colors. A wallet comes in brown, gray, and white colors. There are $(4)(3) = 12$ ways to buy both one purse and one wallet. If **both** items are purchased, the two events occur in combination and the **product rule** applies, so we multiply. The combinations include OB, OG, OW, PB, PG, PW, RB, RG, RW, YB, YG, and YW (where the first letter of each color is used in the combinations).

- A shirt comes in blue, green, purple, and red colors. A hat comes in navy, tan, and white colors. There are $4 + 3$ ways to buy exactly one item. If only one of the items is purchased, **only one** of the events occurs and the **sum rule** applies, so we add. The choices include B, G, P, R, N, T, and W (where the first letter of each color is used).

If a counting problem involves **overlapping groups**, it may help to draw a **Venn diagram**. For example, consider the following problem. There are 28 students in a classroom. Every student in the room will take at least one exam. The only exams offered are in chemistry and physics. 16 students will take the physics exam and 7 students will take both exams. How many students will take only the chemistry exam?

We can draw a **Venn diagram** for this situation as follows.

- Draw two overlapping circles to represent the two overlapping groups: Put chemistry on the left and physics on the right.
- Write 7 in the overlapping region since 7 students will take both exams.
- Since 16 students take the physics exam and 7 students take both exams, there must be $16 - 7 = 9$ students who will only take the physics exam. Write 9 in the remaining portion of the physics circle.
- Since there are 28 students and 16 will take the physics exam, there must be $28 - 16 = 12$ who will not take the physics exam. Since every student will take at least one exam, these 12 students must be taking only the chemistry exam. Write 12 in the remaining portion of the chemistry circle.

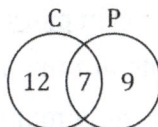

The Venn diagram above illustrates the following:

- $12 + 7 = 19$ students will take the chemistry exam. These students are in the left circle. Of these, 12 will only take the chemistry exam.
- $9 + 7 = 16$ students will take the physics exam. These students are in the right circle. Of these, 9 will take only the physics exam.
- 7 students will take both exams. These students are in the overlapping region.
- $12 + 7 + 9 = 28$ is the total number of students. (It would be wrong to add 19 and 16 because 7 students, who will take both exams, would be counted twice.)

If there are several different cases to work out for what you wish to count, it may be easier to apply the principle of **complementary counting**. This means to count **what you don't want to count** and then subtract. For example, consider the problem of how many three-digit numbers contain at least one 5. In the bullet points below, we solve this problem two different ways. The second method uses complementary counting.

- There are 100 numbers with a 5 as the first digit: 500-599. There are 80 numbers with a 5 as the middle digit (that don't have a 5 as the first digit): 150-159, 250-259, 350-359, 450-459, 650-659, 750-759, 850-859, and 950-959. There are 72 numbers with a 5 as the last digit (that don't have a 5 as the first or middle digit): 105, 115, 125, 135, 145, 165, 175, 185, 195, and the similar sets in the 200's, 300's, 400's, 600's, 700's, 800's, and 900's. (Multiply 9 by 8 to get 72.) Add these up to find a total of $100 + 80 + 72 = 252$ three-digit numbers with at least one 5.
- The more direct way involves **complementary counting**. There are $(9)(10)(10) = 900$ three-digit numbers all together: 100 thru 999. Of these, $(8)(9)(9) = 648$ three-digit numbers don't contain any 5's. (Why? Because there are 8 choices for the first digit – 1, 2, 3, 4, 6, 7, 8, or 9 – and 9 choices for each of the remaining digits – 0, 1, 2, 3, 4, 6, 7, 8, or 9.) Subtract 648 three-digit numbers that don't contain any fives from the 900 three-digit numbers to determine how many three-digit numbers contain at least one five: $900 - 648 = 252$.

It is sometimes necessary to count items in **pairs**. For example, consider the following classic **handshake** problem. If 6 people are in a room and each person shakes hands with every other person exactly once, how many handshakes will occur? A common **mistake** is to multiply 6 by 5, but this is **incorrect** because it counts every handshake twice. The correct answer is $\frac{(6)(5)}{2} = 15$. We first multiply 6 and 5 because each person shakes hands with 5 other people, and then we divide by 2 because handshakes occur in pairs (each handshake involves two people). To see that this answer is correct, let the people be named A, B, C, D, E, and F. The handshakes are AB, AC, AD, AE, AF, BC, BD, BE, BF, CD, CE, CF, DE, DF, and EF. You could use the **combination** formula from Chapter 2 (case 1): $\binom{6}{2} = \frac{6!}{2!(6-2)!} = \frac{6!}{2!4!} = \frac{6(5)}{2} = 10$. (The Case 3 permutation formula from Chapter 1 overcounts because order doesn't matter: AB is the same handshake as BA because the same two people shake hands.)

Example 1. A student reads pages 97-111 in a textbook. How many pages does the student read?

Since both endpoints will be included (pages 97 and 111 will be read), we need to add one after subtracting: $111 - 97 + 1 = 14 + 1 = 15$. Since the answer is small, we can list the pages to check the answer: 97, 98, 99, 100, 101, 102, 103, 104, 105, 106, 107, 108, 109, 110, and 111.

Example 2. A man is on the fifth floor of a building. He wishes to be on the ninth floor. There is one flight of stairs between each floor. How many flights of stairs does he need to climb?

Unlike Example 1, this time we are not counting both of the endpoints. Since the man is already on the fifth floor, he doesn't need to climb a flight of stairs to reach the fifth floor. Don't add one after subtracting: $9 - 5 = 4$. Since the answer is small, we can list the flights that he has to climb. Starting on the fifth floor, he climbs one flight of stairs to reach the sixth floor, another flight of stairs to reach the seventh floor, another flight of stairs to reach to eighth floor, and one last flight of stairs to reach the ninth floor. (Contrast this with Example 1, where the student hadn't yet read page 97. Here, the man is already on the fifth floor.)

Example 3. How many multiples of 3 lie in the range 200-300?

In this range, the first multiple of 3 is 201 (since $3 \times 67 = 201$) and the last multiple of 3 is 300 (since $3 \times 100 = 300$). Divide 300 and 201 each by 3, subtract, and then add one because both endpoints are included: $100 - 67 + 1 = 34$. You can verify that 34 multiples of 3 lie in this range by counting them: 201, 204, 207, 210, 213, 216, 219, 222, 225, 228, 231, 234, 237, 240, 243, 246, 249, 252, 255, 258, 261, 264, 267, 270, 273, 276, 279, 282, 285, 288, 291, 294, 297, and 300.

Example 4. A school offers four art classes – drawing, fashion, graphic design, and painting – and six athletics classes – aerobics, cross country, soccer, tennis, volleyball, and weight training. (A) How many ways can a student choose one of these classes? (B) How many ways can a student choose one art class and one athletics class?

(A) To choose exactly one class, use the <u>**sum**</u> rule: $4 + 6 = 10$. In this case, the student does NOT take both kinds of classes (art and athletics) together. The choices include: D, F, G, P, A, C, S, T, V, and W. (We used the first letter for each class; for example, G stands for graphic design.)

(B) To choose one art class AND one athletics class, use the **product** rule: $(4)(6) = 24$. In this case, the student is taking BOTH kinds of classes together in combination. The combinations include DA, DC, DS, DT, DV, DW, FA, FC, FS, FT, FV, FW, GA, GC, GS, GT, GV, GW, PA, PC, PS, PT, PV, and PW. (We used the first letter for each class; for example, GA stands for graphic design plus aerobics.)

Example 5. A restaurant offers four entrées – chicken, lamb, pork, or vegetarian. Each entrée comes with a choice of soup or salad. The soups include beet, mushroom, and tomato. The salads include house and Caesar. How many ways can a customer order a meal according to these directions?

First, use the <u>**sum**</u> rule for the choice of soup or salad since the customer will select one OR the other (but not both together). There are $3 + 2 = 5$ ways to choose one soup or salad. Now use the **product** rule to combine the entrée with the soup or salad: $(4)(5) = 20$. Using the first letter of the entrée and the first letter of the soup or salad, the combinations are CB, CM, CT, CH, CC, LB, LM, LT, LH, LC, PB, PM, PT, PH, PC, VB, VM, VT, VH, VC. (For example, CB stands for chicken plus beet soup and LC stands for lamb plus Caesar salad.)

Example 6. 43 people ate at a cafeteria. Everybody ate breakfast, lunch, or both. 12 people ate both breakfast and lunch. 27 people ate breakfast. How many people ate lunch?

To solve this problem, make a Venn diagram as follows.

- The two overlapping groups are breakfast and lunch. Draw two overlapping circles. Put breakfast on the left and lunch on the right.
- 12 people ate both breakfast and lunch. Write 12 in the overlapping region.
- Since 27 people ate breakfast and 12 people ate both breakfast and lunch, it follows that $27 - 12 = 15$ people only ate breakfast. Write 15 in the remaining portion of the breakfast circle.
- Since 43 people ate at the cafeteria and 27 people ate breakfast, there must have been $43 - 27 = 16$ people who did not eat breakfast. Since everybody ate breakfast, lunch, or both, these 16 people must have only eaten lunch. Write 16 in the remaining portion of the lunch circle.

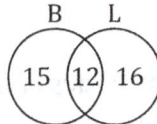

B   L

15 (12) 16

The Venn diagram above shows the following:

- 27 people ate breakfast; 15 people ate breakfast but not lunch.
- 28 people ate lunch; 16 people ate lunch but not breakfast.
- 12 people ate both breakfast and lunch.
- $15 + 16 + 12 = 43$ people ate at the cafeteria.

The answer is that 28 people ate lunch. (Note that the problem asked how many people ate lunch; it didn't ask how many people only ate lunch.)

Example 7. Out of 65 sophomores, 24 have studied French, 36 have studied Spanish, and 13 have studied neither language. (A) How many sophomores have studied both French and Spanish? (B) How many sophomores have studied Spanish but not French?

To solve this problem, make a Venn diagram as follows.

- The two overlapping groups are French and Spanish. Draw two overlapping circles. Put French on the left and Spanish on the right.
- 13 sophomores have studied neither language. Write 13 outside the circles.

- $65 - 13 = 52$ sophomores have studied at least one of these languages.
- $24 + 36 = 60$ is what we get if we add the 24 who have studied French to the 36 who have studied Spanish. Comparing 60 to the 52 who have studied at least one language shows that $60 - 52 = 8$ students have studied both French and Spanish. Write 8 in the overlapping region.
- $24 - 8 = 16$ have studied French but not Spanish, while $36 - 8 = 28$ have studied Spanish but not French. Write these numbers in the remaining parts of the two circles.

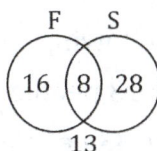

F   S

16 (8) 28

13

The Venn diagram above shows the following:

- 24 sophomores have studied French; 16 have studied French but not Spanish.
- 36 sophomores have studied Spanish; 28 have studied Spanish but not French.
- 8 sophomores have studied both French and Spanish.
- 13 sophomores have studied neither French nor Spanish.
- There are $16 + 28 + 8 + 13 = 65$ sophomores.

(A) 8 sophomores have studied both French and Spanish.

(B) 28 sophomores have studied Spanish but not French.

Example 8. A survey of 100 people revealed that 35 had at least one cat at home, 55 had at least one dog at home, and 22 had both at least one cat and at least one dog at home. (A) How many people had a cat but not a dog? (B) How many people had a dog but not a cat? (C) How many people did not have either a cat or a dog?

To solve this problem, make a Venn diagram as follows.

- The two overlapping groups are people with cats and people with dogs. Draw two overlapping circles. Put cats on the left and dogs on the right.
- 22 people had at least one cat and at least one dog. Write 22 in the overlapping region.
- $35 - 22 = 13$ people had at least one cat, but did not have a dog. Write 13 in the remaining portion of the cats' circle.

- $55 - 22 = 33$ people had at least one dog, but did not have a cat. Write 33 in the remaining portion of the dogs' circle.
- $13 + 33 + 22 = 68$ people had at least one cat or at least one dog.
- $100 - 68 = 32$ people did not have a cat or a dog. Write 32 outside of all of the circles (since these people are excluded from both circles).

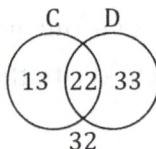

The Venn diagram above shows the following:

- 35 people had at least one cat; 13 people had a cat but not a dog.
- 55 people had at least one dog; 33 people had a dog but not a cat.
- 22 people had both a cat and a dog.
- 32 people did not have a cat or a dog.
- $13 + 22 + 33 + 32 = 100$ people took the survey.

(A) 13 people had a cat but not a dog.

(B) 33 people had a dog but not a cat.

(C) 32 people did not have a cat or a dog.

Example 9. How many four-digit whole numbers contain at least one 7?

Use the method of complementary counting. We will do this in three steps.

- How many four-digit numbers don't contain any 7's? Such numbers have the form $wxyz$, where neither w, x, y, nor z is a 7. There are 8 possible values for w (1, 2, 3, 4, 5, 6, 8, or 9, since a four-digit number can't begin with 0) and 9 possible values for x, y, and z (0, 1, 2, 3, 4, 5, 6, 8, or 9). There are $(8)(9)(9)(9) = 5832$ four-digit numbers that don't contain any 7's.
- How many four-digit numbers are there all together (including 7's)? There are $(9)(10)(10)(10) = 9000$ numbers of the form $abcd$ (where a can be any digit from 1-9 and b, c, and d can be any digit from 0-9).
- Subtract 5832 from 9000 to get 3168.

Example 10. There are 3 boys and 4 girls in a room. Every person shakes hands with every other person exactly once. (A) How many handshakes occur all together? (B) How many handshakes occur where one boy shakes hands with one girl?

(A) First multiply 7 by 6 because each person shakes hands with 6 other people, and then divide by 2 because handshakes occur in pairs (each handshake involves two people): $\frac{7(6)}{2} = 21$. Let the boys be named B, C, and D, and let the girls be named G, H, I, and J. The handshakes are BC, BD, BG, BH, BI, BJ, CD, CG, CH, CI, CJ, DG, DH, DI, DJ, GH, GI, GJ, HI, HJ, and IJ. (Note, for example, that BC is the same handshake as CB because the same pair of people shake hands.) Alternate solution: Use the **combination** formula from Chapter 2 (case 1): $\binom{7}{2} = \frac{7!}{2!(7-2)!} = \frac{7!}{2!5!} = \frac{7(6)}{2} = 21$. (Note: Since order doesn't matter, since BC is the same as CB, these are combinations, not permutations.)

(B) Multiply 3 by 4 to make all of the pairs involving one boy and one girl to get 12. The handshakes are BG, BH, BI, BJ, CG, CH, CI, CJ, DG, DH, DI, and DJ.

Note: If you would like to visualize this problem, see Chapter 11. Part A corresponds to a complete graph, while Part B corresponds to a bipartite graph.

Chapter 3 Problems

Directions: Determine the indicated quantity. For example, "read pages 32-58, 65-82, and 97-121; number of pages read" wants to know how many pages are read all together if all three separate sections are read.

(1) read pages 164-200 and 256-312
number of pages read

(2) read pages 32-58, 65-82, and 97-121
number of pages read

(3) have $17, want to have $52
additional money needed

(4) solve problems 19-33
number of problems solved

(5) read pages 100-200
number of pages read

(6) numbers 100-200
greater than 100 and less than 200

(7) owe $9, want to have $16
additional money needed
(to have $16 after paying the debt)

(8) walk from the 7th floor to the 18th floor
number of flights walked
(one flight connects consecutive floors)

Directions: How many multiples lie in the given range? For example, "40-200; multiples of 8" wants numbers that are evenly divisible by 8 from 40 thru 200 (including 40 and 200), while ">70 and <700; multiples of 7" excludes 70 and 700.

(9) 40-200
multiples of 8

(10) two-digit numbers
multiples of 12

(11) >70 and <700
multiples of 7

(12) >300 and <800
multiples of 9

(13) 1100-2200
multiples of 11

(14) three-digit numbers
multiples of both 2 and 3

(15) four-digit numbers
multiples of both 3 and 5

(16) whole numbers 6-30
multiples of $\frac{2}{3}$

(17) whole numbers >3 and <15
multiples of 0.75

Directions: Each problem below lists options. Use the sum or product rule to find the number of ways to make the specified choice. For example, "4 lunches and 9 dinners; choose 1 lunch and 1 dinner" means to choose 1 of the lunches and 1 of the dinners.

(18) 15 pencils and 20 pens
choose 1 writing utensil

(19) 4 lunches and 9 dinners
choose 1 lunch and 1 dinner

(20) 6 math classes and 9 science classes
choose 1 math class and 1 science class

(21) 7 entrées, 4 soups, and 3 salads
choose entrée with 1 soup or 1 salad

(22) 8 boys and 5 girls
choose 3 boys and 2 girls

(23) 8 boys and 5 girls
choose 1 person

(24) a company has 3 districts
each district has 12 stores
each store has 8 departments
each department has 25 salespeople
choose one salesperson

(25) a company has 5 warehouses
each warehouse has 10 vans
each van holds 60 boxes
each box contains 4 items
choose one item

Directions: Draw a Venn diagram and use it to answer the questions.

(26) 85 people ate pizza, tacos, or both

36 people only ate pizza

23 people ate both pizza and tacos

(A) How many ate pizza?

(B) How many ate tacos?

(C) How many ate tacos, but not pizza?

(27) 73 students attend a school

17 students went to a movie and a dance

36 students went to a dance

21 students did neither

(A) How many only went to a movie?

(B) How many only went to a dance?

(28) 42 campers went boating

24 campers only went boating

56 campers went swimming

no campers did neither

(A) How many campers were there?

(B) How many did both activities?

(C) How many only went swimming?

(29) 150 juniors attend a school

94 took a health class

76 took a PE class

11 did not take health or PE

(A) How many took both?

(B) How many took health, but not PE?

(C) How many took PE, but not health?

Directions: For each question below, use the method of complementary counting to determine the answer. For example, "whole numbers 200-800; contain at least one 3" wants to know how many numbers in the range 200-800 contain at least one 3.

(30) whole numbers 200-800
contain at least one 3

(31) three-digit whole numbers
not a multiple of 6

(32) four-digit whole numbers
contain at least one 0

(33) five-digit whole numbers
contain at least one 1

(34) whole numbers 500-1500
contain at least one 7

(35) three-digit whole numbers
contain at least one 2, but no 8's or 9's

(36) four-digit whole numbers
not a multiple of 9

(37) whole numbers 77-863
not a multiple of 12

Directions: Determine the number of pairs for each problem below. Each handshake that is described occurs exactly once. Only the handshakes described occur.

(38) there are 9 people; everyone shakes hands with everyone else
How many handshakes occur?

(39) there are 8 boys and 6 girls; each boy shakes hands with each girl
How many handshakes occur?

(40) there are 7 boys and 10 girls; each boy shakes hands with every other boy and each girl shakes hands with every other girl
How many handshakes occur?

(41) a convex octagon is drawn on a board
How many ways can a line be drawn that connects two corners that are not adjacent?

4 Random Selections

The **probability** that an event will occur is a number which could be anywhere from 0 to 1. This number corresponds to a percentage from 0% to 100%. This fraction or percentage (however you wish to express it) represents the **likelihood** that the event will occur. For example, if the probability that an event will occur is equal to 0.75, this means that the event is expected to occur 75% of the time, on average.

Probability is related to the odds that an event will occur. For example, suppose that a bag contains three balls, where two are blue and one is red. If one ball is chosen at random, it could be blue or it could be red. The probability that it will be blue is 2/3 while the probability that it will be red is 1/3 (since the bag contains twice as many blue balls as red balls). Thus, a blue ball is twice as likely as a red ball, meaning that the odds favor the ball being blue. (We will return to the topic of odds in Chapter 7.)

Note that probability theory **doesn't** provide a definite outcome for a **single** event to occur. If you choose one ball at random in the previous example, it could be blue or red. We can't say for sure, but we do know that it is twice as likely to be blue. What we can say is what will happen if the event is **repeated a large number of times**. If we repeat the previous example a large number of times, blue will occur approximately 2/3 of the time and red will occur approximately 1/3 of the time.

If every outcome is equally likely and the outcome is **random**, it's simple. To find the probability that a specific outcome will occur, divide the number of ways that the specific outcome can occur by the total number of possible outcomes.

$$\text{probability for a specific outcome} = \frac{\text{number of ways for specific outcome to occur}}{\text{total number of possible outcomes}}$$

When calculating probability, first **define what an outcome is**. Be sure to define an outcome so that all of the outcomes are equally likely. For example, suppose that a bag contains one blue ball, one green ball, and two red balls. To find the probability that a ball selected at random will be a particular color, it would be **incorrect** to think of the outcomes as blue, green, and red because red is more likely. It would be correct to think of the outcomes as blue, green, the first red ball, and the second red ball since each of these four outcomes is equally likely. (We'll continue this example soon.)

In this book, we will assume that the selection process is **fair** unless a problem explicitly states otherwise. (To see an example where the selection process isn't fair, see the discussion of unfair coins in Chapter 6.)

Note that **an outcome may be defined in terms of permutations or combinations**, provided that you are **consistent** in the numerator and denominator. Don't use permutations in the numerator and combinations in the denominator, for example. (Exception: If you are looking for a specific outcome where order matters, then you need to use permutations. For example, the probability of first selecting a blue ball and selecting a red ball next involves a particular order.) For example, to find the probability of selecting 2 red balls, you could define an outcome to be a permutation or a combination of selecting 2 balls. The examples in this chapter include alternate solutions; one solution shows how to solve the problem in terms of combinations and an alternate solution shows how to solve the problem in terms of permutations.

As an example, suppose that a bag contains one blue ball, one green ball, and two red balls. If one ball is selected at random, there are 4 possible outcomes: a blue ball, a green ball, the first red ball, or the second red ball. To find the probability that the ball will be red, divide the number of outcomes for selecting one red ball (which is 2 since there are 2 red balls) by the total number of possible outcomes (which is 4 since there are 4 balls). The probability that the ball will be red equals 2/4, which reduces to 1/2 (which is equivalent to 0.5 or 50%). To find the probability that the ball will be blue, divide the number of outcomes for selecting one blue ball (which is 1 since there is 1 blue ball) by the total number of possible outcomes (which is 4 since there are 4 balls). The probability that the ball will be blue equals 1/4. Similarly, the probability that the ball will be green is 1/4 (since there is 1 green ball). Note that if you add the probability that the ball will be red (50%), the probability that the ball will be blue (25%), and the probability that the ball will be green (25%) together, you get 100%. This shows that there is 100% probability that the ball will have one of the 3 colors.

When selecting more than one item, keep the following points in mind:

- Is each item **replaced** before selecting a new item, or are all of the items kept **without replacement**? Parts B and C of Example 1 illustrate the difference. In the case **with replacement**, permutations are equally likely outcomes, whereas combinations are not. See the note below.

- If the items are selected one at a time, do you care in **which order the items are selected**? If order matters, you definitely need to count permutations (Chapter 1). If order doesn't matter, it isn't necessary to count permutations; in this case, you may count combinations instead (Chapter 2). Example 3 compares a case where order doesn't matter to a case where order does matter. (When order doesn't matter, permutations can still be helpful. See Examples 1-2.)

Note regarding **with replacement**: If the first item is placed back with the other items before selecting a second item, beware that permutations are equally likely outcomes, but combinations are not. For example, if there is 1 blue ball, 1 green ball, and 1 red ball, and the first ball is placed back in the bag before selecting the second ball, there are 9 equally likely permutations (BB, BG, BR, GB, GG, GR, RB, RG, RR), whereas the 6 combinations (BB, BG, BR, GG, GR, RR) are not equally likely. In contrast, if 2 balls are selected **without replacement**, the 6 permutations (BG, BR, GB, GR, RB, RG) are equally likely and the 3 combinations (BG, BR, GR) are also equally likely. The reason for the difference is that **with replacement**, you can select the same color twice (BB, GG, or RR).

Example 1. A bag contains 1 blue ball, 3 green balls, and 4 red balls. (A) Determine the probability of randomly selecting one ball for each color. (B) Determine the probability of randomly selecting two red balls if two balls are selected **without replacement**. (C) Determine the probability of randomly selecting two red balls if the first ball is **replaced** in the bag before selecting the second ball.

(A) First define what an outcome is so that each possible outcome is equally likely. Here, the equally likely outcomes are the different balls that can be selected. The total number of outcomes is 8 (since there are 1 + 3 + 4 = 8 balls). To find the probability of selecting one ball of a specific color, divide the number of ways of selecting a ball of that color by the total number of outcomes (which is 8).

- The probability of selecting one blue ball is 1/8 (or 0.125 or 12.5%).
- The probability of selecting one green ball is 3/8 (or 0.375 or 37.5%).
- The probability of selecting one red ball is 4/8, which reduces to 1/2 (or 0.5 or 50%).

Observe that these probabilities add up to 1 (or 100%).

(B) In our first solution, we define an outcome to be a permutation for selecting two balls. If two balls are selected without replacement (as opposed to putting the first ball back before selecting the second), there are 8 ways to select the first ball (since there are 8 balls in the bag to begin with) and there are 7 ways to select the second ball (since there are only 7 other balls to choose from after the first ball is selected). Multiply 8 by 7 to get the total number of possible outcomes: 56. There are 4 ways that the first ball can be red (since there are 4 red balls to begin with). If the first ball is red, there are 3 ways that the second ball can be red (since only 3 red balls remain in the bag if the first ball is red). Multiply 4 by 3 to get the number of ways that both balls can be red: 12. The probability of selecting two red balls **without replacement** is therefore 12/56, which reduces to 3/14 (which is approximately 0.214 or 21.4%).

Alternate solution: This time, we define an outcome to be a combination for selecting two balls. To find the total number of outcomes, use the combination formula from Chapter 2 to select 2 balls from a bag of 8 balls: $\binom{8}{2} = \frac{8!}{2!(8-2)!} = \frac{8!}{2!6!} = \frac{(8)(7)}{(2)(1)} = 28$. These combinations include: BG_1, BG_2, BG_3, BR_1, BR_2, BR_3, BR_4, G_1G_2, G_1G_3, G_2G_3, G_1R_1, G_1R_2, G_1R_3, G_1R_4, G_2R_1, G_2R_2, G_2R_3, G_2R_4, G_3R_1, G_3R_2, G_3R_3, G_3R_4, R_1R_2, R_1R_3, R_1R_4, R_2R_3, R_2R_4, and R_3R_4 (where B represents the blue ball, G_1, G_2, and G_3, represent the green balls, and R_1, R_2, R_3, and R_4, represent the red balls). To find the number of outcomes where both balls are red, use the combination formula to select 2 red balls from 4 red balls: $\binom{4}{2} = \frac{4!}{2!(4-2)!} = \frac{4!}{2!2!} = \frac{(4)(3)}{(2)(1)} = 6$. These combinations include R_1R_2, R_1R_3, R_1R_4, R_2R_3, R_2R_4, and R_3R_4. The probability of selecting two red balls **without replacement** is therefore 6/28, which reduces to 3/14 (which is approximately 0.214 or 21.4%).

Another alternate solution: The probability of selecting a red ball first is 1/2 (see Part A). If the first ball is red, when selecting the second ball, the bag will contain 1 blue ball, 3 green balls, and 3 red balls. The probability that the second ball will be red after already selecting one red ball is 3/7 (since there will be 3 red balls in the bag out of a total of 7 balls at this point). Multiply the two probabilities (1/2 and 3/7) to get 3/14 (which is approximately 0.214 or 21.4%). Note: We will explore probability rules, like when you can add or multiply probabilities, when we get to Chapter 5. There are rules that tell you when you can or can't multiply probabilities. Before you use this method, you should read about those rules in Chapter 5.

(C) This time, instead of selecting two balls at once, the first ball will be selected and then placed back in the bag before selecting the second ball. There are 8 ways to select each ball since each time one ball is selected, there are 8 balls in the bag. Multiply 8 by 8 to get the total number of outcomes: 64. Each time a ball is selected, there are 4 ways for it to be red (since the first ball is placed back in the bag before selecting the second ball). Multiply 4 by 4 to get the number of outcomes where both balls are red: 16. The probability of selecting two red balls **with replacement** (where the first ball is placed back in the bag before selecting the second ball) is 16/64, which reduces to 1/4 (or 0.25 or 25%). In Part C, an outcome is a permutation for selecting two balls; **with replacement**, we need to work with **permutations** (where R_1R_2 differs from R_2R_1, for example) to get equally likely outcomes (see the note from earlier in the chapter). **Alternate solution**: The probability of selecting one red ball was found to be 1/2 in Part A. Since in Part C the same 8 balls are in the bag when each ball is selected (unlike Part B, where there are only 7 balls in the bag after the first ball is selected), for each ball the probability of it being red is 1/2. Multiply the two probabilities (1/2 and 1/2) to get the probability of both balls being red to get 1/4 (or 0.25 or 25%). Note: We will explore probability rules, like when you can add or multiply probabilities, when we get to Chapter 5. There are rules that tell you when you can or can't multiply probabilities. Before you use this method, you should read about those rules in Chapter 5.

Example 2. A drawer contains 2 black socks and 4 gray socks. (A) Determine the probability of randomly selecting two matching socks if two socks are selected **without replacement**. (B) Determine the probability of selecting two matching socks if three socks are randomly selected **without replacement**.

(A) In our first solution, we define an outcome to be a permutation for selecting two socks. Since we are working with permutations, we will treat B_1B_2 different from B_2B_1, for example. There are 6 ways to select the first sock and 5 ways to select the second sock. The total number of outcomes is $(6)(5) = 30$. There are 2 ways that the first sock can be black. If the first sock is black, there is 1 way that the second sock can also be black. The number of ways for both socks to be black is $(2)(1) = 2$ (B_1B_2 and B_2B_1). There are 4 ways that the first sock can be gray. If the first sock is gray, there are 3 ways that the second sock can also be gray. The number of ways for both socks to be gray is $(4)(3) = 12$. The number of outcomes where both socks are the same color is $2 + 12 = 14$. (Either both are black or both are gray.) The probability of selecting two matching socks **without replacement** is 14/30, which reduces to 7/15 (which is approximately 0.467 or 46.7%).

Alternate solution: This time, we define an outcome to be a combination for selecting two socks. To find the total number of outcomes, use the combination formula from Chapter 2 to select 2 socks from a drawer of 6 socks: $\binom{6}{2} = \frac{6!}{2!(6-2)!} = \frac{6!}{2!4!} = \frac{(6)(5)}{(2)(1)} = 15$. These combinations include: B_1B_2, B_1G_1, B_1G_2, B_1G_3, B_1G_4, B_2G_1, B_2G_2, B_2G_3, B_2G_4, G_1G_2, G_1G_3, G_1G_4, G_2G_3, G_2G_4, and G_3G_4, (where B represents black and G represents gray). To find the number of outcomes where both socks are black, use the combination formula to select 2 black socks from 2 black socks: $\binom{2}{2} = \frac{2!}{2!(2-2)!} = \frac{2!}{2!0!} = \frac{2}{(2)(1)} = 1$. To find the number of outcomes where both socks are gray, use the combination formula to select 2 gray socks from 4 gray socks: $\binom{4}{2} = \frac{4!}{2!(4-2)!} = \frac{4!}{2!2!} = \frac{4(3)}{(2)(1)} = 6$. There are $1 + 6 = 7$ combinations where the socks are the same color. These combinations include B_1B_2, G_1G_2, G_1G_3, G_1G_4, G_2G_3, G_2G_4, and G_3G_4. The probability of selecting two matching socks **without replacement** is therefore 7/15 (which is approximately 0.467 or 46.7%). (B) If 3 socks are selected, there is a 100% probability that two of the socks will be the same color. If the first 2 socks don't match, 1 will be black and 1 will be gray; the third sock will either match the black sock or the gray sock.

Example 3. A bag contains 2 blue balls, 3 green balls, and 5 red balls. If 2 balls are randomly selected **without replacement**, (A) what is the probability that 1 will be blue and 1 will be red in any order and (B) what is the probability that the first ball will be blue and the second ball will be red?

(A) In our first solution, we define an outcome to be a permutation for selecting two balls. If two balls are selected without replacement (as opposed to putting the first ball back before selecting the second), there are 10 ways to select the first ball (since there are 10 balls in the bag to begin with) and there are 9 ways to select the second ball (since there are only 9 other balls to choose from after the first ball is selected). Multiply 10 by 9 to get the total number of possible outcomes: 90. There are 2 ways that the first ball can be blue; if the first ball is blue, there are 5 ways that the second ball can be red. Multiply 2 by 5 to get the number of ways for the first ball to be blue and the second ball to be red: 10. Similarly, there are 5 ways that the first ball can be red; if the first ball is red, there are 2 ways that the second ball can be blue. Multiply 5 by 2 to get the number of ways for the first ball to be red and the second ball to be blue: 10. Add 10 to 10 to get the number of ways for one ball to be blue and one ball to be red: 20. The probability of selecting one blue ball and one red ball in any order **without replacement** is 20/90, which reduces to 2/9 (which is approximately 0.222 or 22.2%). **Alternate solution**: This time, we define an outcome to be a combination for selecting two balls. To find the total number of outcomes, use the combination formula from Chapter 2 to select 2 balls from a bag of 10 balls: $\binom{10}{2} = \frac{10!}{2!(10-2)!} = \frac{10!}{2!8!} = \frac{(10)(9)}{(2)(1)} = 45$.

To find the number of outcomes where 1 of the 2 blue balls is selected and 1 of the 5 red balls is selected, use the Case 4 combination formula (Chapter 2): $\binom{2}{1}\binom{5}{1} = \frac{2!}{1!(2-1)!}\frac{5!}{1!(5-1)!} = \frac{2}{1!1!}\frac{5!}{1!4!} = (2)(5) = 10$. The probability of selecting 1 blue ball and 1 red ball (in any order) **without replacement** is therefore 10/45, which reduces to 2/9 (which is approximately 0.222 or 22.2%).

Another alternate solution: The probability of selecting a blue ball first is 2/10, which reduces to 1/5, and the probability of selecting a red ball first is 5/10, which reduces to 1/2. If the first ball is blue, the probability that the second ball will be red after already selecting one blue ball is 5/9. If the first ball is red, the probability that the second ball will be blue after already selecting one red ball is 2/9. The probability of selecting a blue ball first and then a red ball is $\left(\frac{1}{5}\right)\left(\frac{5}{9}\right) = \frac{1}{9}$ and the probability of selecting a red ball first and then a blue ball is $\left(\frac{1}{2}\right)\left(\frac{2}{9}\right) = \frac{1}{9}$. Add these together to get the probability of selecting one blue ball and one red ball in any order **without replacement**: $\frac{1}{9} + \frac{1}{9} = \frac{2}{9}$ (which is approximately 0.222 or 22.2%). Note: We will explore probability rules, like when you can add or multiply probabilities, when we get to Chapter 5. There are rules that tell you when you can or can't add or multiply probabilities. Before you use this method, you should read about those rules in Chapter 5.

(B) In the first solution to Part A, we found that there are 10 ways to first select one blue ball and then select one red ball, out of 90 possible outcomes. The probability of selecting one blue ball first and one red ball second **without replacement** is therefore 10/90, which reduces to 1/9 (which is approximately 0.111 or 11.1%). Note: Using any method from Part A, you could reason out that one-half of the outcomes where one blue ball and one red ball are selected have the blue ball first, and then simply divide the result from Part A (2/9) by two to get the answer for Part B. Beware that the strategy becomes a little less trivial if three or more balls are selected.

Example 4. A bag contains 8 blue balls and 6 red balls. If 5 balls are randomly selected **without replacement**, what is the probability that 3 balls will be blue and 2 balls will be red if the order in which the balls are selected doesn't matter?

We define an outcome to be a combination for selecting two balls. To find the total number of outcomes, use the combination formula (Chapter 2) to choose 5 balls from a bag of 14 balls: $\binom{14}{5} = \frac{14!}{5!(14-5)!} = \frac{14!}{5!9!} = 2002$. To find the number of outcomes where 3 of the 8 blue balls are selected and 2 of the 6 red balls are selected, use the combination formula for Case 4 (recall Chapter 2): $\binom{8}{3}\binom{6}{2} = \frac{8!}{3!(8-3)!}\frac{6!}{2!(6-2)!} = \frac{8!}{3!5!}\frac{6!}{2!4!} = (56)(15) = 840$. The probability of selecting 3 blue balls and 2 red balls (in any order) **without replacement** is therefore 840/2002, which reduces to 60/143 (which is approximately 0.420 or 42.0%). Note: In this example, the solution would be more involved to consider first selecting one ball, then selecting another ball, etc. Since we will be selecting 3 blue balls and 2 red balls, we would need to consider several cases (one example is blue, red, red, blue, blue; another example is red, blue, blue, red, blue). This is an example where the solution is simple in terms of combinations, but would be more complicated in terms of permutations.

Chapter 4 Problems

Directions: Find the indicated probabilities for each selection, assuming that it is **random**. The letter following the number is the first letter of the color. For example, P(2R) is the probability that both objects are red. As more examples of the notation, P(2 match) is the probability that both objects are the same color, P(1T,1G, any order) is the probability of selecting one tan sock and one gray sock in any order, and P(1B first and then 1R) is the probability of selecting a blue ball first and then selecting a red ball.

(1) A bag contains 4 blue balls, 8 green balls, and 12 red balls. One ball is selected.
P(1B), P(1G), P(1R)

(2) A bag contains 3 blue balls and 6 red balls. Two balls are selected without replacement.
P(2B), P(2R)

(3) A bag contains 5 blue balls and 7 red balls. One ball is selected, placed back in the bag, and then another ball is selected.
P(1B,1R, any order), P(2B), P(2R)

(4) A drawer contains 4 black socks and 8 white socks. Two socks are selected without replacement.
P(1B,1W, any order), P(2 match)

(5) A drawer contains 2 tan, 4 gray, and 6 white socks. Two socks are selected without replacement.
P(1T,1G, any order), P(2 match)

(6) A bag contains 7 blue balls, 4 green balls, and 5 red balls. Two balls are selected without replacement.
P(2G), P(1B first and then 1R)

(7) A bag contains 5 blue balls, 3 green balls, and 7 red balls. Three balls are selected without replacement.
P(1B,1G,1R, any order), P(3 match)

(8) A drawer contains 6 black socks, 4 tan socks, and 8 white socks. Four socks are selected without replacement.
P(4W), P(2 matching pairs)

(9) A bag contains 10 blue balls and 5 red balls. Three balls are selected without replacement.
P(3B), P(3R), P(2B,1R, any order)

(10) A drawer contains 6 tan socks and 10 white socks. Three socks are selected, replacing each before the next selection.
P(3T), P(3W), P(2T first and then 1W)

(11) The letters of the word NUMBER are randomly arranged.
P(2 consecutive vowels),
P(begin and end with a vowel)

(12) Three digits of 42,175 are randomly selected to form a three-digit number.
P(even number), P(digits add up to 13),
P(doesn't include a 7)

(13) A two-digit number is randomly chosen.
P(a multiple of 2), P(a multiple of 5), P(a multiple of 10)

(14) Every possible 3-letter subset of the word ALGEBRA appears on its own tile. One tile is selected at random.
P(no vowels), P(at least 2 vowels)

(15) A class has 5 boys and 7 girls. A team of 3 students is randomly selected.
P(3 boys), P(3 girls),
P(1 boy, 2 girls, any order)

(16) A box contains 4 pencils, 5 pens, and 6 markers. Three items are selected without replacement.
P(3 markers), P(2 pencils, 1 pen, any order)

5 Probability Concepts

In this chapter, we will explore a variety of probability concepts. Many of the concepts are useful for solving problems or checking that answers are self-consistent.

If two events occur, it is important to distinguish between the **intersection** and the **union** of the two events. The probability that one event **and** another event **both** occur is referred to as an **intersection**. The probability that one event **or** another event occurs is referred to as a **union**. We will explore intersections first, then unions, and then discuss other probability concepts.

$P(A \cap B)$ represents the probability that events A **and** B **both** occur. The symbol $\cap$ represents an **intersection** (as in the intersection of two sets) and may be read as the word "and." Before calculating $P(A \cap B)$, first determine if A and B are **independent** (meaning that the outcome of one doesn't influence the outcome of the other) or if A and B are **dependent** (where one outcome influences the other outcome).

If two events A and B are **independent** (meaning that the outcome of one doesn't influence the outcome of the other) and **both** events are to occur, the probability that both events will occur equals the **product** of the probabilities for each event to occur: $P(A \cap B) = P(A)P(B)$. For example, if a blue bag consists of three balls numbered 1, 2, and 3 and a red bag consists of four balls numbered 1, 2, 3, and 4, the probability that a 2 is randomly chosen from the blue bag and a 3 is randomly chosen from the red bag is $P(B2 \cap R3) = P(B2)P(R3) = \left(\frac{1}{3}\right)\left(\frac{1}{4}\right) = \frac{1}{12}$. These events are independent because selecting a ball from the blue bag doesn't affect the result of selecting a ball from the red bag. Since both events occur and they are independent, we multiply the probabilities. If three or more events all occur and are independent, multiply all of the probabilities together: $P(A \cap B \cap C) = P(A)P(B)P(C)$. See Example 5.

If two events A and B are **dependent** (meaning that the outcome of one influences the outcome of the other) and **both** events occur, you will need to find the **conditional probability** before you find $P(A \cap B)$. The **conditional probability** $P(B|A)$ represents the probability that B will occur once A has already occurred. The probability that A and B both occur can be found as $P(A \cap B) = P(A)P(B|A)$. For example, consider a bag that contains one blue ball and two red balls. We wish to find the probability that a red ball is selected first and the blue ball is selected second **without replacement**. In this example, the events are dependent; after the first ball is selected, there will be fewer balls left in the bag for the second selection. We will use the conditional probability formula. Let $P(R)$ represent the probability of selecting a red ball first and $P(B|R)$ represent the probability of selecting a blue ball second after a red ball has already been selected. Since there are initially 3 balls in the bag and 2 of them are red, $P(R) = \frac{2}{3}$. After a red ball has already been selected, there will be 2 balls in the bag, 1 of which is blue, such that $P(B|R) = \frac{1}{2}$. Use the conditional probability formula: $P(R \cap B)$ $= P(R)P(B|R) = \left(\frac{2}{3}\right)\left(\frac{1}{2}\right) = \frac{1}{3}$. Note that two events occur (two balls are selected; the first event is selecting the first ball and the second event is selecting the second ball) in this example and that the second event depends on the outcome of the first event. Conditional probability works the same way if there are three or more events. If three events occur and if each event depends on the outcome of the previous event, then $P(A \cap B \cap C) = P(A)P(B|A)P(C|A \cap B)$, where $P(A)$ is the probability that A occurs, $P(B|A)$ is the probability that B occurs if A has already occurred, and $P(C|A \cap B)$ is the probability that C occurs if A and B have already occurred. See Example 5.

$P(A \cup B)$ represents the probability that A **or** B will occur. The symbol $\cup$ stands for **union** (as in the union of two sets) and may be read as the word "or." Before calculating $P(A \cup B)$, first determine whether or not the two events are **mutually exclusive**.

- If A and B are **mutually exclusive**, this means that if one occurs, the other can't occur. (An alternative way to say that A and B are mutually exclusive is to call them **disjoint**.) For example, suppose that a bag contains 4 blue balls, 3 green balls, 2 red balls, and 1 yellow ball. A single ball is to be selected and we want the probability that the ball will be green or red. Since a single ball can't be both green and red, the events are mutually exclusive. If a green ball is selected, we know that the ball isn't red, and vice-versa.

- If one event occurs but this doesn't prevent the other event from occurring, then the two events are **not** mutually exclusive. For example, suppose that a bag contains a blue ball with the number 1 on it, a blue ball with the number 2 on it, a red ball with the number 1 on it, and a red ball with the number 2 on it. A single ball is to be selected and we want the probability that it will be red or have the number 2 on it. Since a ball could be red and have the number 2 on it, the events aren't mutually exclusive; the color red occurring doesn't prevent the number 2 from occurring.

If A and B are **mutually exclusive** (also referred to as **disjoint**), the probability that one of the events will occur equals the **sum** of the probabilities for each event to occur: $P(A \cup B) = P(A) + P(B)$. For example, suppose that a bag contains 4 blue balls, 3 green balls, 2 red balls, and 1 yellow ball, and we want the probability that a single randomly selected ball will be green or red. If the outcome is green, it can't also be red, and vice-versa, meaning that these events are mutually exclusive. In that case, we may add the probabilities for each event to occur. The probability that it will be green is $P(G) = \frac{3}{10}$ (since there are 3 green balls out of a total of $4 + 3 + 2 + 1 = 10$ balls) and the probability that it will be red is $P(R) = \frac{2}{10} = \frac{1}{5}$ (since there are 2 red balls out of a total of 10 balls). Since the events are mutually exclusive, $P(G \cup R) = P(G) + P(R) = \frac{3}{10} + \frac{2}{10} = \frac{5}{10} = \frac{1}{2}$.

If A and B are **not** mutually exclusive, to find the probability that either A **or** B occurs, but not both, the addition rule is modified as follows.

$$P(A \cup B) = P(A) + P(B) - P(A \cap B)$$

The last term, $P(A \cap B)$, represents the probability that A and B both occur; this term accounts for the fact that the two events **aren't** mutually exclusive. First find $P(A \cap B)$ as we previously discussed for the intersection of two events, and then use the above formula to find the union of the two events, $P(A \cup B)$. For example, suppose that a bag contains a blue ball with a 1 on it, a blue ball with a 2 on it, a red ball with a 1 on it, and a red ball with a 2 on it, and we want the probability that a single randomly selected ball will be red or have the number 2 on it. If the outcome is red, it could also be a 2, which means these events **aren't** mutually exclusive, so we need to use the modified sum formula. The probability that a ball will be red is $P(R) = \frac{2}{4} = \frac{1}{2}$ (since there are 2 red balls out of a total of 4 balls) and the probability that a ball will have a 2 on it is $P(2) = \frac{2}{4} = \frac{1}{2}$ (since there are 2 balls with a 2 on them out of a total of 4 balls). Since the events **aren't** mutually exclusive, we also need to find the probability that a ball is both red and a 2. These events are independent, such that $P(R \cap 2) = P(R)P(2) = \left(\frac{1}{2}\right)\left(\frac{1}{2}\right) = \frac{1}{4}$. (This should make sense: Out of 4 balls, there is 1 ball that is both red and a 2.) The modified sum formula gives $P(A \cup B) = P(A) + P(B) - P(A \cap B) = \frac{1}{2} + \frac{1}{2} - \frac{1}{4} = \frac{3}{4}$. (This should also make sense. Out of 4 balls, there is only 1 ball that isn't red or a 2: the blue ball with a 1 on it. The other 3 balls are either red or number 2.)

Here is a quick summary of the rules for $P(A \cap B)$ (called an **intersection**, where A **and** B **both** occur) and $P(A \cup B)$ (called a **union**, where A **or** B occurs).

- If A and B are **independent** (the outcome of one doesn't influence the other), $P(A \cap B) = P(A)P(B)$.
- If B **depends** on the outcome of A, $P(A \cap B) = P(A)P(B|A)$, where $P(B|A)$ is the probability that B will occur once A has already occurred.
- If A and B are **mutually exclusive** (meaning that if one occurs, the other can't occur), $P(A \cup B) = P(A) + P(B)$.
- If the occurrence of one event doesn't prevent the other from occurring (that is, A and B **aren't** mutually exclusive), $P(A \cup B) = P(A) + P(B) - P(A \cap B)$.

We will now explore other probability rules. Note that probability always lies in the range $0 \leq P(A) \leq 1$. If you ever get an answer for probability that is greater than one (like $\frac{5}{4}$) or that is negative, you know that you made a mistake.

- If $P(A) = 0$, the event is **impossible**. For example, if a bag contains nothing but white blocks, the probability of selecting a black block is zero.
- If $P(A) = 1$, the event is **certain**. For example, if a bag contains nothing but white blocks, the probability of selecting a white block is one.
- If $0 < P(A) < 1$, the event is possible, but not certain.

A **sample space** refers to the set of all **possible outcomes**. For example, if two coins are tossed simultaneously, the same space includes 4 elements: HH, HT, TH, and TT (where H is heads and T is tails). Suppose that $S_1, S_2, \ldots, S_N$ are **mutually exclusive** (or **disjoint**) subsets that form a sample space. (If three or more subsets are mutually exclusive, this means that any two subsets must be mutually exclusive.) Such a division of a sample space (specifically, where the subsets are mutually exclusive and where their union is the sample space) is referred to as a **partition**. If A is an event in the sample space, then the probability that A occurs is given by the formula below, which is referred to as the **total probability**, where N is the total number of subsets. Since the subsets are mutually exclusive, $P(A) = P(S_1 \cap A) + P(S_2 \cap A) + \cdots + P(S_N \cap A)$. Use the conditional probability formula $P(S_k \cap A) = P(S_k)P(A|S_k)$ to rewrite the previous equation as follows. The formula below is known as the **law of total probability**.

$$P(A) = P(S_1)P(A|S_1) + P(S_2)P(A|S_2) + \ldots + P(S_N)P(A|S_N)$$

Note that the conditional probability $P(A|S_k)$ is the probability that A will occur once S_k has already occurred.

As an example, consider a drawer where two-thirds of the socks are black and one-third of the socks are white. Of the black socks, three-fourths are long and one-fourth are short. Of the white socks, three-fifths are long and two-fifths are short. What is the probability of randomly selecting a long sock from the drawer? In this example, the sample space consists of black socks (B) and white socks (W); these are all of the possible outcomes for the color. In this example, B and W are mutually exclusive; if a sock is B, it can't also be W, and vice-versa. Since B and W are all of the possible outcomes for color and since B and W are mutually exclusive, they form a partition with $N = 2$ colors. Let L represent the event where a long sock is selected. The total probability formula gives $P(L) = P(B)P(L|B) + P(W)P(L|W)$. Since two-thirds of the socks are black and one-third are white, $P(B) = \frac{2}{3}$ and $P(W) = \frac{1}{3}$. Here, $P(L|B)$ is the probability that L will occur once B has already occurred; the problem states that $P(L|B) = \frac{3}{4}$. Similarly, $P(L|W)$ is the probability that L will occur once W has already occurred; the problem states that $P(L|W) = \frac{3}{5}$. Plug these fractions into the total probability formula: $P(L) = \left(\frac{2}{3}\right)\left(\frac{3}{4}\right) + \left(\frac{1}{3}\right)\left(\frac{3}{5}\right) = \frac{1}{2} + \frac{1}{5} = \frac{5}{10} + \frac{2}{10} = \frac{7}{10}$.

Note that we may write $P(S_k \cap A)$ either of two equivalent ways. We may write it as $P(S_k \cap A) = P(S_k)P(A|S_k)$, where $P(A|S_k)$ is the probability that A will occur once S_k has already occurred, or we may write it as $P(A \cap S_k) = P(A)P(S_k|A)$, where $P(S_k|A)$ is the probability that S_k will occur once A has already occurred. These two ways are equivalent because $P(S_k \cap A) = P(A \cap S_k)$, since each represents the probability that S_k and A both occur. This means that $P(S_k)P(A|S_k) = P(A)P(S_k|A)$. If we rearrange this, we arrive at **Baye's theorem**:

$$P(S_k|A) = \frac{P(S_k)P(A|S_k)}{P(A)}$$

If we rewrite the denominator using the law of total probability, we get **Baye's formula**:

$$P(S_k|A) = \frac{P(S_k)P(A|S_k)}{P(S_1)P(A|S_1) + P(S_2)P(A|S_2) + \ldots + P(S_N)P(A|S_N)}$$

As with the law of total probability, in order to use Baye's theorem or Baye's formula, $S_1, S_2, \ldots, S_N$ must be **mutually exclusive** (or **disjoint**) subsets that form a sample space (meaning that they form a **partition**), and A is an event in the sample space (though A is generally **not** the same event as any of the S_k's, as you can see by reviewing the previous example).

Let's apply Baye's formula to the previous example. We will use Baye's formula to find $P(B|L)$ and $P(W|L)$, which are the probabilities that black or white occurs once long has already occurred. Recall that L is the event that a long sock is selected; here, L is like A. The sample space was partitioned into black (B) and white (W) socks; these are S_1 and S_2. In the equations below, we already found the denominator to be $\frac{7}{10}$ in the previous example. Recall also that $P(B) = \frac{2}{3}$, $P(W) = \frac{1}{3}$, $P(L|B) = \frac{3}{4}$, and $P(L|W) = \frac{3}{5}$.

$$P(B|L) = \frac{P(B)P(L|B)}{P(B)P(L|B) + P(W)P(L|W)} = \frac{\left(\frac{2}{3}\right)\left(\frac{3}{4}\right)}{7/10} = \frac{1/2}{7/10} = \frac{1}{2} \div \frac{7}{10} = \frac{1}{2} \times \frac{10}{7} = \frac{5}{7}$$

$$P(W|L) = \frac{P(W)P(L|W)}{P(B)P(L|B) + P(W)P(L|W)} = \frac{\left(\frac{1}{3}\right)\left(\frac{3}{5}\right)}{7/10} = \frac{1/5}{7/10} = \frac{1}{5} \div \frac{7}{10} = \frac{1}{5} \times \frac{10}{7} = \frac{2}{7}$$

Recall the principle of **complementary counting** from Chapter 3. There is a similar rule for probability. If $P(A)$ represents the probability that event A will occur, then the **complementary** probability $P(A^c)$ represents the probability that event A won't occur.

Here, A^c is the complement of A. The **<u>complement rule</u>** of probability is $P(A) + P(A^c)$ $= 1$, which states that there is 100% probability that either A will occur or A won't occur. As an example, suppose that a bag contains a blue ball, a green ball, a red ball, a purple ball, and an orange ball. If $P(R)$ represents the probability that a randomly selected ball will be red, its complement $P(R^c)$ represents the probability that it won't be red. In this example, $P(R^c)$ represents the probability that the ball will be blue, green, purple, or orange. Since there are five balls, in this example $P(R) = \frac{1}{5}$ and $P(R^c) = \frac{4}{5}$. Observe that $P(R) + P(R^c) = \frac{1}{5} + \frac{4}{5} = 1$.

The **<u>complement rule</u>** is handy when it is easier to find the probability that an event **<u>won't occur</u>** than it is to find the probability that an event will occur. For example, suppose that two bags each consist of 4 balls numbered 1, 2, 3, and 4. One ball is to be randomly selected from each bag, and we would like to find the probability that at least one of the balls is a 2. If $P(X)$ is the probability that at least one ball is a 2, then the complementary probability $P(X^c)$ is the probability that neither ball is a 2. Note that $P(X^c)$ is the probability that both balls are not 2's. The probability that one selected ball isn't a 2 is 3/4 (since, in each bag, there are 4 balls and 3 of them aren't a 2); these probabilities are independent since selecting a ball from one bag doesn't affect the result of selecting a ball from the other bag. Since both events occur and they are independent, $P(X^c) = P(A \cap B) = P(A)P(B) = \left(\frac{3}{4}\right)\left(\frac{3}{4}\right) = \frac{9}{16}$, where A and B are the events of selecting one ball from each bag and not getting a 2. According to the complement rule, $P(X) + P(X^c) = 1$. To find $P(X)$, subtract $P(X^c)$ from both sides: $P(X) = 1 - P(X^c)$. Now plug in $P(X^c) = \frac{9}{16}$ to get $P(X) = 1 - \frac{9}{16} = \frac{16}{16} - \frac{9}{16} = \frac{7}{16}$. The probability that at least one of the balls is a 2 equals $P(X) = \frac{7}{16}$. Check the answer:

- The probability that both balls are 2's is $\left(\frac{1}{4}\right)\left(\frac{1}{4}\right) = \frac{1}{16}$.
- The probability that only the first ball is a 2 is $\left(\frac{1}{4}\right)\left(\frac{3}{4}\right) = \frac{3}{16}$.
- The probability that only the second ball is a 2 is $\left(\frac{3}{4}\right)\left(\frac{1}{4}\right) = \frac{3}{16}$.
- The probability that at least one ball is a 2 is $\frac{1}{16} + \frac{3}{16} + \frac{3}{16} = \frac{7}{16}$.

Example 1. A bag contains 1 blue ball, 2 green balls, and 3 red balls. Determine the probability of randomly selecting one blue ball or one red ball if a single ball is selected. Since we want a single ball to be blue **or** red, this question involves a **union**. We want $P(B \cup R)$, where B is blue and R is red. Since a single ball can't be both blue and red, these events are **mutually exclusive**: $P(B \cup R) = P(B) + P(R)$. Note that $P(B) = \frac{1}{6}$ and $P(R) = \frac{1}{2}$ since 1 out of 6 balls are blue and 3 out of 6 balls are red. This gives $P(B \cup R) = \frac{1}{6} + \frac{1}{2} = \frac{1}{6} + \frac{3}{6} = \frac{4}{6} = \frac{2}{3}$.

Alternate solution: First find $P(G) = \frac{2}{6} = \frac{1}{3}$. Observe that $P(G)$ is the complement to what the question asks for: $P(B \cup R) = P(G^c) = 1 - P(G) = 1 - \frac{1}{3} = \frac{2}{3}$.

Example 2. A bag contains 3 blue balls and 3 red balls. For each color, the 3 balls are numbered 1, 2, and 3. Determine the probability of selecting one ball that is blue or one ball that has the number 2 on it.

Since we want a single ball to be blue **or** to have the number 2 on it, this question involves a **union**. We want $P(B \cup 2)$, where B is blue and 2 means the ball has a 2 on it. These events **aren't** mutually exclusive? (Why? Because one possible outcome is a blue ball with the number 2 on it. An outcome of blue doesn't prevent an outcome of 2 from occurring.) Therefore, we need to use the modified sum formula: $P(B \cup 2) = P(B) + P(2) - P(B \cap 2)$. Note that $P(B) = \frac{1}{2}$ and $P(2) = \frac{1}{3}$ since 3 out of 6 balls are blue and 2 out of 6 balls are numbered 2. The modified sum formula requires that we first find $P(B \cap 2)$, which is the probability that a ball is blue **and** also number 2; this is an **intersection**. If the ball is blue, it doesn't affect the chances that it will be a 2 and vice-versa. Therefore, the events of blue or 2 are independent, such that $P(B \cap 2) = P(B)P(2) = \left(\frac{1}{2}\right)\left(\frac{1}{3}\right) = \frac{1}{6}$. (This should make sense: Out of 6 balls, there is 1 ball that is both blue and a 2.) The modified sum formula gives $P(B \cup 2) = P(B) + P(2) - P(B \cap 2) = \frac{1}{2} + \frac{1}{3} - \frac{1}{6} = \frac{3}{6} + \frac{2}{6} - \frac{1}{6} = \frac{4}{6} = \frac{2}{3}$. (This should also make sense. Out of 6 balls, there 2 balls that aren't blue or a 2: the red ball with a 1 on it and the red ball with a 3 on it. The other 4 balls include 3 blue balls and 1 red ball with a 2 on it.)

Example 3. A bag contains 3 blue balls and 2 red balls. One ball is selected, <u>replaced</u> in the bag, and then a second ball is selected. Determine the probability of selecting (A) a blue ball first then a red ball, (B) a red ball first then a blue ball, (C) one blue ball and one red ball in any order, (D) two blue balls, (E) two red balls, and (F) two balls of the same color.

(A) Since we want one blue ball <u>and</u> one red ball to <u>both</u> occur, this question involves an <u>intersection</u>. We want $P(B \cap R)$. Since the first ball will be placed back in the bag before the second ball is selected, the events are <u>independent</u>: $P(B \cap R) = P(B)P(R)$. Note that $P(B) = \frac{3}{5}$ and $P(R) = \frac{2}{5}$ since 3 out of 5 balls are blue and 2 out of 5 balls are red. (Since the first ball is placed back in the bag, there are still 3 blue balls and 2 red balls in the bag during the second selection.) This gives $P(B \cap R) = \left(\frac{3}{5}\right)\left(\frac{2}{5}\right) = \frac{6}{25}$.

(B) Since the first ball is replaced in the bag before the second ball is selected, the answer is the same as for Part A: $P(R \cap B) = \left(\frac{2}{5}\right)\left(\frac{3}{5}\right) = \frac{6}{25}$.

(C) Part C is the <u>union</u> of Parts A and B. The events from Parts A and B are <u>mutually exclusive</u>; the balls might come blue first and red second or they might come red first and blue second, but it can't happen both ways. Add the answers from Parts A and B:
$P(1B, 1R, \text{any order}) = P(B \cup R) + P(R \cup B) = \frac{6}{25} + \frac{6}{25} = \frac{12}{25}$.

(D) This is like Part A, except that both balls are blue; $P(B) = \frac{3}{5}$ for each ball since the first ball is replaced in the bag before the second selection: $P(B \cap B) = \left(\frac{3}{5}\right)\left(\frac{3}{5}\right) = \frac{9}{25}$. (This isn't the intersection of the same event with itself. These are two distinct events: the first selection being blue and the second selection being blue.)

(E) This is like Part D, except that both balls are red; $P(R) = \frac{2}{5}$ for each ball since the first ball is replaced in the bag before the second selection: $P(R \cap R) = \left(\frac{2}{5}\right)\left(\frac{2}{5}\right) = \frac{4}{25}$. Check the answers to Parts C, D, and E for consistency: $\frac{12}{25} + \frac{9}{25} + \frac{4}{25} = \frac{25}{25} = 1$.

(F) Part F is the <u>union</u> of Parts D and E, which are <u>mutually exclusive</u>. Add the answers from Parts D and E: $P(\text{same color}) = P(B \cup B) + P(R \cup R) = \frac{9}{25} + \frac{4}{25} = \frac{13}{25}$.

Example 4. A bag contains 3 blue balls and 2 red balls. Two balls are randomly selected **without replacement**. Determine the probability of selecting (A) a blue ball first then a red ball, (B) a red ball first then a blue ball, (C) one blue ball and one red ball in any order, (D) two blue balls, (E) two red balls, and (F) two balls of the same color.

(A) Since we want one blue ball **and** one red ball to **both** occur, this question involves an **intersection**. We want $P(B \cap R)$. Since there are fewer balls in the bag when the second ball is selected, the second event **depends** on the outcome of the first event. Since there are 5 balls in the bag and 3 are blue when the first ball is selected, $P(B) = \frac{3}{5}$. Since there are 4 balls left in the bag and 2 are red when the second ball is selected, the probability that the second ball will be red after a blue ball has already been selected is $P(R|B) = \frac{2}{4} = \frac{1}{2}$. Use the **conditional probability** formula: $P(B \cap R) = P(B)P(R|B)$
$= \left(\frac{3}{5}\right)\left(\frac{1}{2}\right) = \frac{3}{10}$.

(B) This is like Part A, except for the order. Since there are 5 balls in the bag and 2 are red, $P(R) = \frac{2}{5}$. Since there are 4 balls left in the bag and 3 are blue when the second ball is selected, the probability that the second ball will be blue after a red ball has already been selected is $P(B|R) = \frac{3}{4}$. Use the **conditional probability** formula: $P(R \cap B)$
$= P(R)P(B|R) = \left(\frac{2}{5}\right)\left(\frac{3}{4}\right) = \frac{6}{20} = \frac{3}{10}$. The answer is the same as for Part A because the numerators were effectively swapped: $\left(\frac{3}{5}\right)\left(\frac{2}{4}\right)$ equals $\left(\frac{2}{5}\right)\left(\frac{3}{4}\right)$.

(C) Part C is the **union** of Parts A and B. The events from Parts A and B are **mutually exclusive**. Add the answers from Parts A and B: $P(1B, 1R, \text{any order}) = P(B \cup R) +$
$P(R \cup B) = \frac{3}{10} + \frac{3}{10} = \frac{6}{10} = \frac{3}{5}$.

Alternate solution: Using the combination method from Chapter 4, there are $\binom{3}{1}\binom{2}{1}$
$= \frac{3!}{1!2!}\frac{2!}{1!1!} = (3)(2) = 6$ ways to choose one blue ball and one red ball in any order, and there are $\binom{5}{2} = \frac{5!}{2!3!} = \frac{(5)(4)}{(2)(1)} = 10$ ways to choose 2 balls out of 5. Divide 6 by 10 to get
$P(1B, 1R, \text{any order}) = \frac{6}{10} = \frac{3}{5}$.

(D) This is like Part A, except that both balls are blue. Since there are 5 balls in the bag and 3 are blue when the first ball is selected, $P(B_1) = \frac{3}{5}$. Since there are 4 balls left in the bag and 2 are blue when the second ball is selected, the probability that the second ball will be blue after a blue ball has already been selected is $P(B_2|B_1) = \frac{2}{4} = \frac{1}{2}$.

Use the **conditional probability** formula: $P(B_1 \cap B_2) = P(B_1)P(B_2|B_1) = \left(\frac{3}{5}\right)\left(\frac{1}{2}\right) = \frac{3}{10}$.

Alternate solution: Using the combination method from Chapter 4, there are $\binom{3}{2} = \frac{3!}{1!2!} = 3$ ways to choose 2 blue balls from 3 blue balls, and there are $\binom{5}{2} = \frac{5!}{2!3!} = \frac{(5)(4)}{(2)(1)} = 10$ ways to choose 2 balls out of 5. Divide 3 by 10 to get $P(2B) = \frac{3}{10}$.

(E) This is like Part D, except that both balls are red. Since there are 5 balls in the bag and 2 are red when the first ball is selected, $P(R_1) = \frac{2}{5}$. Since there are 4 balls left in the bag and 1 is red when the second ball is selected, the probability that the second ball will be red after a red ball has already been selected is $P(R_2|R_1) = \frac{1}{4}$. Use the **conditional probability** formula: $P(R_1 \cap R_2) = P(R_1)P(R_2|R_1) = \left(\frac{2}{5}\right)\left(\frac{1}{4}\right) = \frac{2}{20} = \frac{1}{10}$.

Check the answers to Parts C, D, and E for consistency: $\frac{3}{5} + \frac{3}{10} + \frac{1}{10} = \frac{6}{10} + \frac{4}{10} = \frac{10}{10} = 1$.

Alternate solution: Using the combination method from Chapter 4, there is $\binom{2}{2} = \frac{2!}{2!0!} = 1$ way to choose 2 red balls from 2 red balls, and there are $\binom{5}{2} = \frac{5!}{2!3!} = \frac{(5)(4)}{(2)(1)} = 10$ ways to choose 2 balls out of 5. Divide 1 by 10 to get $P(2R) = \frac{1}{10}$.

(F) Part F is the **union** of Parts D and E, which are **mutually exclusive**. Add the answers from Parts D and E: $P(\text{same color}) = P(B_1 \cup B_2) + P(R_1 \cup R_2) = \frac{3}{10} + \frac{1}{10} = \frac{4}{10} = \frac{2}{5}$.

Example 5. A bag contains 5 blue balls, 4 green balls, and 3 red balls. Three balls are randomly selected. Determine the probability of selecting (A) one ball of each color if each ball is **replaced** in the bag before making the next selection, (B) one ball of each color **without replacement**, (C) three blue balls if each ball is **replaced** in the bag before making the next selection, and (D) three blue balls **without replacement**.

(A) Since we want one blue ball, one green ball, **and** one red ball to **all** occur, this question involves an **intersection**. Let us first find the probability for blue first, then green, then red: $P(B \cap G \cap R)$. Since each ball will be placed back in the bag before the next ball is selected, the events are **independent**: $P(B \cap G \cap R) = P(B)P(G)P(R)$

$= \left(\frac{5}{12}\right)\left(\frac{4}{12}\right)\left(\frac{3}{12}\right) = \left(\frac{5}{12}\right)\left(\frac{1}{3}\right)\left(\frac{1}{4}\right) = \frac{5}{144}$. (Since each ball is placed back in the bag, there are still 5 blue balls, 4 green balls, and 3 red balls in the bag during each selection.) Note that there are a total of $5 + 4 + 3 = 12$ balls. The probability for BGR (blue first, green second, red last) is $\frac{5}{144}$. It's also $\frac{5}{144}$ for BRG, GBR, GRB, RBG, and RGB. To find the probability of selecting one ball of each color in any order, add the probabilities for these 6 permutations together: P(1B,1G,1R, any order) $= \frac{5}{144} + \frac{5}{144} + \frac{5}{144} + \frac{5}{144} + \frac{5}{144} + \frac{5}{144} = \frac{30}{144} = \frac{5}{24}$.

(B) Since there are fewer balls in the bag when the second and third balls are selected, the second and third events **depend** on the outcome of the prior events. Since there are 12 balls in the bag and 5 are blue when the first ball is selected, $P(B) = \frac{5}{12}$. Since there are 11 balls left in the bag and 4 are green when the second ball is selected, the probability that the second ball will be green after a blue ball has already been selected is $P(G|B) = \frac{4}{11}$. Since there are 10 balls left in the bag and 3 are red when the third ball is selected, the probability that the third ball will be red after a blue ball and green ball have already been selected is $P(R|B \cap G) = \frac{3}{10}$. Use the **conditional probability** formula: $P(B \cap G \cap R) = P(B)P(G|B)P(R|B \cap G) = \left(\frac{5}{12}\right)\left(\frac{4}{11}\right)\left(\frac{3}{10}\right) = \frac{60}{1230} = \frac{1}{22}$. This is just one of 6 permutations: BGR, BRG, GBR, GRB, RBG, and RGB. The probability of selecting one ball of each color in any order is P(1B,1G,1R, any order) $= \frac{1}{22} + \frac{1}{22} + \frac{1}{22} + \frac{1}{22} + \frac{1}{22} + \frac{1}{22} = \frac{6}{22} = \frac{3}{11}$.

Alternate solution: Using the method from Chapter 4, there are $\binom{5}{1}\binom{4}{1}\binom{3}{1} = \frac{5!}{1!4!}\frac{4!}{1!3!}\frac{3!}{1!2!} = (5)(4)(3) = 60$ ways to choose one blue ball, one green ball, and one red ball in any order, and there are $\binom{12}{3} = \frac{12!}{3!9!} = \frac{(12)(11)(10)}{(3)(2)(1)} = 220$ ways to choose 3 balls out of 12. Divide 60 by 220 to get $P(1B,1G, 1R, \text{any order}) = \frac{60}{220} = \frac{3}{11}$.

(C) This is similar to Part A, except for selecting three blue balls. $P(B \cap B \cap B) = P(B)P(B)P(B) = \left(\frac{5}{12}\right)\left(\frac{5}{12}\right)\left(\frac{5}{12}\right) = \frac{125}{1728}$. (Since each ball is placed back in the bag, there are still 5 blue balls, 4 green balls, and 3 red balls in the bag during each selection.)

(D) This is similar to Part B, except for selecting three blue balls. Since there are 12 balls in the bag and 5 are blue when the first ball is selected, $P(B_1) = \frac{5}{12}$. Since there are 11 balls left in the bag and 4 are blue when the second ball is selected, the probability that the second ball will be blue after a blue ball has already been selected is $P(B_2|B_1) = \frac{4}{11}$. Since there are 10 balls left in the bag and 3 are blue when the third ball is selected, the probability that the third ball will be blue after two blue balls have already been selected is $P(B_3|B_1 \cap B_2) = \frac{3}{10}$. Use the **conditional probability** formula:

$$P(B_1 \cap B_2 \cap B_3) = P(B_1)P(B_2|B_1)P(B_3|B_1 \cap B_2) = \left(\frac{5}{12}\right)\left(\frac{4}{11}\right)\left(\frac{3}{10}\right) = \frac{60}{1230} = \frac{1}{22}.$$ Note: B_1, B_2, and B_3 **don't** refer to specific balls (unlike Chapter 4, where we did use subscripts to refer to specific balls); with the conditional probability formula, when the same color ball is to be selected in different events, we are using the subscripts to indicate that a ball of that color is being selected first, second, third, etc. (This example has 5 blue balls, but only 3 balls are selected.)

Alternate solution: Using the method from Chapter 4, there are $\binom{5}{3} = \frac{5!}{3!2!} = \frac{(5)(4)}{(2)(1)} = \frac{20}{2} = 10$ ways to choose 3 blue balls from 5 blue balls, and there are $\binom{12}{3} = \frac{12!}{3!9!} = \frac{(12)(11)(10)}{(3)(2)(1)} = 220$ ways to choose 3 balls out of 12. Divide 10 by 220 to get $P(3B) = \frac{10}{220} = \frac{1}{22}$.

Example 6. A product is manufactured at one of three factories. The largest factory makes 60% of the products, of which 2% are defective. The medium factor makes 25% of the products, of which 4% are defective. The smallest factory makes 15% of the products, of which 5% are defective. (A) What is the probability that a product purchased at random is defective? (B) If a product is defective, what is the probability that it was manufactured at the largest factory?

(A) Use the **law of total probability**. Let L, M, and S represent the largest, medium, and smallest factories, and let D stand for a defective product. According to the problem, $P(L) = 60\% = 0.6$, $P(M) = 25\% = 0.25$, $P(S) = 15\% = 0.15$, $P(D|L) = 2\% = 0.02$, $P(D|M) = 4\% = 0.04$, and $P(D|S) = 5\% = 0.05$. Note that $P(D|L)$ represents the probability that D will occur once L has already occurred; this means that if it is known that a product was manufactured at the largest factory, then $P(D|L)$ is the probability that the product will be defective. Use the total probability formula: $P(D) = P(L)P(D|L) + P(M)P(D|M) + P(S)P(D|S) = (0.6)(0.02) + (0.25)(0.04) + (0.15)(0.05) = 0.012 + 0.01 + 0.0075 = 0.0295 = 2.95\%$.

(B) Use **Baye's theorem**. The denominator, $P(D) = 0.0295$, was found in Part A.

$$P(L|D) = \frac{P(L)P(D|L)}{P(D)} = \frac{(0.6)(0.02)}{0.0295} = \frac{0.012}{0.0295} = \frac{24}{59} \approx 0.407 = 40.7\%$$

Example 7. A drawer contains 6 black socks, 4 gray socks, and 2 white socks. If socks are selected at random **without replacement**, how many socks must be selected in order to guarantee that the selected socks include at least one pair of matching socks? What if we want to have a pair of matching black socks?

Work out the worst-case scenario. The first three socks could be different colors, so **4 socks** are needed to guarantee a pair. The first seven socks could include 1 black, 4 gray, and 2 white, so **8 socks** are needed to guarantee a pair of black socks.

Example 8. A bag contains 5 blue balls, 3 green balls, and 1 red ball. Two balls are randomly selected **without replacement**. What is the probability that at least one of the balls is green?

We will use the **complement rule**. Let $P(X)$ be the probability that at least one ball is green. Then $P(X^c)$ is the probability that neither ball is green. Since there are fewer balls in the bag during the second selection, we need to use the conditional probability formula: $P(X^c) = P(Y)P(Z|Y)$, where $P(Y)$ is the probability that the first ball is blue or red and $P(Z|Y)$ is the probability that the second ball is blue or red after a blue or red ball has already been selected. Since there are $5 + 1 = 6$ blue or red balls out of a total of $5 + 3 + 1 = 9$ balls initially, $P(Y) = \frac{6}{9} = \frac{2}{3}$. Since there are 5 blue or red balls out of a total of 8 balls after a blue or red ball has already been selected, $P(Z|Y) = \frac{5}{8}$. This gives $P(X^c) = P(Y)P(Z|Y) = \left(\frac{2}{3}\right)\left(\frac{5}{8}\right) = \frac{10}{24} = \frac{5}{12}$. According to the complement rule, $P(X) + P(X^c) = 1$. To find $P(X)$, subtract $P(X^c)$ from both sides: $P(X) = 1 - P(X^c)$. Now plug in $P(X^c) = \frac{5}{12}$ to get $P(X) = 1 - \frac{5}{12} = \frac{12}{12} - \frac{5}{12} = \frac{7}{12}$. The probability that at least one of the balls is green equals $P(X) = \frac{7}{12}$.

Chapter 5 Problems

Directions: Find the indicated probabilities for each selection **using techniques from this chapter**, assuming that it is **random**. As examples of the notation, P(B or R) is the probability that the ball is blue or red, P(1B,1W, any order) is the probability that a black sock and white sock will be selected in any order, P(2R) is the probability for two red balls, and P(2 match) is the probability that both objects are the same color.

(1) A bag contains 4 blue balls, 3 green balls, and 2 red balls. A single ball is selected.

P(B or G), P(B or R), P(G or R)

(2) A bag contains 4 blue balls and 4 red balls. For each color, the balls are numbered 1-4. A single ball is selected.

P(B or 3), P(odd number), P(not a 4)

(3) A bag contains 5 blue balls, 5 green balls, 3 red balls, and 2 yellow balls. A single ball is selected.

P(B or G), P(G or R), P(B, G, or Y)

(4) A bag contains 5 blue balls numbered 1-5 and 3 red balls numbered 1-3. A single ball is selected.

P(B or 2), P(R or 1), P(1, 3, or 4)

(5) A drawer contains 2 black socks and 2 white socks. One sock is selected, placed back in the drawer, and then another sock is selected.
P(1B first then 1W), P(2 match)

(6) A drawer contains 2 black socks and 2 white socks. Two socks are selected without replacement.
P(1B,1W, any order), P(2 match)

(7) A drawer contains 3 black socks and 1 white sock. One sock is selected, placed back in the drawer, and then another sock is selected.
P(1B first then 1W), P(2 match)

(8) A drawer contains 3 black socks and 1 white sock. Two socks are selected without replacement.
P(1B first then 1W), P(2B)

(9) A bag contains 6 blue balls and 4 red balls. One ball is selected, placed back in the bag, and then another ball is selected.

P(1B,1R, any order), P(2 match)

(10) A bag contains 9 blue balls and 6 red balls. Three balls are selected without replacement.

P(2B,1R, any order), P(3B), P(at least 1 red)

(11) A bag contains 8 blue balls, 3 green balls, and 4 red balls. Two balls are selected without replacement.

P(2B), P(2R), P(at least 1 green)

(12) A bag contains 7 blue balls, 5 green balls, and 3 red balls. Three balls are selected without replacement.

P(3B), P(3G), P(1 of each color)

Directions: Socks are selected at random. Determine how many socks must be selected **without replacement** in order to guarantee that the indicated matching pairs of socks are found. Ignore Part A when answering Part B; they are two separate cases.

(13) A drawer contains 8 black socks, 10 tan socks, and 6 white socks.
(A) Make 1 matching pair.
(B) Make 1 matching black pair.

(14) A drawer contains 13 black socks, 9 gray socks, and 5 white socks.
(A) Make 1 matching black pair.
(B) Make 1 matching white pair.

(15) A drawer contains 12 pink socks, 14 orange socks, and 8 yellow socks.
(A) Make 2 matching pairs.
(B) Make 2 matching pink pairs.

(16) A drawer contains 22 black socks, 16 gray socks, and 24 white socks.
(A) Make 3 matching pairs.
(B) Make 1 matching pair for every color.

Directions: A product is manufactured at one of the factories listed. For each factory, first find the probability that a product is defective. Next, if a product is known to be defective, find the probability that it was manufactured at factory A.

(17) Factory A makes 50% of the products, of which 3% are defective. Factory B makes 30% of the products, of which 2% are defective. Factory C makes 20% of the products, of which 1% are defective.

(18) Factory A makes 40% of the products, of which 0.5% are defective. Factory B makes 35% of the products, of which 2% are defective. Factory C makes 25% of the products, of which 4% are defective.

6 Dice and Coins

A single flipped **coin** has two possible outcomes: heads or tails. For a **fair** coin, each outcome is equally likely, meaning that the probability that it will be heads is 50% and the probability that it will be tails is also 50%. It is possible to engineer a coin to be **unfair** (by making the coin weighted), such that one outcome is more likely than the other. For example, if a coin is weighted so that it comes up heads 54% of the time and tails 46% of the time (even after a very large number of flips), that coin is unfair. Note that the probability of one coin coming up heads and the probability of one coin coming up tails add up to 100%.

In the United States, the most common coins include quarters, dimes, nickels, and pennies. A penny is worth one cent, meaning that 100 pennies are worth one dollar. A nickel is worth 5 cents, a dime is worth 10 cents, and a quarter is worth 25 cents.

Note that the word **dice** may be used in the singular or the plural form, whereas the word **die** can only be singular. Some people use die for singular and dice for plural, but other people use the word dice whether it is singular or plural. The former group would say "He rolled one die" and "She rolled two dice" whereas the latter group would say "He rolled one dice" and "She rolled two dice." According to the dictionary, both cases are considered to be acceptable. So if you prefer to use the word dice whether you are talking about one or more dice, that's fine, and if you prefer to use die for just one and dice for two or more, that's also fine.

In this book, we will use **die** for exactly one and **dice** when referring to two or more.

The following kinds of dice are relatively common. For our purposes, the important feature of each kind of dice listed below is the **number of faces**.
- The most common playing dice are shaped like cubes and have 6 square faces.
- Dodecahedral dice have 12 pentagonal faces.
- Icosahedral dice have 20 triangular faces.
- Octahedral dice have 8 triangular faces.

- A die shaped like a pentagonal trapezohedron has 10 kite-shaped faces. A kite is a quadrilateral with two pairs of congruent adjacent sides (meaning that each pair of adjacent sides have the same length). A classic kite that kids fly on a windy day has the same shape.

- Tetrahedral dice have 4 triangular faces. A unique property of tetrahedral dice is that no face points up. Some tetrahedral dice put numbers near the vertices so that the top vertex determines the outcome; other tetrahedral dice put numbers near the edges so that the bottom face determines the outcome. Both methods of numbering have 4 possible outcomes.

- Many dice number the faces starting with one. For example, standard dice shaped like cubes have the numbers 1, 2, 3, 4, 5, and 6, and standard icosahedral dice have the numbers 1-20.

- Dice don't have to number the faces in order starting with one. A common alternative is to number the faces in tens. For example, a pentagonal trapezohedron die may number the faces 0, 10, 20, 30, 40, 50, 60, 70, 80, and 90. A pair of dice shaped like pentagonal trapezohedrons may have one die with the numbers 1-10 and another with the numbers 0-90, such that when the two dice are rolled together any number from 1 to 100 is possible (found by adding the values of the two dice together).

- Nonstandard dice may have anything on the faces. For example, a cube could have 2's on three of the faces and 4's on three of the faces, or an octahedron could have different letters on each face. The possibilities are endless.

When one fair die is rolled, each outcome is equally likely. For example, for a fair die shaped like a cube, each of the 6 faces is equally likely to land up, meaning that there is a probability of $\frac{1}{6}$ for any particular side to land face up. It's also possible to create **loaded dice** that are unfair (by using weights), such that some outcomes are more likely than others.

For **fair** coins or **fair** dice, we may calculate probabilities using formulas from Chapters 4-5. This is illustrated in Examples 1-4.

For **unfair** coins or dice, we will calculate probabilities using formulas from Chapter 5. We will explore unfair coins or dice in Examples 5-7. (For unfair coins or dice, the outcomes aren't equally likely, so we **can't** use the probability formula from Chapter 4 where we divide the number of ways for a specific outcome to occur by the total number of possible outcomes.)

Let's compare a fair coin to an unfair coin for a specific example. A fair coin shows heads 50% of the time and tails 50% of the time. Suppose that a particular unfair coin is weighted such that it shows heads 30% of the time and tails 70% of the time. (It must be understood that these percentages are averaged over a sufficiently large number of flips.) We will find the probabilities of the different possible outcomes if a coin is flipped two times. The two flips are independent since the outcome of the first flip doesn't affect the outcome of the second flip. We'll start with the fair coin. Recall from Chapter 5 that we multiply probabilities for independent events when both of the events occur.

If the **fair** coin is flipped twice, the probability that heads will show twice is $P(H \cap H)$ $= \left(\frac{1}{2}\right)\left(\frac{1}{2}\right) = \frac{1}{4}$, the probability that tails will show twice is $P(T \cap T) = \left(\frac{1}{2}\right)\left(\frac{1}{2}\right) = \frac{1}{4}$, the probability of getting heads first and then tails is $P(H \cap T) = \left(\frac{1}{2}\right)\left(\frac{1}{2}\right) = \frac{1}{4}$, and the probability of getting tails first and then heads is $P(T \cap H) = \left(\frac{1}{2}\right)\left(\frac{1}{2}\right) = \frac{1}{4}$. (Observe that the probabilities add up to one.)

If the **unfair** coin is flipped twice, the probability that heads will show twice is $P(H \cap H) = (0.3)(0.3) = 0.09$, the probability that tails will show twice is $P(T \cap T) = (0.7)(0.7) = 0.49$, the probability of getting heads first and then tails is $P(H \cap T) = (0.3)(0.7) = 0.21$, and the probability of getting tails first and then heads is $P(T \cap H) = (0.7)(0.3) = 0.21$. (Observe that $0.09 + 0.49 + 0.21 + 0.21 = 1$.)

Example 1. Three fair coins are flipped at once. What is the probability that exactly two of the coins will show tails?

Since each coin may be heads (H) or tails (T), there are $2 \times 2 \times 2 = 2^3 = 8$ possible outcomes for flipping three coins at once. If two coins show tails and one coin shows heads, we need permutations of TTH. Using Case 2 from Chapter 1 (for the repeated letter), there are $\frac{3!}{2!} = \frac{6}{2} = 3$ permutations of TTH. These include HTT, THT, and TTH. (Sure, you could easily list these without using the permutation formula, but if there are a large number of coins, you'll want to know the formula.) The probability that exactly two of the coins will show tails is $P(2T) = \frac{3}{8}$ (or 0.375 or 37.5%). The eight possible outcomes include HHH, HHT, HTH, THH, HTT, THT, TTH, and TTT.

<u>Alternate solution</u>: There are $\frac{3!}{2!} = \frac{6}{2} = 3$ permutations of TTH. Each permutation has a probability of $\left(\frac{1}{2}\right)\left(\frac{1}{2}\right)\left(\frac{1}{2}\right) = \frac{1}{8}$ of occurring. The probability that exactly two of the coins will show tails is $P(2T) = (3)\left(\frac{1}{8}\right) = \frac{3}{8}$. **<u>When it comes to unfair coins</u>**, it will be simplest to use this method.

<u>Another alternate solution</u>: There are $\binom{3}{2} = \frac{3!}{2!(3-2)!} = \frac{3!}{2!1!} = 3$ ways to choose 2 out of 3 coins to be tails. If we label the coins C_1, C_2, and C_3, the combinations are C_1C_2, C_1C_3, and C_2C_3. There are $2^3 = 8$ possible outcomes. The probability that exactly two of the coins will show tails is $P(2T) = \frac{3}{8}$.

Note: The solution to this example would be the same whether the same fair coin were flipped three different times or if three different fair coins were flipped at once (or if three fair different coins were flipped one time each but at different times). Challenge: Can you think of a problem where it would make a difference whether the same coin was flipped multiple times or if multiple coins were flipped at once?

Example 2. Five fair coins are flipped at once. What is the probability that at least two of the coins will show heads?

Notice the difference in wording in the first two examples: This example wants "at least two" coins to be heads, whereas the first example wanted "exactly two" coins to be tails. In this example, we want 2, 3, 4, or 5 of the coins to show heads. It would be easier to find how many times 0 or 1 of the coins show heads, and then apply the complement rule from Chapter 5. There is 1 way to have 0 heads: TTTTT. Using permutations, there are $\frac{5!}{4!} = 5$ ways to have 1 coin heads up: HTTTT, THTTT, TTHTT, TTTHT, and TTTTH. (We divided by 4! according to Case 2 of Chapter 1 because the T is repeated 4 times.) There are $2^5 = 32$ possible outcomes. The probability that fewer than 2 coins will show heads is $P(<2H) = \frac{6}{32} = \frac{3}{16}$. Use the **complement rule** to find the probability that at least 2 of the coins will show heads: $P(\geq 2H) = 1 - P(<2H)$ $= 1 - \frac{3}{16} = \frac{16}{16} - \frac{3}{16} = \frac{13}{16}$ (or 0.8125 or 81.25%). Since there are six ways to have 0 or 1 coins show heads (HTTTT, THTTT, TTHTT, TTTHT, TTTTH, and TTTTT), this leaves $32 - 6 = 26$ ways to have at least 2 coins show heads: $\frac{26}{32} = \frac{13}{16}$.

Alternate solution: There are $1 + 5 = 6$ permutations with 0 or 1 heads showing. Each permutation has a probability of $\left(\frac{1}{2}\right)\left(\frac{1}{2}\right)\left(\frac{1}{2}\right)\left(\frac{1}{2}\right)\left(\frac{1}{2}\right) = \frac{1}{32}$ of occurring. This gives $P(<2H) = 6\left(\frac{1}{32}\right) = \frac{3}{16}$ and $P(\geq 2H) = 1 - P(<2H) = 1 - \frac{3}{16} = \frac{16}{16} - \frac{3}{16} = \frac{13}{16}$.

Another alternate solution: There is $\binom{5}{0} = \frac{5!}{0!(5-0)!} = \frac{5!}{0!5!} = 1$ way to choose 0 heads out of 5 coins and there are $\binom{5}{1} = \frac{5!}{1!(5-1)!} = \frac{5!}{1!4!} = 5$ ways to choose 1 head out of 5 coins. This gives $1 + 5 = 6$ ways for 0 or 1 coins to show heads. The six ways to have 0 or 1 coins show heads include TTTTT (no coins are heads), HTTTT (only C_1 is heads), THTTT (only C_2 is heads), TTHTT (only C_3 is heads), TTTHT (only C_4 is heads), and TTTTH (only C_5 is heads). There are $2^5 = 32$ possible outcomes. The probability that fewer than 2 coins will show heads is $P(<2H) = \frac{5+1}{32} = \frac{6}{32} = \frac{3}{16}$. According to the **complement rule**, $P(\geq 2H) = 1 - P(<2H) = 1 - \frac{3}{16} = \frac{16}{16} - \frac{3}{16} = \frac{13}{16}$.

Example 3. Two standard, fair 6-sided dice are rolled at once. What is the probability that the sum of the dice will equal 8?

There are $6 \times 6 = 6^2 = 36$ possible outcomes for rolling two 6-sided dice. There are 5 permutations where the numbers showing on the top face of the dice add up to 8: $2+6, 3+5, 4+4, 5+3,$ and $6+2$. The probability that the sum will be 8 is $P(\text{sum} = 8) = \frac{5}{36}$ (which is approximately 0.139 or 13.9%).

Alternate solution: There are 5 permutations where the two dice have a sum of 8. Each permutation has a probability of $\left(\frac{1}{6}\right)\left(\frac{1}{6}\right) = \frac{1}{36}$ of occurring. The probability that both dice will sum to 8 is $P(\text{sum} = 8) = 5\left(\frac{1}{36}\right) = \frac{5}{36}$. **When it comes to unfair dice**, it will be simplest to use this method.

Example 4. Three fair octahedral dice are rolled at once. Each die has the letters T, R, I, A, N, G, L, and E on its sides. What is the probability that all three dice will show vowels on the top face?

An octahedron has 8 sides. There are $8 \times 8 \times 8 = 8^3 = 512$ possible outcomes for rolling three 8-sided dice. Each die has 3 sides with vowels (A, E, and I). Each vowel may appear multiple times since more than one die can show the same letter. There are $3 \times 3 \times 3 = 3^3 = 27$ outcomes with three vowels: AAA, AAE, AAI, AEA, AEE, AEI, AIA, AIE, AII, EAA, EAE, EAI, EEA, EEE, EEI, EIA, EIE, EII, IAA, IAE, IAI, IEA, IEE, IEI, IIA, IIE, and III. The probability that all three dice will show vowels on the top face is $P(3 \text{ vowels}) = \frac{27}{512}$ (which is approximately 0.0527 or 5.27%).

Alternate solution: There are 27 outcomes with three vowels. Each outcome has a probability of $\left(\frac{1}{8}\right)\left(\frac{1}{8}\right)\left(\frac{1}{8}\right) = \frac{1}{512}$ of occurring. The probability that all three dice will show vowels is $P(3 \text{ vowels}) = 27\left(\frac{1}{512}\right) = \frac{27}{512}$.

Example 5. An unfair coin is twice as likely to show tails as it is to show heads. (A) What is the probability that a single flip will result in heads? (B) What is the probability that a single flip will result in tails? (C) If it is flipped four times, what is the probability that it will show tails exactly two times?

(A) We are told that a tail is twice as likely as a head for a single flip. We can express this as $P(T) = 2P(H)$. For a single flip, we know that the probabilities of all of the possible outcomes must sum to 100%: $P(T) + P(H) = 1$. Substitute $P(T) = 2P(H)$ into the equation $P(T) + P(H) = 1$ to get $2P(H) + P(H) = 1$, which simplifies to $3P(H) = 1$. Divide by 3 on both sides: $P(H) = \frac{1}{3}$ (which is approximately 0.333 or 33.3%).

(B) Plug $P(H) = \frac{1}{3}$ into $P(T) = 2P(H)$ to get $P(T) = \frac{2}{3}$ (which is approximately 0.667 or 66.7%).

(C) If two coins show tails and two coins shows heads, we need permutations of TTHH. Using Case 2 from Chapter 1, there are $\frac{4!}{2!2!} = \frac{24}{4} = 6$ permutations of TTHH. (We divided by 2! for the 2 T's and for the 2 H's.) These include HHTT, HTHT, HTTH, THHT, THTH, and TTHH. We will now solve this problem using the method shown in the first alternate solution to Example 1. Since each permutation involves 2 H's and 2 T's, each permutation has a probability of $P(H)P(H)P(T)P(T) = \left(\frac{1}{3}\right)\left(\frac{1}{3}\right)\left(\frac{2}{3}\right)\left(\frac{2}{3}\right) = \frac{4}{81}$. Multiply this by 6 (since there are 6 permutations of TTHH) to find the probability that tails will show exactly two times: $P(2T) = (6)\left(\frac{4}{81}\right) = \frac{24}{81} = \frac{8}{27}$ (which is approximately 0.296 or 29.6%).

Note: We could alternatively use the combination formula $\binom{4}{2} = \frac{4!}{2!(4-2)!} = \frac{4!}{2!2!} = 6$ to find the number of ways to choose 2 coins to be tails. This is the same as the number of permutations of TTHH, which is $\frac{4!}{2!2!} = \frac{24}{4} = 6$. Compare the solution to Examples 1-2 with their second alternate solutions.

Example 6. An unfair coin has a probability of $\frac{5}{8}$ of showing heads. If it is flipped five times, what is the probability that it will show heads exactly three times?

If three coins show heads and two coins shows tails, we need permutations of HHHTT. Using Case 2 from Chapter 1, there are $\frac{5!}{3!2!} = \frac{120}{(6)(2)} = 10$ permutations of HHHTT. These include HHHTT, HHTHT, HHTTH, HTHHT, HTHTH, HTTHH, THHHT, THHTH, THTHT, and TTHHH. Since each permutation involves 3 H's and 2 T's, each permutation has a probability of $P(H)P(H)P(H)P(T)P(T) = \left(\frac{5}{8}\right)^3 \left(\frac{3}{8}\right)^2 = \left(\frac{125}{512}\right)\left(\frac{9}{64}\right) = \frac{1125}{32,768}$. Multiply this by 10 (since there are 10 permutations of HHHTT) to find the probability that heads will show exactly three times: $P(3H) = (10)\left(\frac{1125}{32,768}\right) = \frac{11,250}{32,768} = \frac{5625}{16,384}$ (which is approximately 0.343 or 34.3%).

<u>Note</u>: As mentioned at the end of Example 5, we could alternatively use the combination formula $\binom{5}{3} = \frac{5!}{3!(5-3)!} = \frac{5!}{3!2!} = 10$ to find the number of ways to choose 3 coins to be heads, since this equals the number of permutations of HHHTT.

Example 7. An unfair 6-sided die has probabilities $P(1) = P(3) = P(5) = \frac{1}{9}$ and $P(2) = P(4) = P(6) = \frac{2}{9}$. (Observe that $\frac{1}{9} + \frac{1}{9} + \frac{1}{9} + \frac{2}{9} + \frac{2}{9} + \frac{2}{9} = 1$.) If the die is rolled twice, what is the probability that the two numbers rolled will sum to 8?

There are 5 permutations where the numbers showing on the top face of the dice add up to 8: 2+6, 3+5, 4+4, 5+3, and 6+2. We will now solve this problem using the method shown in the alternate solution to Example 3. Three of the permutations (2+6, 4+4, and 6+2) involve two even numbers. Each of these permutations has a probability of $P(even)P(even) = \left(\frac{2}{9}\right)\left(\frac{2}{9}\right) = \frac{4}{81}$. Multiply this by 3 since there are three such permutations: $(3)\left(\frac{4}{81}\right) = \frac{4}{27}$. Two of the permutations (3+5 and 5+3) involve two odd numbers. Each of these permutations has a probability of $P(odd)P(odd) = \left(\frac{1}{9}\right)\left(\frac{1}{9}\right) = \frac{1}{81}$. Multiply this by 2 since there are two such permutations: $(2)\left(\frac{1}{81}\right) = \frac{2}{81}$. Add $\frac{4}{27}$ to $\frac{2}{81}$ to find the probability that the sum will be 8: $P(\text{sum} = 8) = \frac{4}{27} + \frac{2}{81} = \frac{12}{81} + \frac{2}{81} = \frac{14}{81}$ (which is approximately 0.173 or 17.3%).

Chapter 6 Problems

Directions: Find the indicated probabilities. As examples of the notation, P(1,2,3, any order) means the dice show one 1, one 2, and one 3 in any order, P(H's=30 cents) means that the coins with heads add up to **exactly** 30 cents, and P(more H's on N's) means that there are more heads on the nickels than on the dimes.

(1) 4 fair coins are flipped at once.
P(2T), P(3H), P(≥3T), P(4 of a kind)

(2) 6 fair coins are flipped at once.
P(3H), P(4T), P(more H than T)

(3) 2 standard, fair 6-sided dice are rolled at once.
P(doubles), P(sum=7), P(sum≤4)

(4) 3 standard, fair 6-sided dice are rolled at once.
P(at least two 5's), P(1,2,3, any order), P(sum=15)

(5) 5 fair nickels and 3 fair dimes are flipped at once.

P(H's=30 cents), P(more H's on N's)

(6) A fair quarter, fair dime, and fair nickel are flipped at once.

P(Q and D match), P(T's≥30 cents)

(7) 2 standard, fair 6-sided dice are rolled at once.

P(product=12), P(only 1's and/or 2's)

(8) 3 fair 8-sided dice numbered 1-8 are rolled at once.

P(same number **not** on all 3 dice),

P(3 different numbers)

(9) 1 fair blue coin and 3 fair red coins are flipped at once.

P(3T), P(3T if it's known that blue is T), P(3T if it's known that blue is H)

(10) 2 fair coins, 1 double-headed coin, and 2 double-tailed coins are flipped at once.

P(3T), P(3H)

(11) 1 standard, fair 6-sided die and 1 fair 12-sided die numbered 1-12 are rolled at once.

P(sum=14), P(sum=15), P(12-sided die>6-sided die)

(12) 1 fair 6-sided die has letters C, E, N, T, E, and R on its sides. Another fair 6-sided die has letters R, A, D, I, U, and S. Both dice are rolled at once.

P(2 vowels), P(1 vowel and 1 consonant)

(13) 1 fair coin has numbers 1 and 2 on its sides. Another fair coin has numbers 2 and 3 on its sides. A third fair coin has numbers 3 and 4 on its sides. All three coins are flipped at once.
P(sum=7), P(2 coins match)

(14) Three fair coins are flipped at once. All three coins are flipped a second time. P(same number of heads for each flip)

(15) 3 standard, fair 6-sided dice are rolled at once.
P(two 5's and one 4 in any order),
P(either of the two most likely sums)

(16) 3 fair 12-sided dice numbered 1-12 are rolled at once.
P(all 3 dice show 2-digit numbers),
P(at least 1 die shows a 2-digit number)

(17) An unfair coin is three times as likely to show heads as tails. It is flipped once.

P(H), P(T)

(18) An unfair coin shows heads 60% of the time. It is flipped 3 times.

P(1H), P(2H), P(3H), P($\geq$2T)

(19) An unfair coin has a probability of 5/8 of showing tails. This coin and a fair coin are flipped at once.

P(2H), P(2T), P(1H)

(20) A loaded 6-sided die shows 5 every time. This and 2 standard, fair 6-sided dice are rolled at once.

P(three 5's), P(sum=12),

P(3 different numbers)

(21) 1 fair coin and 1 standard, fair 6-sided die are flipped/rolled at once. P(H and 2), P(H or 2), P(T and ≥3)

(22) A bag contains 2 fair coins and 1 double-tailed coin. One coin is picked at random and flipped 3 times.
P(1T), P(2T), P(3T), P(0T)
If 3T occurs, find P(coin is double-tailed).

(23) A standard, fair 6-sided die is rolled 5 times.
P(4 occurs exactly 3 times),
P(4 occurs more than 2 occurs)

(24) An unfair 6-sided die has probabilities P(1)=P(6)=1/12, P(2)=P(5)=1/4, and P(3)=P(4)=1/6. The die is rolled 3 times.
P(only 2's and/or 5's), P(sum=12)

(25) 4 standard, fair 6-sided dice in 4 different colors are rolled at once. The red die is the thousands place, the blue die is the hundreds place, the yellow die is the tens place, and the gray die is the units place. This makes a 4-digit number. P(>3452)

(26) A fair blue die has five 3's and one 6 on its sides. A fair green die has three 2's and three 5's on its sides. A fair red die has two 1's and four 4's on its sides. All three dice are rolled at once. P(B beats G), P(G beats R), P(R beats B) Does something seem strange about this?

7 Odds

Since odds involve ratios, we will quickly review ratios before discussing odds. A **ratio** separates two numbers by a colon, like 5:8. A ratio of the form a:b is equivalent to the fraction $\frac{a}{b}$. For example, 5:8 is equivalent to $\frac{5}{8}$; it can also be expressed as the decimal 0.625 or the percentage 62.5%. This book assumes that the reader knows how to convert between fractions, decimals, and percents. If you're not fluent with this, we recommend that you take a moment to review this since it is a valuable arithmetic skill. If needed, many calculators can do these conversions for you:

- To convert a fraction to a decimal on a calculator, simply divide. For example, to convert $\frac{5}{6}$ to a decimal, divide $5 \div 6$ to get the repeating decimal 0.83333333.

- Many calculators can convert a decimal to a fraction. For example, the TI-30XS is relatively inexpensive and has a button for this. If you enter 0.35 and then press the f◄►d button, it will convert 0.35 to the fraction $\frac{7}{20}$.

- To convert a decimal to a percent, multiply by 100%. For example, $0.4 = 40\%$.

- To convert a percent to a decimal, divide by 100%. For example, $8\% = 0.08$.

When you solve for the odds, first you get a fraction, and then you need to convert that fraction to a ratio. For example, if you solve for the odds and get the fraction $\frac{3}{2}$, you then express the fraction as the ratio 3:2. **If you obtain a whole number when you solve for the odds**, express the whole number as a fraction with a denominator of one. For example, if you solve for the odds and obtain the whole number 8, rewrite the whole number 8 as the fraction $\frac{8}{1}$, and then express the fraction as the ratio 8:1.

If you know the odds and wish to solve for probability (which we will learn how to do soon), first express the odds as a fraction. For example, if the odds are 3:5, first express the odds as the fraction $\frac{3}{5}$.

Here is another useful fraction skill that we will use. Recall that the way to divide by a fraction is to multiply by its **reciprocal**. For example, $\frac{3}{4} \div \frac{3}{5} = \frac{3}{4} \times \frac{5}{3} = \frac{15}{12} = \frac{5}{4}$.

Odds and probability are similar in that they both express the likelihood that an event will occur, but they are different in that they express the likelihood in different ways. If every outcome is equally likely and the outcome is random, recall from Chapter 4 that the **probability** that the event will occur equals the number of ways for the specific outcome to occur divided by the total number of outcomes. In comparison, the **odds** represent the ratio of the probability that an event will occur to its **complement** (which is the probability that the event won't occur). Let p represent the **probability** that an event will occur; it is a fraction in the range $0 \leq p \leq 1$. The **complement** to p is equal to $1 - p$ (since, according to Chapter 5, a probability and its complement add up to 1). Let o represent the **odds** that an event will occur. The odds o and the corresponding probability p are related by the following formula:

$$\text{odds} = o = \frac{p}{1 - p}$$

Following are a few examples:

- If $p = \frac{1}{2}$, then $1 - p = \frac{1}{2}$ and $o = \frac{1/2}{1/2} = \frac{1}{2} \div \frac{1}{2} = \frac{1}{2} \times \frac{2}{1} = \frac{2}{2} = 1$. In this case, the odds are 1:1, meaning that the event and its complement are equally likely to occur. The odds that a fair coin will come up heads are 1:1.

- If $p = \frac{1}{6}$, then $1 - p = \frac{5}{6}$ and $o = \frac{1/6}{5/6} = \frac{1}{6} \div \frac{5}{6} = \frac{1}{6} \times \frac{6}{5} = \frac{1}{5}$. In this case, the odds are 1:5, meaning that the complement is 5 times as likely to occur as the event. The odds that a standard, fair 6-sided die will show a 2 are 1:5; it is 5 times as likely to show a different number (a 1, 3, 4, 5, or 6) as it is to show a 2.

- If $p = \frac{3}{4}$, then $1 - p = \frac{1}{4}$ and $o = \frac{3/4}{1/4} = \frac{3}{4} \div \frac{1}{4} = \frac{3}{4} \times \frac{4}{1} = 3$. In this case, the odds are 3:1, meaning that the event is 3 times as likely to occur as its complement. If the odds of a team winning are 3:1, the team is expected to be 3 times as likely to win as it is to lose. (Odds of 3:1 correspond to a probability of 3/4.)

If the two parts of a ratio share a common factor, the ratio can be **reduced**. Divide each part of the ratio by the greatest common factor, the same way that you would reduce a fraction. For example, the ratio 8:12 can be reduced to the ratio 2:3 by dividing 8 and 12 each by 4. It's exactly the same as reducing the fraction $\frac{8}{12}$ to the fraction $\frac{2}{3}$ by dividing the numerator and denominator each by four: $\frac{8}{12} = \frac{8 \div 4}{12 \div 4} = \frac{2}{3}$.

If you know the odds, we can invert the formula to solve for the probability. If the odds are in the form $o = a{:}b$, first express this as the fraction $o = \frac{a}{b}$. Replace o with $\frac{a}{b}$ in the formula $o = \frac{p}{1-p}$ to get $\frac{a}{b} = \frac{p}{1-p}$. Cross multiply to get $a(1 - p) = bp$. Distribute the a to get $a - ap = bp$. Add ap to both sides: $a = ap + bp$. Factor out the p to get $a = p(a + b)$. Finally, divide by $a + b$ on both sides to obtain the following formula:

$$\text{probability} = p = \frac{a}{a + b}$$

(If you need the complementary probability, it is $1 - p = 1 - \frac{a}{a+b} = \frac{a+b}{a+b} - \frac{a}{a+b} = \frac{b}{a+b}$.)

To find probability from the odds, first identify a and b as shown below:

- If $o = 3{:}2$, then $a = 3$ and $b = 2$, such that $p = \frac{3}{3+2} = \frac{3}{5}$. Since $a > b$, $p > \frac{1}{2}$.
- If $o = 1{:}7$, then $a = 1$ and $b = 7$, such that $p = \frac{1}{1+7} = \frac{1}{8}$. Since $a < b$, $p < \frac{1}{2}$.

Example 1. If the probability that a team will win a game is 20%, what are the odds that the team will win the game?

The probability that the team will win is $p = 20\%$. First convert this to a fraction: $p = \frac{20}{100} = \frac{1}{5}$. Use the formula for odds: $o = \frac{p}{1-p} = \frac{1/5}{1-1/5} = \frac{1/5}{4/5} = \frac{1}{5} \div \frac{4}{5} = \frac{1}{5} \times \frac{5}{4} = \frac{5}{20} = \frac{1}{4}$. Now express the fraction $\frac{1}{4}$ as the ratio 1:4. The odds are 1:4 (which is read as "1 to 4"). Although 5:20 would technically be correct, 1:4 is considered to be a better answer because the ratio has been reduced. The ratio 5:20 reduces to 1:4 (if you divide 5 and 20 each by 5).

Example 2. A bag contains balls of various colors. The odds that a randomly selected ball will be red are 2:9. What is the probability that a randomly selected ball will be red?

First compare 2:9 to the general form $o = a{:}b$ to see that $a = 2$ and $b = 9$. Use the formula for probability: $p = \frac{a}{a+b} = \frac{2}{2+9} = \frac{2}{11}$.

Chapter 7 Problems

Directions: The exercises below express the probability of some outcome as a fraction or percent. For each probability, express the odds that the outcome will occur as a ratio.

(1) 2/3

(2) 1/3

(3) 3/8

(4) 25%

(5) 5/6

(6) 4/9

Directions: The exercises below give the odds that some outcome will occur as a ratio. For each case, determine the probability that the outcome will occur as a fraction.

(7) 5:2

(8) 1:8

(9) 4:11

(10) 5:7

(11) 3:4

(12) 7:3

8 Cards

A great variety of card games are played with a standard deck. A standard deck of playing cards has 52 cards divided into 4 <u>suits</u>: hearts (♥), diamonds (♦), spades(♠), and clubs (♣). Two suits are red: hearts (♥) and diamonds (♦). Two suits are black: spades (♠) and clubs (♣). Each suit consists of 13 cards: ace (A), 2, 3, 4, 5, 6, 7, 8, 9, 10, jack (J), queen (Q), and king (K). The jack (J), queen (Q), and king (K) are called <u>face cards</u>. In games where cards have point values, a face card typically counts as 10 points (the same as a 10); in some games, like Poker, face cards are considered more valuable than a 10. The ace sometimes counts as the highest card and sometimes counts as the lowest card. In some games (like Poker or Blackjack), the ace can be used as a high card or as a low card; in other games (like Cribbage), it is only used one way or the other. Most games are played with a single deck of cards. A few games are played with multiple decks of cards; for example, in order to make it more difficult for players to use their memory to predict which cards remain in the deck, Blackjack is often played with multiple decks.

Some games are played with **wildcards**. A wildcard can be used in place of any standard card. When one or more jokers are included in a game, the joker is typically wild. The joker isn't the only card that can be wild; for example, a few variations of Poker allow deuces (which are 2's) to be wild, and in Crazy Eights, the 8's are wild.

Some games use special cards that aren't part of a standard deck. For example, Uno includes reverse and skip cards, which affect the order in which players play their cards. In Old Maid, every card is nonstandard. We will briefly discuss features of a few common games before discussing probability.

In <u>Poker</u>, the following kinds of hands are listed from best to worst:
- five of a kind (only possible when using wildcards, like 9♥-9♦-9♠-9♣-joker)
- royal flush (A, K, Q, J, 10 of the same suit, like A♠-K♠-Q♠-J♠-10♠)
- straight flush (all cards are in order in the same suit, like J♦-10♦-9♦-8♦-7♦)
- four of a kind (4 of the same card, like 7♥-7♦-7♠-7♣)

- full house (3 of one card and 2 of another, like J♥-J♦-J♣-5♦-5♠)
- flush (all cards have the same suit, like K♠-J♠-8♠-7♠-3♠)
- straight (all cards are in order, like Q♣-J♦-10♣-9♥-8♠)
- three of a kind (3 of the same card, like 10♥-10♦-10♣)
- two pair (2 pairs, like A♥-A♣-6♦-6♠)
- one pair (1 pair, like 7♦-7♣)
- high card (none of the above, like Q♦-J♠-9♣-7♠-4♥, where the queen is high)

There are many variations of Poker. In Draw Poker, each player receives 5 cards face down and may replace one or more cards by discarding them and drawing new cards from the deck. In Community Card Poker (like Texas Hold 'em), each player receives an incomplete hand face down, which is combined with shared cards that are face up. In Stud Poker (like Seven-Card Stud), each player receives some cards face up and other cards face down.

In **Blackjack**, players are dealt two cards and may draw additional cards with the goal of making the highest hand with a value not greater than 21. If your cards add up to more than 21, you lose the hand (this is called going bust). The ace (A) may count as either 1 point or 11 points. Face cards (J, Q, and K) are worth 10 points each. Other cards are worth their numerical value (for example, a 6 is worth 6 points). If you are dealt one ace (A) and either a 10 or a face card (J, Q, or K), this is called blackjack; two cards add up to 21 points. As an example, if you are dealt a K and a 7, you have $10 + 7 = 17$ points. You can choose to hold (keep what you have) and hope the dealer busts (if the dealer currently has 16 or less, the dealer will draw a card), or you can draw a card to try to improve your score. If you draw a 4, your score will be $10 + 7 + 4 = 21$ points; if you draw a 3 or lower, your score will be less than 21 points (you may keep what you have; drawing another card is very risky); and if you draw a 5 or higher, your score will be more than 21 points (you go bust and lose the hand).

Many card games (like Rummy, Cribbage, and Phase 10) involve runs or sets. In a **run**, 3 or more cards appear in order. For example, a 5, 6, and 7 make a short run, while an 8, 9, 10, J, and Q make a run of five cards. Many games (like Rummy) require a run to occur in the **same suit**, like 10♣-J♣-Q♣. In a **set**, 3 or more cards are the same, like 4♥-4♦-4♠.

Games like Uno or Crazy Eights involve playing a card that matches either the suit or the value of the previously played card. For example, if the last card played was a 5 of spades (5♠), the next card must either be a 5 or a spade (♠).

Some games (like Bridge, Spades, and Hearts) involve **tricks**, which are cards that are played and won in each round. In many of these games, all 52 cards are dealt to 4 players (such that each player receives 13 cards). Each player plays one card in one round (so there are 13 rounds per deal). The player who wins the trick is generally the player who played the highest card in the round, unless a trump card is played (for example, in Spades, the spades are trump cards, such that spades count higher than any other suit). Players are often required to follow suit unless they are out of the suit; for example, if the first player plays a diamond, everyone must play a diamond, unless a player doesn't have any diamonds to play. The player who wins the trick tends to play the first card in the next round. Scoring and strategy varies widely from one game to another, but is based on the tricks that are won.

One thing virtually all card games have in common is that players must make **decisions**. In Draw Poker, players decide which cards (if any) to discard in order to try to improve their hands. In Blackjack, players decide whether to draw a new card or to hold what they have. In Rummy, players decide whether to draw a card from the deck or the discard pile, which card to discard, and when to play runs or sets from their hands. In Uno, players decide whether to play a card of the same suit, a card of the same value, a special card (like a wildcard, reverse card, or skip card), or to draw from the deck. **Probability** is one factor that can help make a better decision.

For example, it may help to know that (in a standard deck) 26 cards are red and 26 cards are black (such that 1 out of 2 cards is red), that there are 13 cards of each suit (such that 1 out of 4 cards is a heart), that there are 12 face cards (such that 3 out of 13 cards is a jack, queen, or king), or that 4 cards are sevens (such that 1 out of 13 cards is a seven). For example, if your hand includes three hearts, a spade, and a club, then there are $13 - 3 = 10$ hearts in the $52 - 5 = 47$ cards that you don't see, such that the probability of drawing two more hearts in the next two cards is $\frac{(10)(9)}{(47)(46)} = \frac{45}{1081}$ (or about 4%); see Example 5.

Note that there are other factors in a game that can affect probabilities. For example, if more than one hand has already been played from the same deck, the ability to remember some of the cards that have already been played helps you know which cards remain in the deck. Out of 52 cards, there is a 1 in 13 chance of getting a 4, but if you remember that no 4's have been played yet and about half the deck remains, then there is about a 2 in 13 chance of getting a 4.

Other issues include how well the cards are shuffled, whether any of the cards have wrinkles or marks that make them easy to identify, or if a player's facial expressions or mannerisms offer clues as to which cards are in that player's hand. Reading facial expressions, finger motions, changes in the sound of a voice, etc. are important aspects of playing Poker in person.

Familiarity with probabilities is helpful, but is not the only factor in formulating a strategy for playing cards. In this book, we will assume that the games are **fair** (unless otherwise stated) and that **the only knowledge that a player has is the information stated in the problem**.

Example 1. A player is dealt 2 cards from a standard deck of cards. Find the probability and the odds that the player will have blackjack.

There are $\binom{52}{2} = \frac{52!}{2!(52-2)!} = \frac{52!}{2!50!} = \frac{(52)(51)}{(2)(1)} = \frac{2652}{2} = 1326$ ways to choose 2 cards out of 52. To make blackjack, one card must be a 10, J, Q, or K (there are 16 such cards) and one card must be an A (there are 4 aces). There are $\binom{16}{1}\binom{4}{1} = \frac{16!}{1!15!}\frac{4!}{1!3!} = (16)(4)$ = 64 ways to choose 1 out of 16 J's, Q's, K's, or 10's and also choose 1 out of 4 A's. The probability of being dealt blackjack is $\frac{64}{1326} = \frac{32}{663}$ (which is approximately 0.0483 or 4.83%). To find the **odds**, use the formula from Chapter 7: $o = \frac{p}{1-p} = \frac{32/663}{631/663} = \frac{32}{631}$. The odds are 32:631 (which is approximately 1 out of 20; divide 631 by 32 to see this).
Alternate solution: There are 52 ways to deal the first card and 51 ways to deal the second card (since one card has already been dealt). This makes a total of $(52)(51) = 2652$ permutations where 2 cards are dealt from a 52-card deck. There are 16 ways that the first card can be a 10, J, Q, or K and 4 ways that the second card can be an A.

There are 4 ways that the first card can be an A and 16 ways that the second card can be a 10, J, Q, or K. This makes $(16)(4) + (4)(16) = 64 + 64 = 128$ ways to be dealt blackjack. The probability of being dealt blackjack is $\frac{128}{2652} = \frac{32}{663}$.

Another alternate solution: The probability that the first card is a 10, J, Q, or K is $\frac{16}{52} = \frac{4}{13}$ (since the deck has four 10's, four J's, four Q's, and 4 K's) and the probability that the second card is an A (after one card has already been drawn) is $\frac{4}{51}$ (since the deck has four A's). The probability that the first card is an A is $\frac{4}{52} = \frac{1}{13}$ and the probability that the second card (after an A has already been drawn) is a 10, J, Q, or K is $\frac{16}{51}$. The probability of being dealt blackjack is $\left(\frac{4}{13}\right)\left(\frac{4}{51}\right) + \left(\frac{1}{13}\right)\left(\frac{16}{51}\right) = \frac{16}{663} + \frac{16}{663} = \frac{32}{663}$.

Example 2. A player is dealt 5 cards from a standard deck of cards. Find the probability and the odds that the player is dealt a flush (but not a straight or royal flush).

There are $\binom{52}{5} = \frac{52!}{5!(52-5)!} = \frac{52!}{5!47!} = \frac{(52)(51)(50)(49)(48)}{(5)(4)(3)(2)(1)} = \frac{311,875,200}{120} = 2,598,960$ ways to choose 5 cards out of 52. There are $\binom{13}{5}\binom{4}{1} = \frac{13!}{5!8!}\frac{4!}{1!3!} = \frac{(13)(12)(11)(10)(9)}{(5)(4)(3)(2)(1)}\binom{4}{1} = \frac{154,440}{120}(4) = 1287(4) = 5148$ ways to choose 5 cards of the same suit. (Why? There are 4 suits to choose from and each suit has 13 cards. Note that $\binom{13}{5}$ is the number of ways to have 5 cards of a specific suit, and we multiply by $\binom{4}{1} = 4$ because there are 4 possible suits.) However, 5148 includes all kinds of flushes, including straight and royal flushes. We need to subtract out the straight and royal flushes. The number of ways to make a straight or royal flush is $\binom{10}{1}\binom{4}{1} = \frac{10!}{1!9!}\frac{4!}{1!3!} = (10)(4) = 40$. (Why? A straight flush can be A-2-3-4-5, 2-3-4-5-6, 3-4-5-6-7, up to 9-10-J-Q-K, and a royal flush is 10-J-Q-K-A. There are 10 such flushes in a given suit; multiply by 4 suits to make 40 straight or royal flushes.) Subtract $5148 - 40 = 5108$ to find the number of flushes that aren't straight or royal. The probability of being dealt a flush (that isn't straight or royal) is $\frac{5108}{2,598,960} = \frac{1277}{649,740}$ (which is approximately 0.00197 or 0.197%). To find the **odds**, use the formula from Chapter 7: $o = \frac{p}{1-p} = \frac{1277/649,740}{648,463/649,740} = \frac{1277}{648,463}$. The odds are 1277:648,463 (which is approximately 1 out of 500; divide 648,463 by 1277 to see this).

Example 3. A player is dealt 5 cards from a standard deck of cards. What are the probability and the odds that the player will have 3 of a kind (but not 4 of a kind or full house)?

There are $\binom{52}{5} = \frac{52!}{5!(52-5)!} = \frac{52!}{5!47!} = \frac{(52)(51)(50)(49)(48)}{(5)(4)(3)(2)(1)} = \frac{311,875,200}{120} = 2,598,960$ ways to choose 5 cards out of 52. The next part can be a little tricky. You have to make sure that you account for all 5 cards. We will do this in pieces:

- There are 13 values to choose from (2, 3, 4, 5, 6, 7, 8, 9, 10, J, Q, K, and A). We want to choose one of these values for the 3 of a kind. For one of these values, there are 4 cards available (one heart, one diamond, one spade, and one club). This gives $\binom{13}{1}\binom{4}{3}$; the $\binom{13}{1}$ chooses the value and $\binom{4}{3}$ chooses the 3 suits.

- We also need to choose 2 cards that aren't the same as the card for the 3 of a kind. We also want these 2 cards to be different (so we don't get a full house). For each card, there are 4 cards available (one for each suit). This gives $\binom{12}{2}\binom{4}{1}\binom{4}{1}$. Note that $\binom{12}{2}$ automatically chooses two different values (so we don't have to worry about a full house). The two $\binom{4}{1}$'s choose the suits for each of these cards.

Put this all together: $\binom{13}{1}\binom{4}{3}\binom{12}{2}\binom{4}{1}\binom{4}{1} = \frac{13!}{1!12!}\frac{4!}{3!1!}\frac{12!}{2!10!}\left(\frac{4!}{1!3!}\right)^2 = (13)(4)(66)(4)^2$ $= 54,912$. The probability of being dealt a 3 of a kind (that isn't a 4 of a kind or a full house) is $\frac{54,912}{2,598,960} = \frac{88}{4165}$ (which is approximately 0.0211 or 2.11%). To find the **odds**, use the formula from Chapter 7: $o = \frac{p}{1-p} = \frac{88/4165}{4077/4165} = \frac{88}{4077}$. The odds are 88:4077 (which is approximately 1 out of 46; divide 4077 by 88 to see this).

Alternate solution: There are $\binom{52}{5} = \frac{52!}{5!(52-5)!} = \frac{52!}{5!47!} = \frac{(52)(51)(50)(49)(48)}{(5)(4)(3)(2)(1)} = \frac{311,875,200}{120}$ $= 2,598,960$ ways to choose 5 cards out of 52. There are $\binom{4}{3} = 4$ ways to choose 3 out of 4 aces. We need to choose 2 more cards; call them X and Y. There are $52 - 4 = 48$ ways to choose X so that it isn't an ace. There are $48 - 4 = 44$ ways to choose Y so that it isn't an ace or the same as X. However, we have twice as many XY combinations as we need. For example, when X = 3 and Y = 8, it's the same as when X = 8 and Y =

3. So we will divide by 2 to correct for double counting. Finally, we will multiply by 13 because 3 of a kind could have been made with cards other than an aces. Putting all this together, we get $(4)(48)(44)\left(\frac{1}{2}\right)(13) = 54,912$. The probability of being dealt a 3 of a kind (that isn't a 4 of a kind or a full house) is $\frac{54,912}{2,598,960} = \frac{88}{4165}$.

Example 4. In Blackjack, a player is dealt K♥ and 5♣ from a standard deck of cards. Also visible on the table are: 9♣, A♠, 4♠, J♥, and Q♦. If the player draws one card, what is the probability that the player won't bust?

There are $52 - 7 = 45$ cards that are not visible. Since face cards (J, Q, and K) are worth 10 points each, the player's current score is $10 + 5 = 15$. Since $21 - 15 = 6$, the player needs to draw a 6 or lower in order not to bust. The original 52-card deck had $(6)(4) = 24$ cards that were 6 or lower (since there are four A's, four 2's, four 3's, four 4's, four 5's, and four 6's, and since an A may count as just 1 point instead of 11 points if desired). However, 3 of these cards (a 4, a 5, and an ace) are visible. This leaves $24 - 3 = 21$ cards that are not visible. The probability that the player won't bust after drawing one card is $\frac{21}{45} = \frac{7}{15}$ (which is approximately 0.467 or 46.7%).

Example 5. In Draw Poker, a player is dealt the following cards from a standard deck: J♥, 10♣, 5♥, 4♥, and 3♠. The player discards 10♣ and 3♠, and draws two new cards to replace them. What is the probability that the player will make a flush?

There are $52 - 5 = 47$ cards that the player doesn't see. The are $\binom{47}{2} = \frac{47!}{2!45!} = \frac{(47)(46)}{2} = 1081$ ways to choose 2 cards from 47 cards. There are $13 - 3 = 10$ hearts remaining. There are $\binom{10}{2} = \frac{10!}{2!8!} = \frac{(10)(9)}{2} = 45$ ways to choose 2 out of 10 hearts. The probability that the next two cards are both hearts is $\frac{45}{1081}$ (which is approximately 0.0416 or 4.16%).

Alternate solution: There are 47 ways to deal the next card and 46 ways to deal the card after that. This makes $(47)(46) = 2162$ permutations. There are 10 ways for the first card to be a heart and 9 ways for the following card to also be a heart. This makes $(10)(9) = 90$ ways for both cards to be hearts. The probability that the next two cards are both hearts is $\frac{90}{2162} = \frac{45}{1081}$.

Example 6. A player has the following 7 cards: 8♣, 9♣, 10♣, 3♥, 3♠, 3♣, and A♦. There is one other card showing on the table: 5♣. The player draws one card from the deck. What is the probability that the player will have a run or set of four cards?

There are $52 - 7 - 1 = 44$ cards that the player doesn't see. There are 44 ways to draw one card. Which cards does the player need in order to make a run of 4 cards or a set of 4 cards? In order to extend the run 8♣, 9♣, 10♣, the player either needs to draw 7♣ or J♣. In order to make a set of four 3's, the player needs to draw 3♦. There are $2 + 1 = 3$ ways that the next card dealt can extend a run or set to 4 cards. The probability that the next card will make a run or set of 4 cards is $\frac{3}{44}$ (which is approximately 0.0682 or 6.82%).

Example 7. A player is dealt 5 cards from a deck of 54 cards: a standard deck plus 2 jokers. The joker counts as a wildcard. What are the probability and the odds that the player will have 5 of a kind?

There are $\binom{54}{5} = \frac{54!}{5!(54-5)!} = \frac{54!}{5!49!} = \frac{(54)(53)(52)(51)(50)}{(5)(4)(3)(2)(1)} = \frac{379,501,200}{120} = 3,162,510$ ways to choose 5 cards out of 54. The player could make 5 of a kind using one or two jokers:

- The player could draw four cards of the same value and one joker. There are $\binom{13}{1}\binom{4}{4}\binom{2}{1} = \frac{13!}{1!12!}\frac{4!}{4!0!}\frac{2!}{1!1!} = (13)(1)(2) = 26$ ways to choose 4 of one card plus 1 out of 2 jokers. We first choose 1 of 13 values, then choose all 4 of the suits for that value, and then choose 1 of the 2 jokers.

- The player could draw three cards of the same value and two jokers. There are $\binom{13}{1}\binom{4}{3}\binom{2}{2} = \frac{13!}{1!12!}\frac{4!}{3!1!}\frac{2!}{2!0!} = (13)(4)(1) = 52$ ways to choose 3 of one card plus 2 out of 2 jokers. We first choose 1 of 13 values, then choose 3 of the 4 suits for that value, and then choose both of the jokers.

This makes $26 + 52 = 78$ ways to choose 5 of a kind. The probability of being dealt a 5 of a kind is $\frac{78}{3,162,510} = \frac{1}{40,545}$ (which is approximately 0.0000247 or 0.00247%). To find the **odds**, use the formula from Chapter 7: $o = \frac{p}{1-p} = \frac{1/40,545}{40,544/40,545} = \frac{1}{40,544}$. The odds are 1:40,544 (which is approximately 1 out of 40,000).

Alternate solution: There are $\binom{54}{5} = \frac{54!}{5!(54-5)!} = \frac{54!}{5!49!} = \frac{(54)(53)(52)(51)(50)}{(5)(4)(3)(2)(1)} = \frac{379,501,200}{120}$
$= 3,162,510$ ways to choose 5 cards out of 54. The player could make 5 of a kind using one or two jokers:

- There is 1 way to choose all 4 aces. There are 2 ways to choose 1 of the 2 jokers. This makes $(1)(2) = 2$ ways to make 5 of a kind with 4 aces and 1 joker. Multiply by 13 since 4 of a kind could be made with cards other than aces: $(2)(13) = 26$.

- There are $\binom{4}{3} = 4$ ways to choose 3 out of 4 aces. There is 1 ways to choose both of the jokers. This makes $(4)(1) = 4$ ways to make 5 of a kind with 3 aces and 2 jokers. Multiply by 13 since 3 of a kind could be made with cards other than aces: $(4)(13) = 52$.

This makes $26 + 52 = 78$ ways to choose 5 of a kind. The probability of being dealt a 5 of a kind is $\frac{78}{3,162,510} = \frac{1}{40,545}$.

Example 8. A special deck has 18 cards. There are 6 cards for each of 3 colors: red, green, or blue. The cards of each color are numbered 1-6. A player is dealt 3 cards. Find the probability that the player receives a run of 3 cards of the same color.

There are $\binom{18}{3} = \frac{18!}{3!15!} = \frac{(18)(17)(16)}{(3)(2)(1)} = 816$ ways to choose 3 cards out of 18. A run of 3 cards could be 1-2-3, 2-3-4, 3-4-5, or 4-5-6. There are 4 such runs of each color for a total of $(4)(3) = 12$ possible runs. The probability of being dealt a run of 3 cards of the same color is $\frac{12}{816} = \frac{1}{68}$ (which is approximately 0.0147 or 1.47%).

Example 9. A player draws 2 cards from a standard deck of cards. Find the probability that both cards are face cards if the first card is placed back in the deck before the second card is drawn.

This problem involves **replacement** (recall Chapter 4). Since the first card is placed back in the deck, all 52 cards are in the deck when each card is drawn. There are 12 face cards (J, Q, and K for each of 4 suits). The probability that both cards are face cards is $\left(\frac{12}{52}\right)\left(\frac{12}{52}\right) = \left(\frac{3}{13}\right)\left(\frac{3}{13}\right) = \frac{9}{169}$ (which is approximately 0.0533 or 5.33%). If the first card isn't placed back in the deck, the answer would be $\left(\frac{12}{52}\right)\left(\frac{11}{51}\right) = \frac{11}{221}$.

Chapter 8 Problems

Directions: Find the indicated probabilities or odds. <u>**Cards are dealt from a standard, fair 52-card deck without replacement, unless stated otherwise**</u>. No other cards are known except for those stated in the problem. As examples of the notation, P(a ♥ and a ♣, any order) is the probability of getting a heart and club in any order, P(5-9) is the probability of a 5, 6, 7, 8, or 9, and o(full house) is the odds of getting a full house.

(1) A player draws 1 card.
P(♦), P(face card or ♠), P(5-9), P(black)

(2) A player is dealt 2 cards.
P(pair), P(both ♣'s), P(a ♥ and a ♣, any order)

(3) A player is dealt 2 cards.
P(both black), P(both face cards),
P(red face card, black ace, any order)

(4) A player draws 2 cards. The first card is placed back in the deck before drawing the second card.
P(pair), P(both ♣'s), P(a ♥ and a ♣, any order)

(5) A player is dealt 3 cards.

P(run of 3, same color), P(set of 3)

Here, an ace may start or end a run.

(6) A player is dealt 3 cards.

P(all ♦'s),

P(one pair plus one different card)

(7) A player is dealt 4 cards.

P(run of 4, same color), P(set of 4)

Here, an ace may start or end a run.

(8) A player is dealt 2 cards from a 54-card deck: a standard deck + 2 jokers.

P(2 jokers), P(1 joker), P(pair)

(9) A player is dealt 4 cards.

P(2 pairs, but not 4 of a kind)

(10) A player is dealt 4 cards.

P(straight, but not a flush)

(11) A 24-card deck has 3 suits: ▲, ■, ●. Cards are numbered 1-8 in each suit.

A player is dealt 3 cards.

P(set of 3), P(sum=21),

P(▲, ■, ●, any order)

(12) A pile of cards has just the face cards from a standard deck.

A player is dealt 4 cards.

P(3 of a kind, but not 4 of a kind),

P(2 pairs, but not 4 of a kind), P(4 of a kind)

(13) Dealer has J♦ and a face-down card. Also on table: Q♠, 5♦, 2♣, A♥, K♣, 6♠.

P(dealer has blackjack), P(dealer<16)

(14) Player has 8♣ and 7♥. Also on table: A♥, 5♥, K♠.

Player draws exactly one card.

P(21), P(≤21), P(bust)

(15) Player has K♠, J♦, 9♠, 6♠, 4♣.

Player discards J♦, 4♣; draws 2 cards.

P(flush)

(16) Player has A♥, A♠, 10♦, 5♦, 2♣.

Player discards 10♦, 5♦, 2♣; draws 3 cards.

P(full house), P(3 of a kind, but not 4 of a kind or full house)

(17) A player is dealt 5 cards.
P(straight, but not flush),
o(straight, but not flush)

(18) A player is dealt 5 cards.
P(4 of a kind), o(4 of a kind)

(19) A player is dealt 5 cards.
P(full house), o(full house)

(20) A player is dealt 5 cards.
P(2 pairs, but not 4 of a kind or full house),
o(2 pairs, but not 4 of a kind or full house)

(21) A player is dealt 2 cards from a 54-card deck: a standard deck + 2 jokers. P(royal flush)

(22) A player is dealt 7 cards. (There are <u>no</u> jokers.) The 5 best cards make the hand. P(royal flush), o(royal flush)

9 Birthdays

Suppose that there are 30 people in a room, and we wish to find the probability that at least two of them have the same birthday (meaning the same month and day). If you're thinking 30 people is a small number compared to 365 days, you're making the wrong comparison. You want to know if 2 people share the same birthday, so what you really need to be thinking about is: "How many **pairs** of people are there?" With 30 people, there are $\binom{30}{2} = \frac{30!}{2!28!} = \frac{(30)(29)}{2} = 435$ pairs. There are more pairs in the room than there are days in the year. It turns out that there is a better than 70% chance that, in a room full of 30 random people, at least 2 will share the same birthday. We will work out this calculation shortly, but first we'll begin with simpler problems.

We will **assume that none of the people were born on February 29 (Leap Year)**. This assumption keeps the calculation simpler so that you can focus on the main idea.

Let's start with a room of 2 people. If there are just 2 people in a room, the probability that they share the same birthday is $\frac{1}{365}$. That's highly unlikely (but still possible).

What if there are 3 people in the room? It's easier to first find the probability that no 2 people have the same birthday. Let A, B, and C represent the 3 people. There are 365 days that A could be born on. This leaves 364 days that B could be born on and not share a birthday with A, and that leave 363 days that C could be born on and not share a birthday with A or B. The probability that A, B, and C were all born on different days is P(all different) $= \left(\frac{364}{365}\right)\left(\frac{363}{365}\right)$. From the **complement rule**, the probability that at least 2 people share a birthdays is P(at least 2 same) $= 1 - \left(\frac{364}{365}\right)\left(\frac{363}{365}\right)$. This works out to 0.0082. That's less than 1% (still rather unlikely).

If there are 4 people in the room, we get P(at least 2 same) $= 1 - \left(\frac{364}{365}\right)\left(\frac{363}{365}\right)\left(\frac{362}{365}\right)$. This works out to 0.016. That's 1.6%. It's still a small percentage, but it's about twice as likely as when there were 3 people in the room. Each person we add is significant.

Continuing the progression, we obtain the following formula. If there are N people in the room (where $N < 365$), the probability that at least 2 people share a birthday is:

$$P(\text{at least 2 same}) = 1 - \frac{(364)(363)(362) \cdots (365 - N + 1)}{365^{N-1}}$$

The three dots $(\cdots)$ mean to keep multiplying until you get to $(365 - N + 1)$. For example, when $N = 4$, we get $1 - \frac{(364)(363)(362)}{365^3}$, which agrees with the formula in the previous paragraph. If we multiply by $\frac{365}{365}$ on the right, the formula becomes:

$$P(\text{at least 2 same}) = 1 - \frac{(365)(364)(363)(362) \cdots (365 - N + 1)}{365^N}$$

We can use the combination formula (Chapter 2) to rewrite the formula as:

$$P(\text{at least 2 same}) = 1 - \frac{N!}{365^N}\binom{365}{N}$$

This formula is convenient if you are using a calculator that can do combinations. (You might find probability functions in a menu or by pressing a PRB button, for example.) To see that this formula is equivalent to the previous one, if we plug in $N = 4$, we get

$$1 - \frac{4!}{365^4}\binom{365}{4} = 1 - \frac{4!}{365^4}\frac{365!}{4!361!} = 1 - \frac{(365)(364)(363)(362)}{365^4} = 1 - \frac{(364)(363)(362)}{365^3}.$$

When we get to 23 people, we reach an important benchmark. If there are at least 23 people in the room, the probability that at least 2 people share a birthday exceeds 50%; it's more likely than not that at least 2 people share a birthday.

$$P(\text{at least 2 same}) = 1 - \frac{23!}{365^{23}}\binom{365}{23} \approx 0.507$$

Returning to our original question, if there are 30 people in a room, we get:

$$P(\text{at least 2 same}) = 1 - \frac{30!}{365^{30}}\binom{365}{30} \approx 0.706$$

With 30 people, there is more than a 70% chance that at least 2 people will share a birthday.

(Our formula assumes that the selection process is fair and random. In a community where people are more likely to give birth in the fall than at other times of the year, for example, this would change the formula. Or if you look around the room and see that two people are identical twins, that makes the experiment seem unfair.)

There are a couple of formulas that give good **approximations** to the birthday formula. One of these is $1 - \left(\frac{364}{365}\right)^{\frac{N(N-1)}{2}}$. For example, when $N = 30$, we get $1 - \left(\frac{364}{365}\right)^{435}$, which is approximately equal to 0.697 (which is close to the value 0.706 that we obtained previously). Another is $1 - e^{-N^2/730}$. When $N = 30$, this gives 0.709. (Where did the 'magic' number 730 come from? It's twice the number of days in a year.)

Example 1. There are 8 people in a room. What is the probability that at least two of the people have the same birthday?

Set $N = 8$ in the formula.

$$P(\text{at least 2 same}) = 1 - \frac{8!}{365^8}\binom{365}{8} \approx 0.0743$$

The answer is about 7.43%.

Example 2. A computer program is made that produces a random integer k in the range $0 \le k \le 9$. The program produces 6 random values for k. What is the probability that at least 2 of the values for k are the same?

Instead of 365 days in a year, this problem involve 10 possible values for k: 0, 1, 2, 3, 4, 5, 6, 7, 8, 9. Modify the formula to use 10 in place of 365. Since there are 6 random values for k and we want to know if any 2 values of k are the same, in the birthday formula, 6 is analogous to the number of people in the room. Plug in $N = 6$.

$$P(\text{at least 2 same}) = 1 - \frac{6!}{10^6}\binom{10}{6} = 1 - \frac{720}{1,000,000}(210) = 1 - \frac{189}{1250} = \frac{1061}{1250}$$

The answer is $\frac{1061}{1250}$ (which equals 0.8488 or 84.88%).

Chapter 9 Problems

Directions: Find the indicated probabilities.

(1) There are 6 people in a room.

P(≥2 same birthday)

(2) There are 17 people in a room.

P(≥2 same birthday)

(3) There are 4 people in a room.

P(≥2 born on same day of the week)

(4) A bag has 15 balls numbered 1-15. A person selects one ball at random, looks at the number, and places it back in the bag. 10 different people do this.

P(≥2 same number)

10 Coloring and Arranging

In this and the next two chapters, we will explore some probability problems that involve a visual or geometric element. This chapter focuses on coloring regions or arranging items.

Suppose that N people sit in a **row** with N chairs. For this case, there are $N!$ ways for the people to arrange themselves. This is the number of **permutations** (Chapter 1); order matters in an arrangement (whereas for combinations, order doesn't matter). As an example, if 4 people sit in a row of 4 chairs, there are $4! = 24$ ways for the people to arrange themselves. If we let A, B, C, and D represent the people, the 24 ways are: ABCD, ABDC, ACBD, ACDB, ADBC, ADCB, BACD, BADC, BCAD, BCDA, BDAC, BDCA, CABD, CADB, CBAD, CBDA, CDAB, CDBA, DABC, DACB, DBAC, DBCA, DCAB, and DCBA.

If there are restrictions or conditions on the arrangements, or if only a subset is arranged, then the permutation formula is modified (recall Chapter 1). See Examples 2-3.

Also, note that the arrangements don't need to involve people sitting in chairs. For example, there are $N!$ ways to arrange N books on a bookshelf.

If N people sit in N chairs **around** a table, the answer is smaller. Why? Because of what is called **rotational symmetry**. Two seating arrangements are the same if they have rotational symmetry, which means that the clockwise order is the same in each case. For example, all 4 arrangements shown below are equivalent because they have the same clockwise order. If you start at A and go clockwise in each diagram below, you will see that each seating arrangement has the order ABCD.

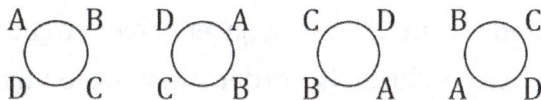

Due to rotational symmetry, it doesn't matter where the first person sits. Let one person sit first. After one person sits, there are $N - 1$ people left to sit. There are $(N - 1)!$ ways for the remaining people to arrange themselves. The result is that there are $(N - 1)!$ ways for N people to sit in N chairs **around** a table. For example, suppose that 4 people sit in 4 chairs around a table. Let A, B, C, and D represent the people. There are $(4 - 1)! = 3! = 6$ ways for these people to arrange themselves. These 6 arrangements are illustrated below.

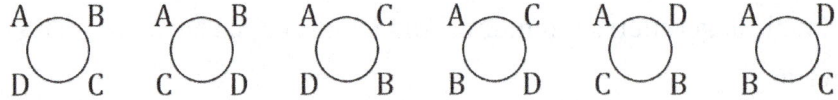

If the problem is to **color** objects (rather than merely arrange objects), the problem is somewhat different. For example, suppose that 3 cars are arranged in a row and that each car is to be painted one of 4 colors: black, white, gray, or red. If no restrictions are given about how the cars are to be painted, there are $(4)(4)(4) = 4^3 = 64$ ways to paint the cars. In general, if there are N objects arranged in a row and if there are C colors to choose from, there are C^N ways to color the objects.

However, if there are any **restrictions**, the number is less. For example, suppose that we don't want to paint two consecutive cars the same color. If there are 3 cars and 4 colors, there are $(4)(3)(3) = 36$ ways to paint the cars so that two adjacent cars don't have the same color. The first car may be any of the 4 colors. The second car has 3 choices (it can't be the same color as the first car). The third car similarly has 3 choices (it can't be the same color as the second car). The 36 allowed permutations are: BGB, BGR, BGW, BRB, BRG, BRW, BWB, BWG, BWR, GBG, GBR, GBW, GRB, GRG, GRW, GWB, GWG, GWR, RBG, RBR, RBW, RGB, RGR, RGW, RWB, RWG, RWR, WBG, WBR, WBW, WGB, WGR, WGW, WRB, WRG, and WRW.

If the objects to be **colored** are arranged in a **loop**, this also reduces the number. For example, suppose that we wish to buy 4 chairs to place around a table, where each chair may be blue, green, or red. (There are plenty of chairs available in every color.) Suppose also that we don't want any two adjacent chairs to be the same color. If two permutations have the same clockwise order, they are equivalent. First place one chair. Let's place a blue chair on the west edge (from the top view). There are 5 ways to do this. If we list the colors in the order west, north, east, south, the 5 permutations are: BGBG, BGBR, BGRG, BRBR, and BRGR. (Note that the last color can't be the same as the first color because then two adjacent chairs would be the same color. That's why BGRB and BRGB aren't on the list.) If none of the chairs are blue, we get 1 more permutation: GRGR. This makes a total of $5 + 1 = 6$ permutations.

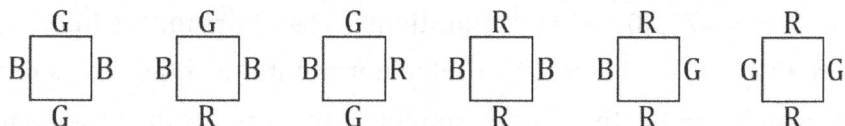

Let's look at three cases of **rotational symmetry** for this example. Note that RGRG and GRGR are equivalent since they have the same clockwise order, as shown below. In each case, if you start at green and work clockwise, the order is GRGR.

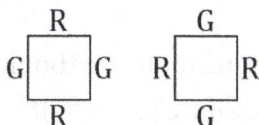

Also note that BGBR and BRBG are equivalent since they have the same clockwise order. This example of rotational symmetry is a little **trickier**. If you start at the west blue chair in each diagram below and go clockwise, you will get BGBR for the left diagram and BRBG for the right diagram, yet they have the same clockwise order. Try starting at the west blue in the left diagram, but the east blue in the right diagram, and travel clockwise. Now you will get BGBR for both diagrams.

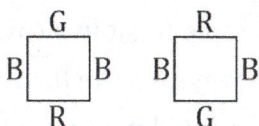

Similarly, if we start out by placing a blue chair at a different side, it will be equivalent to one of the first 6 permutations. As an example, both diagrams below show the same permutation. One diagram started with B to the north; the other started with B to the west. In each case, if you start at blue and work clockwise, the order is BGRG.

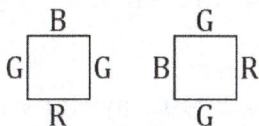

Beware: We use the concept of **rotational symmetry** to count the number of unique outcomes when a question asks for "how many ways." However, if a question asks for **probability**, you want to work with **equally likely outcomes**, which may not be the same as the number of unique outcomes. This means that you might need to **disregard rotational symmetry for the purpose of calculating probabilities**. See Example 8.

Example 1. How many different ways can 12 people be arranged in 12 chairs if (A) the chairs form a straight line or (B) the chairs form a circle?

(A) There are $12! = 479,001,600$ permutations if the chairs form a line.

(B) There are $(12 - 1)! = 11! = 39,916,800$ permutations if the chairs form a circle. Once one person is seated, this is the number of ways to arrange them clockwise. If the first person sits in a different chair, regardless of how the other 11 people sit, this will have the same clockwise order as one of the previous permutations, such that $11!$ is the total number of permutations.

Example 2. A person has 9 different math textbooks. How many different ways are there to arrange 6 of the textbooks on a bookshelf?

Since this involves a subset (and no elements are repeated), use the Case 3 formula from Chapter 1: $\frac{9!}{(9-6)!} = \frac{9!}{3!} = \frac{362,880}{6} = 60,480$.

Example 3. Three brothers and four other people will sit in a row of seven chairs. If the seating assignment is random, what is the probability that all three brothers will sit next to each other?

There are $7! = 5040$ ways for 7 people to sit in a row of 7 chairs. If the brothers sit in the first 3 chairs, there are $3! = 6$ ways for the brothers to sit in 3 consecutive chairs and there are $4! = 24$ ways for the other 4 people to sit in the next 4 chairs. This makes $(6)(24) = 144$ ways for the brothers to sit in the first 3 chairs. There are 144 ways for the brothers to sit in chairs 1-3, 2-4, 3-5, 4-6, or 5-7, so we multiply 144 by 5 to get $(144)(5) = 720$ ways for the three brothers to sit next to each other. The probability that all three brothers will sit next to each other is $\frac{720}{5040} = \frac{1}{7}$ (which is approximately 0.143 or 14.3%).

<u>Alternate solution</u>: There are $7! = 5040$ ways for 7 people to sit in a row of 7 chairs. Now think of the three brothers sitting next to each other as a single group. There are $5! = 120$ ways to arrange one group and 4 other people. There are $3! = 6$ ways to arrange the brothers within their group of 3 chairs. This makes $(120)(6) = 720$ ways for the three brothers to sit next to each other. The probability that all three brothers will sit next to each other is $\frac{720}{5040} = \frac{1}{7}$.

Another alternate solution: This time we will work with combinations rather than permutations, meaning that we will disregard the order of the arrangement. There are 5 ways to choose 3 consecutive chairs (when order doesn't matter): chairs 1-3, chairs 2-4, chairs 3-5, chairs 4-6, or chairs 5-7. There are $\binom{7}{3} = \frac{7!}{3!4!} = \frac{(7)(6)(5)}{(3)(2)(1)} = 35$ ways to choose 3 chairs out of 7. The probability that all three brothers will sit next to each other is $\frac{5}{35} = \frac{1}{7}$.

Example 4. Seven balls numbered 1-7 are arranged in a circle. If the arrangement is random, what is the probability that the balls will be in order from 1 thru 7?

There are $(7 - 1)! = 6! = 720$ ways to arrange 7 balls in a circle. (This is similar to Part B of Example 1.) There are only 2 ways for the balls to be in order from 1 to 7. The balls could have the clockwise order 1, 2, 3, 4, 5, 6, 7 or they could have the clockwise order 7, 6, 5, 4, 3, 2, 1 (which you might prefer to think of as the counter-clockwise order 1, 2, 3, 4, 5, 6, 7). The probability that all 7 balls will be in numerical order is $\frac{2}{720} = \frac{1}{360}$ (which is approximately 0.00278 or 0.278%).

Example 5. A coloring page has four umbrellas arranged in a row. Each umbrella is to be colored one of three colors: red, blue, or green. How many different ways are there to color the umbrellas if (A) there are no restrictions or (B) no two adjacent umbrellas may be the same color?

(A) Any of the 4 umbrellas can be any of the 3 colors. There are $3^4 = 81$ ways to place 4 umbrellas in a straight line without restrictions. A few examples include RRRR, BGRB, GRRB, BBRB, and RGBR.

(B) The first umbrella can be any of the 3 colors. The second umbrella can be one of 2 colors (since it can't be the same as the first umbrella). There are similarly 2 colors available for the third umbrella, and similarly for the last umbrella. This makes a total of $(3)(2)(2)(2) = 24$ ways to color the umbrellas. The allowed permutations are: BGBG, BGBR, BGRB, BGRG, BRBG, BRBR, BRGB, BRGR, GBGB, GBGR, GBRB, GBRG, GRBG, GRBR, GRGB, GRGR, RBGB, RBGR, RBRB, RBRG, RGBG, RGBR, RBRB, and RBRG.

Example 6. At a restaurant, some of its menus are printed on a white background, while the others are printed on a black background. There are plenty of menus of each color. How many different ways are there to arrange five menus in a circle if (A) there are no restrictions or (B) if at most three consecutive menus may be the same color? (A) The key is to watch out for rotational symmetry. If any two permutations have the same clockwise order, they are equivalent. Without restrictions, five menus can be arranged in a circle the following ways:

- There are 2 ways for all five menus to be the same color.

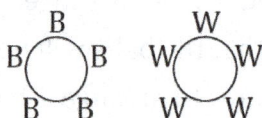

- There are 2 ways for four of the menus to be the same color. Regardless of which menu is the lone color, the other menus will still be four in a row, such that the clockwise order will be equivalent to BBBBW or to WWWWB.

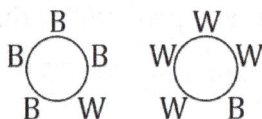

- There are 4 ways for to make a full house (that is, three menus of one color and two menus of the other color). You can either put all of each color together (first and third diagrams) or you can have one pair together and the others mixed (second and fourth diagrams).

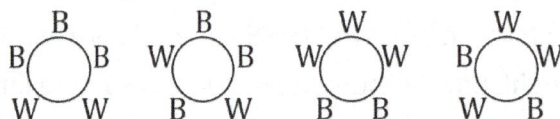

Any other way you might try to draw a full house, it will have the same clockwise order as one of these. For example, the two diagrams below have the same clockwise order. If you start at the W that's in between the two B's, in each diagram, the clockwise order is WBWWB.

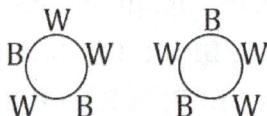

This makes a total of $2 + 2 + 4 = 8$ ways to arrange the menus without restrictions.

(B) If you don't want to have more than 3 consecutive menus of the same color, there are just 4 possible arrangements. (The first 4 arrangements from Part A are excluded.)

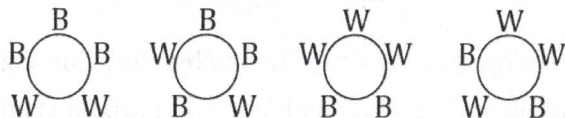

Example 7. A computer displays five dogs in a row. Each dog has one of three colors: blue, green, or red. The computer chooses the colors randomly, except that no two adjacent dogs may be the same color. What is the probability that three of the dogs will be red?

The first dog has three choices (blue, green, or red). Each of the remaining dogs has two choices (it can't be the same color as the previous dog). This makes a total of $(3)(2)(2)(2)(2) = 48$ possible arrangements. In order for three dogs to be red, the first, middle, and last dogs must be red. Since each of the other two dogs must be blue or green, this leaves $(2)(2) = 4$ possibilities: RBRBR, RBRGR, RGRBR, and RGRGR. The probability that at least three of the dogs will be red is $\frac{4}{48} = \frac{1}{12}$ (which is approximately 0.0833 or 8.33%).

Example 8. Four chairs are to be placed around a table. Each chair may be blue or red. There are plenty of chairs of each color. (A) How many different arrangements are there? (B) From a probability perspective, are the different arrangements from Part A equally likely (if the selection process is random)? If not, discuss what this means, and identify the set of equally likely outcomes. (C) For each arrangement in Part A, find the probability that it will occur (if the selection is random).

(A) Chairs may be arranged in the following ways:

- There are 2 ways for all four chairs to be the same color.

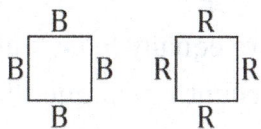

- There are 2 ways for three chairs to be the same color. Regardless of which chair is the lone color, the other chairs will still be three in a row, such that the clockwise order will be equivalent to BBBR or to RRRB.

```
        B           R
    B  [   ] R   R [   ] B
        B           R
```

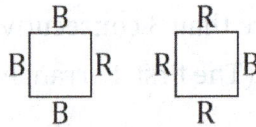

- There are 2 ways for two chairs to be each color. You can either put the pairs together (left diagram) or you can have them mixed (right diagram).

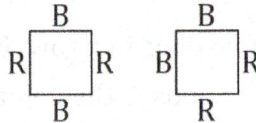

```
        B           B
    R  [   ] R   B [   ] R
        B           R
```

Any other way you might try to draw two of each color, it will have the same clockwise order as one of these. For example, the two diagrams below have the same clockwise order: BBRR.

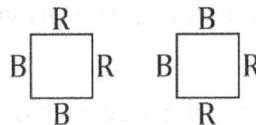

```
        R           B
    B  [   ] R   B [   ] R
        B           R
```

This makes a total of $2 + 2 + 2 = 6$ ways to arrange the menus without restrictions.

(B) The 6 arrangements from Part A are **not** equally likely if a chair of either color is equally likely at each position. To understand why, imagine that a person flips a fair coin and places a blue chair if the coin shows heads and a red chair if the coin show tails. Since there are 4 chairs, there will be 4 coin flips. There are with $2^4 = 16$ equally likely outcomes for flipping a fair coin 4 times. The 16 diagrams below illustrate the 16 possible outcomes for the 4 coin tosses.

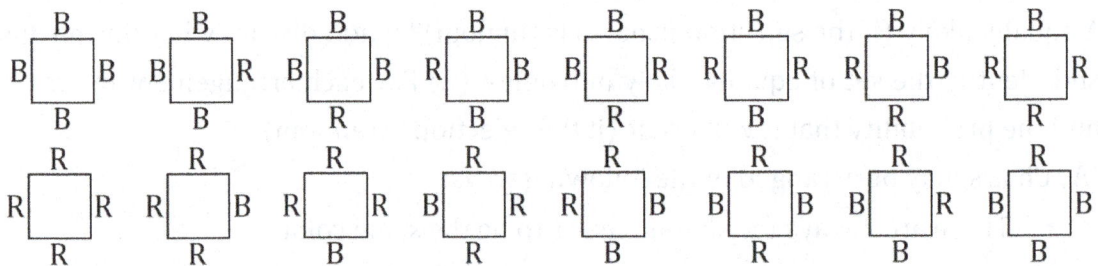

```
     B      B      B      B      B      B      B      B
  B[ ]B  B[ ]R  B[ ]B  R[ ]B  B[ ]R  R[ ]R  R[ ]B  R[ ]R
     B      B      R      B      R      B      R      R

     R      R      R      R      R      R      R      R
  R[ ]R  R[ ]B  R[ ]R  B[ ]R  R[ ]B  B[ ]B  B[ ]R  B[ ]B
     R      R      B      R      B      R      B      B
```

The 16 diagrams shown above are equally likely outcomes. Some of these outcomes are rotationally equivalent, but counting unique diagrams is not the same thing as counting equally likely outcomes. We need to find equally likely outcomes in order to calculate probabilities. **When a question asks you to find probability, you may need to disregard the idea of rotational symmetry to find the equally likely outcomes.** (We encountered a similar issue in the solution to Problem 14 in Chapter 4.)

(C) Each of the 16 equally likely outcomes found in Part B is one of the 6 unique cases from Part A. To find the probabilities, we need to count how many of the equally likely outcomes from Part B corresponds to each case from Part A.

- There is 1 way to have 4 blue chairs. The probability that all four chairs will be blue is $P(4B) = \frac{1}{16}$. There is similarly 1 way to have zero blue chairs. The probability that no chairs will be blue is $P(0B) = \frac{1}{16}$.

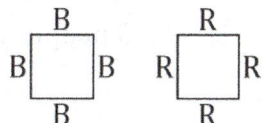

- There are 4 ways to have 3 blue chairs. The probability that 3 chairs will be blue is $P(3B) = \frac{4}{16} = \frac{1}{4}$. There are similarly 4 ways to have 1 blue chair. The probability that 1 chair will be blue is $P(1B) = \frac{4}{16} = \frac{1}{4}$.

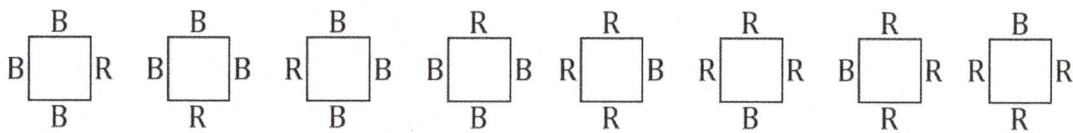

- There are 4 ways to have 2 blue chairs where each pair is together. The probability for this is $P(BBRR) = \frac{4}{16} = \frac{1}{4}$.

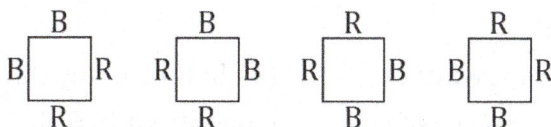

- There are 2 ways to have 2 blue chairs where the blue and red chairs are mixed rather than paired. The probability for this is $P(BRBR) = \frac{2}{16} = \frac{1}{8}$.

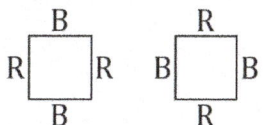

Observe that $\frac{1}{16} + \frac{1}{16} + \frac{1}{4} + \frac{1}{4} + \frac{1}{4} + \frac{1}{8} = \frac{1}{16} + \frac{1}{16} + \frac{4}{16} + \frac{4}{16} + \frac{4}{16} + \frac{2}{16} = \frac{16}{16} = 1$.

Chapter 10 Problems

Directions: Find the indicated numbers or probabilities. Assume that the selections are fair and random. For counting questions, account for **rotational symmetry** as shown in the examples (but for probability questions, work with equally likely outcomes).

(1) In how many different ways can 6 people sit in a row of 6 chairs?

(2) In how many different ways can 5 people sit in 5 chairs around a table?

(3) In how many different ways can 8 books be arranged on one shelf?

(4) In how many different ways can 6 people sit in 6 chairs around a table?

(5) A class has 10 students. In how many different ways can 4 of the students stand in a line?

(6) A group has 5 members. In how many different ways can 3 of the members sit in 3 chairs around a table?

(7) In how many different ways can 2 sisters and 5 other people stand in a line if the sisters are separated?

(8) In how many different ways can 3 girls and 3 boys sit in 6 chairs around a table if girls don't next to each other?

(9) 3 kites are in a row. Each kite will be one of 5 colors: blue, green, red, tan, or yellow. In how many different ways can this be done?

(10) 5 placemats are set around table. Each placemat will be one of 3 colors: black, white, or gray. In how many different ways can this be done?

(11) 5 unicorns are in a row. Each unicorn will be one of 3 colors: blue, green, or red. In how many different ways can this be done if two adjacent unicorns can't be the same color?

(12) 3 chairs are around a table. Each chair will be one of 4 colors: black, white, orange, or yellow. In how many different ways can this be done if two chairs next to each other can't be the same color?

(13) 5 balls numbered 1-5 are arranged in a line. (All five numbers are used.)

P(first ball is 3 and last ball is 4)

(14) A father, son, and 5 other people sit around a table.

P(father and son sit next to each other)

(15) 4 rings are in a row. Each ring will be one of 5 colors: silver, gold, platinum, nickel, or copper. Two adjacent rings can't be the same color.

P(only 2 of the colors are used)

(16) 3 chairs are placed around a table. Each chair will be one of 3 colors: blue, green, or red.

P(1 chair of each color)

(17) 6 balls are placed in a row. A die is rolled to determine the color of each ball. If the die is 1 or 2, a ball is blue. If the die is 3 or 4, a ball is green. If the die is 5 or 6, a ball is red. (There are plenty of balls of each color.)

P(no green balls)

(18) A bag contains 4 blue balls, 4 green balls, and 4 red balls. One ball is grabbed at a time (without replacement) until 6 balls are placed in a row.

P(no green balls); why is the answer different from Exercise 17?

(19) 5 people sit around a table.

Each person flips a coin once.

P(exactly 3 heads, but not all next to each other)

11 Shapes and Grids

In this chapter, we will explore a few examples of counting problems that arise in the context of shapes and grids.

For a polygon, we may wish to count the number of diagonals. Note that a **<u>diagonal</u>** is a line segment that connects two non-adjacent vertices, whereas an **<u>edge</u>** connects two adjacent vertices. How many diagonals can be drawn for the hexagon below?

F A
E B
D C

Each vertex can connect to 3 non-adjacent vertices. For example, A can connect to C, D, and E, which aren't adjacent to A. However, the answer isn't 3 times 6. Why not? If you multiply 3 by 6, you will double-count the diagonals. For example, you will count diagonal AD once from vertex A and then you will count it again from vertex D. So if you multiply 3 by 6, you need to divide by 2 to correct for double-counting. There are $\frac{(3)(6)}{2} = 9$ diagonals: AC, AD, AE, BD, BE, BF, CE, CF, DF. (Note, for example, that EC is the same as CE.) We encountered a similar issue in Chapter 3 when we considered the handshaking problem (which we'll revisit and illustrate later in this chapter).

Lines aren't the only kinds of shapes that may be counted. Polygons may be counted. For example, how many triangles are there in the diagram below?

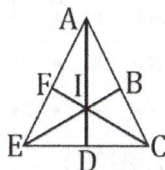

A
F I B
E C
D

- There is 1 large triangle: ACE.
- 3 big triangles involve the centroid (point I): ACI, AEI, CEI.
- 6 big triangles involve midpoints: ABE, ACD, ACF, ADE, BCE, and CEF.
- 6 small triangles involve the centroid: ABI, BCI, CDI, DEI, EFI, and AFI.

There are a total of $1 + 3 + 6 + 6 = 16$ triangles in the diagram above. It's very easy to make a mistake, so we'll boost our confidence by calculating the answer again using a different method. All of the triangles have vertices at 7 points: A, B, C, D, E, F, and I. This time, we'll figure out the answer using these 7 points:

- There are $\binom{7}{3} = \frac{7!}{3!4!} = \frac{(7)(6)(5)}{(3)(2)(1)} = 35$ ways to choose 3 of these 7 points.
- There are 6 sets of 3 points that are collinear: ABC, ADI, AEF, BEI, CDE, and CFI. Since 3 collinear points don't make a triangle (they make a line segment), we'll need to subtract these 6 sets from 35.
- B and F don't connect, so we need to subtract 5 more sets of 3 points: ABF, BCF, BDF, BEF, and BFI.
- B and D don't connect, so we need to subtract 4 more sets of 3 points: ABD, BCD, BDE, and BDI. (Don't count BDF again. We did that in the previous step.)
- D and F don't connect, so we need to subtract 4 more sets of 3 points: ADF, CDF, DEF, and DFI. (Again, we've already counted BDF.)

This makes $35 - 6 - 5 - 4 - 4 = 35 - 11 - 8 = 35 - 19 = 16$, which matches our previous answer.

An $M \times N$ **grid** has M rows and N columns. A row is horizontal; a column is vertical. For example, a 3×4 grid is shown below; it has 3 rows and 4 columns. The rows are indicated by the letters A-C. The columns are indicated by the numbers 1-4. Any point on the grid can be labeled by its corresponding row and column, such as B3. For the grid shown below, how many squares or rectangles can be formed by connecting four dots with horizontal and vertical lines?

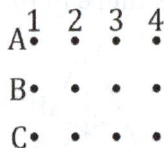

$$
\begin{array}{c c c c}
 & 1 & 2 & 3 & 4 \\
A & \bullet & \bullet & \bullet & \bullet \\
B & \bullet & \bullet & \bullet & \bullet \\
C & \bullet & \bullet & \bullet & \bullet \\
\end{array}
$$

- There is 1 large rectangle: A1A4C4C1.
- There are 2 large squares: A1A3C3C1 and A2A4C4C2.
- There are 3 tall, narrow rectangles: A1A2C2C1, A2A3C3C2, and A3A4C4C3.
- There are 2 short, wide rectangles: A1A4B4B1 and B1B4C4C1.
- There are 4 short rectangles that are 2 units wide: A1A3B3B1, A2A4B4B2, B1B3C3C1, and B2B4C4C2. (The list continues onto the next page.)

- There are 6 small squares: A1A2B2B1, A2A3B3B2, A3A4B4B3, B1B2C2C1, B2B3C3C2, and B3B4C4C3.
- (Although it would be geometrically possible to make a square with diagonal edges, the problem specifically asked us to use horizontal and vertical edges.)

There are a total of $1 + 2 + 3 + 2 + 4 + 6 = 18$ such squares or rectangles.

Another thing one might count on a grid is **paths**. Given a rectangular grid, one might start at the top left corner and proceed to the bottom right corner moving right or down one step at a time. The diagram below shows one possible path for a 3 × 4 grid. It starts at A1, travels 2 units right to A3, 2 units down to C3, and one unit right to C4. Moving only right or down (never up or left), starting at A1, how many paths lead to C4 for the grid shown below?

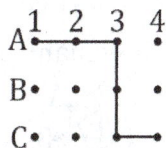

The long way is to count them:

- 1 way is to go all the way right and then down: A1-A4-C4.
- 2 ways go right to A3 and then down: A1-A3-B3-B4-C4 and A1-A3-C3-C4.
- 3 ways go right to A2 and then down: A1-A2-B2-B4-C4, A1-A2-B2-B3-C3-C4, and A1-A2-C2-C4.
- 4 ways go down first: A1-B1-B4-C4, A1-B1-B3-C3-C4, A1-B1-B2-C2-C4, and A1-C1-C4.

There are a total of $1 + 2 + 3 + 4 = 10$ paths. Fortunately, there is a much simpler way to calculate the answer. See the next paragraph.

It turns out that if you count the total number of steps (both right and down), you can use the **combination formula** from Chapter 2 to answer this question. Every path will involve 3 steps to the right and 2 steps down for a total of $3 + 2 = 5$ steps. You may choose the number of steps to the right (3 in this problem) or the number of steps down (2 in this problem) out of the **total number of steps** (5 in this problem). Either way, you will get $\binom{5}{3} = \binom{5}{2} = \frac{5!}{3!2!} = \frac{(5)(4)}{(2)(1)} = 10$ combinations.

Why does the combination formula work give the answer for the number of paths on a grid? In the previous example, we were taking 5 steps. Each step has to be right or down. There will be 3 steps right and 2 steps down. Now compare this to a familiar problem. Flip 5 coins where 3 will be heads and 2 will be tails. There are $\binom{5}{3} = \frac{5!}{3!2!} =$ 10 outcomes: HHHTT, HHTHT, HHTTH, HTHHT, HTHTH, HTTHH, THHHT, THHTH, THTHH, TTHHH. This is equivalent to the 10 paths: RRRDD, RRDRD, RRDDR, RDRRD, RDRDR, RDDRR, DRRRD, DRRDR, DRDRR, DDRRR. Since there are two choices at every junction (right or down), it's very much like flipping a coin.

We will now consider two types of graphs. In a **complete graph**, every vertex connects to every other vertex. A line that joins any two vertices is called an **edge**. The notation K_N represents a complete graph with N vertices. As an example, the complete graph K_6 is shown below; it has 6 vertices. How many edges does K_6 have?

Use the combination formula (Chapter 2) to find the total number of pairs of vertices: $\binom{6}{2} = \frac{6!}{2!4!} = \frac{(6)(5)}{2} = 15$. This agrees with the **handshaking formula** from Chapter 3. If A, B, C, D, E, and F represent 6 people and everybody shakes hands with everybody else, the complete graph K_6 illustrates the handshaking solution. There are $\frac{(6)(5)}{2} = 15$ handshakes. Recall from Chapter 3 that the division by 2 corrects for double counting. For K_6, the edges are: AB, AC, AD, AE, AF, BC, BD, BE, BF, CD, CE, CF, DE, DF, and EF. (Note, for example, that CA is the same as AC.)

Recall that earlier in this chapter we were counting diagonals of a polygon. Observe that K_6 can be drawn by first drawing a hexagon and then drawing all of the diagonals. Of the 15 edges, 6 are not diagonals: AB, BC, CD, DE, EF, and AF. This gives us a formula for the diagonals of a convex polygon: $\binom{N}{2} - N = \frac{N(N-1)}{2} - N$. For example, for K_6, set $N = 6$ to get $\binom{6}{2} - 6 = \frac{(6)(5)}{2} - 6 = 15 - 6 = 9$. This agrees with the example earlier in the chapter where we found that a convex hexagon has 9 diagonals.

A second kind of graph that we will consider is a complete bipartite graph. A **complete bipartite graph** (or **bigraph** for short) has two sets of vertices where edges connect all of the vertices of one set to those of the second set. (No vertices in the same set are connected though.) The notation $K_{M,N}$ represents a complete bipartite graph with M vertices in one set and N vertices in the second set. For example, the complete bipartite graph $K_{3,4}$ is shown below. It has a set of 3 vertices (A, B, and C) and a set of 4 vertices (D, E, F, and G). Note that edges connect A, B, and C to D, E, F, and G (but no edges connect A, B, or C to each other or connect D, E, F, or G to each other). How many edges does $K_{3,4}$ have?

$K_{3,4}$ has $(3)(4) = 12$ edges. (This time we don't divide by two. There is no double counting to correct for.) The 12 edges are: AD, AE, AF, AG, BD, BE, BF, BG, CD, CE, CF, and CG. A complete bipartite graph represents a different kind of handshaking problem. If A, B, and C represent boys while D, E, F, and G represent girls, then the 12 edges of $K_{3,4}$ represent handshakes where every boy shakes hands with every girl (but where two boys don't shake hands and two girls don't shake hands).

Example 1. If a diagonal is randomly drawn in a regular decagon, what is the probability that the diagonal will pass through its center?

A regular decagon has 10 equal sides (and equal interior angles). We discussed how to count the diagonals of a polygon twice in this chapter. When we discussed complete graphs, we found a formula for the number of diagonals: $\binom{N}{2} - N$. Set $N = 10$ to get $\binom{10}{2} - 10 = \frac{10!}{2!8!} - 10 = \frac{(10)(9)}{2} - 10 = 45 - 10 = 35$. (The complete graph K_{10} has 45 edges; 10 of these are edges of the decagon; the other 35 are diagonals.) How many of the 35 diagonals pass through the center? 5 of them. (It may help to review the complete graph K_6, which we drew using a regular hexagon and which has 3 diagonals passing through its center: AD, BE, and CF.) If a diagonal is randomly drawn, the probability that it will pass through the center of the decagon is $\frac{5}{35} = \frac{1}{7}$ (which is approximately 0.143 or 14.3%).

Example 2. The figure below has several triangles. If 3 different vertices are randomly selected, what is the probability that they will be vertices for one of those triangles?

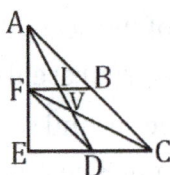

What exactly is the question asking? If we happen to pick A, F, and I, they do form one of the triangles (AFI), but if we happen to pick B, C, and D, they don't form one of the triangles. That is, BCD isn't one of the triangles because there isn't a line BD in the diagram. The question wants to know the probability that the three points will all have lines connecting them like AFI (in contrast to BCD). Start out by counting the triangles in the figure.

- 10 triangles involve A: ABF, ABI, ACD, ACE, ACF, ACV, ADE, ADF, AFI, and AFV.
- 1 triangle involves B but not A: BCF.
- 3 triangles involve C but not A or B: CDF, CDV, and CEF.
- 3 triangles involve D but not A-C: DEF, DFI, and DFV.
- (Every triangle involving E has already been counted.)
- 1 triangle involves F but not A-E: FIV.
- (Every triangle involving I and V has already been counted.)

There are $10 + 1 + 3 + 3 + 1 = 18$ triangles. There are 8 vertices in the diagram: A, B, C, D, E, F, I, and V. There are $\binom{8}{3} = \frac{8!}{3!5!} = \frac{(8)(7)(6)}{(3)(2)(1)} = 56$ ways to choose 3 out of 8 points. The probability that 3 randomly selected vertices will be one of the 18 triangles that we counted is $\frac{18}{56} = \frac{9}{28}$ (which is approximately 0.321 or 32.1%). Since it's easy to make a mistake counting these triangles, we will do it with a different method below to boost our confidence in the answer.

- There are $\binom{8}{3} = \frac{8!}{3!5!} = \frac{(8)(7)(6)}{(3)(2)(1)} = 56$ ways to choose 3 out of 8 points.

- Subtract 9 sets of 3 points that are collinear: ABC, ADI, ADV, AEF, AIV, BFI, CDE, CFV, and DIV. (Note that the 4 collinear points A, D, I, and V make $\binom{4}{3} = \frac{4!}{3!1!} = 4$ sets of 3: ADI, ADV, AIV, and DIV.)

- Subtract 6 sets of 3 points that involve BD (since no line joins B to D): ABD, BCD, BDE, BDF, BDI, and BDV.
- Subtract 5 sets of 3 points that involve BE: ABE, BCE, BEF, BEI, and BEV. (Don't count BDE again. We did that in the previous step.)
- Subtract 4 sets of 3 points that involve BV: ABV, BCV, BFV, and BIV. (Don't count BDV or BEV again. We counted those earlier.)
- Subtract 6 sets of 3 points that involve CI: ACI, BCI, CDI, CEI, CFI, and CFV.
- Subtract 4 sets of 3 points that involve EI: AEI, DEI, EFI, and EIV. (Don't count BEI or CEI again. We counted those earlier.)
- Subtract 4 sets of 3 points that involve EV: AEV, CEV, DEV, and EFV. (Don't count BEV or EIV again. We counted those earlier.)

Subtract: $56 - 9 - 6 - 5 - 4 - 6 - 4 - 4 = 18$ matches our previous answer.

Example 3. If 4 different points are randomly selected for the grid shown below, what is the probability that they will all be the vertices of a square or rectangle with horizontal and vertical sides?

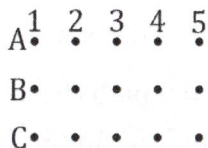

$$
\begin{array}{c c c c c}
 & 1 & 2 & 3 & 4 & 5 \\
A & \bullet & \bullet & \bullet & \bullet & \bullet \\
B & \bullet & \bullet & \bullet & \bullet & \bullet \\
C & \bullet & \bullet & \bullet & \bullet & \bullet \\
\end{array}
$$

There are $(3)(5) = 15$ points in the grid. There are $\binom{15}{4} = \frac{15!}{4!11!} = 1365$ ways to choose 4 of the 15 points. Four points can form a square or rectangle with horizontal and vertical sides in the following ways:

- There is 1 rectangle that is 4 units wide and 2 units tall (A1A5C5C1).
- There are 2 rectangles that are 3 units wide and 2 units tall (like A1A4C4C1).
- There are 3 squares that are 2 units wide (like A2A4C4C2).
- There are 4 rectangles that are 1 unit wide and 2 units tall (like A2A3C3C2).
- There are 2 rectangles that are 4 units wide and 1 unit tall (like A1A5B5B1).
- There are 4 rectangles that are 3 units wide and 1 unit tall (like B2B5C5C2).
- There are 6 rectangles that are 2 units wide and 1 unit tall (like A2A4B4B2).
- There are 8 squares that are 1 unit wide (like B3B4C4C3).

- (Although it would be geometrically possible to make a square with diagonal edges, the problem specifically asked us to use horizontal and vertical edges.)

There are a total of $1 + 2 + 3 + 4 + 2 + 4 + 6 + 8 = 30$ squares or rectangles with horizontal and vertical edges. The probability that all 4 randomly selected points will be the vertices of one of these squares or rectangles is $\frac{30}{1365} = \frac{2}{91}$ (which is approximately 0.0220 or 2.20%).

Example 4. Moving only right or down (never up or left), a path that begins at A1 and ends at C5 is randomly selected. What is the probability that it passes through B4?

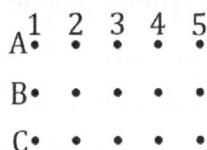

$$A\overset{1}{\bullet} \quad \overset{2}{\bullet} \quad \overset{3}{\bullet} \quad \overset{4}{\bullet} \quad \overset{5}{\bullet}$$

$$B\bullet \quad \bullet \quad \bullet \quad \bullet \quad \bullet$$

$$C\bullet \quad \bullet \quad \bullet \quad \bullet \quad \bullet$$

Each path involves 4 steps to the right and 2 steps down for a total of $4 + 2 = 6$ steps. There are $\binom{6}{2} = \frac{6!}{2!4!} = \frac{(6)(5)}{2} = 15$ such paths. To find how many pass through B4, first find that there are $\binom{4}{1} = 4$ paths from A1 to B4 (since B4 is 3 units right + 1 unit down from A1) and $\binom{2}{1} = 2$ paths from B4 to C5 (since C5 is 1 unit right + 1 unit down from B4). These combine to make $(4)(2) = 8$ paths from A1 to C5 that pass through B4. (The 8 paths are: A1A4B4B5C5, A1A4C4C5, A1A3B3B5C5, A1A3B3B4C4C5, A1A2B2B5C5, A1A2B2B4C4C5, A1B1B5C5, and A1B1B4C4C5.) If one of the 15 paths is randomly selected, the probability that it will pass through B4 is $\frac{8}{15}$ (which is approximately 0.533 or 53.3%).

Example 5. In the diagram below, (A) if one edge is randomly selected, what is the probability that it will involve point A, and (B) if 3 different vertices are randomly selected, what is the probability that the triangle will involve edge DE?

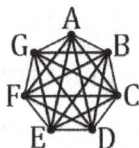

(A) There are 7 vertices (A-G). Since every vertex connects to every other vertex, this is the complete graph K_7. There are $\binom{7}{2} = \frac{7!}{2!5!} = \frac{(7)(6)}{2} = 21$ ways to choose 2 out of 7

vertices (and each edge connects one pair of vertices). Vertex A connects to each of the other 6 vertices: AB, AC, AD, AE, AF, and AG. The probability that a randomly selected edge will involve point A is $\frac{6}{21} = \frac{2}{7}$ (which is approximately 0.286 or 28.6%).

(B) There are $\binom{7}{3} = \frac{7!}{3!4!} = \frac{(7)(6)(5)}{(3)(2)(1)} = 35$ ways to choose 3 out of 7 vertices (to form a triangle). Edge DE is a part of 5 triangles: ADE, BDE, CDE, DEF, and DEG. The probability that a triangle formed by randomly selecting vertices will involve edge DE is $\frac{5}{35} = \frac{1}{7}$ (which is approximately 0.143 or 14.3%).

Example 6. In the diagram below, if two different edges are randomly selected, what is the probability that they will intersect at a point other than A, B, C, D, E, or F?

This is the complete bipartite graph (or bigraph) $K_{3,3}$. It has two sets of 3 vertices; one set is A, B, and C, while the other set is D, E, and F. Every vertex from one set is connected to every vertex of the other set (but no vertices within a set are connected). There are $(3)(3) = 9$ edges. These are AD, AE, AF, BD, BE, BF, CD, CE, and CF. Looking at the diagram, there are 7 points of intersection that are **not** point A, B, C, D, E, or F; these are the points where the edges cross. Three edges cross at the center point; 3 pairs of edges cross there (AF&BE, AF&CD, and BE&CD). Two edges cross at each of the other 6 points (AE&BD, AE&CD, AF&BD, AF&CE, BF&CD, and BF&CE). This makes a total of $3 + 6 = 9$ pairs of intersecting edges. There are $\binom{9}{2} = \frac{9!}{2!7!} = \frac{(9)(8)}{2} = 36$ ways to choose 2 out of 9 edges. Since 9 of these pairs intersect, the probability that 2 randomly selected edges intersect is $\frac{9}{36} = \frac{1}{4}$ (or 0.25 or 25%).

Chapter 11 Problems

Directions: Find the indicated probabilities, assuming that the selection is __random__.

(1) A regular octagon is drawn such that its top and bottom edges are horizontal. One diagonal is randomly drawn.
P(the diagonal is horizontal)

(2) Two diagonals are randomly drawn for a regular octagon.
P(the diagonals are parallel)

(3) The figure below has many triangles. 3 vertices are randomly selected.
P(all 3 belong to one of those triangles)

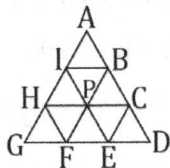

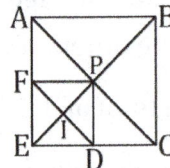

(4) The figure below has many triangles. 3 vertices are randomly selected.
P(all 3 belong to one of those triangles)

(5) In the grid below, 4 points are randomly selected.

P(form a square or rectangle with horizontal and vertical sides)

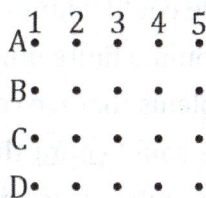

(6) The same grid is for Problems 5-6. Moving only right or down, a random path begins at A1 and ends at D5.

P(path passes through C3)

```
   1  2  3  4  5
A  •  •  •  •  •
B  •  •  •  •  •
C  •  •  •  •  •
D  •  •  •  •  •
```

(7) In the figure below, 1 triangle is randomly selected.

P(one edge of the triangle is AD)

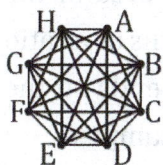

(8) Below, AB = BC = CD = DE = FG = GH and the top row is parallel to the bottom row. Two edges are randomly selected.

P(edges are parallel)

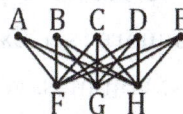

12 Geometric Probability

When we considered the problem of grabbing balls of various colors from a bag, we had a finite number of balls that we could count. Similarly, when we considered the problem of rolling dice, we could count a finite number of dice and count the number of dots on each face. All of the problems that we considered in the previous chapters were **discrete** in the sense that we could **count** the outcomes. (Discrete means that there are separate entities like balls, dots, cards, or birthdays that can be counted.) In contrast, many geometric problems are **continuous** in that they can't be counted. For example, consider the picture below where a circle is inscribed in a square.

If a point inside the square is selected at random, what is the probability that it will lie inside of the circle? We can't 'count' the points inside the circle or square (since the number of points is infinite), yet we can still calculate the probability.

The way to calculate geometric probability is to find a ratio of two suitable measurements (such as length, area, or volume). The two measurements need to correspond (so that you don't compare apples to oranges, so to speak). For the question asked in the previous paragraph, we would divide the area of the circle by the area of the square (see Example 1), but in other problems we will find a ratio of lengths or a ratio of volumes. Whether you should work with length, area, or volume depends on the geometry of the problem and what the question asks for. Compare the examples.

The following geometric formulas may be useful:
- The are of a triangle is $\frac{bh}{2}$, where b is the base and h is the height.
- The area of a square is L^2, where L is the length of one side.
- The area of a rectangle is LW, where L is length and W is width.
- The area of a circle is πR^2, where $\pi \approx 3.141592654$ is the constant **pi** and R is the radius of the circle.
- The **Pythagorean theorem** is $a^2 + b^2 = c^2$, where a and b are the legs and c is the hypotenuse of a **right triangle**.

- Two triangles are **similar** if they have the same shape but not the same size. This means that they have the same interior angles, but the lengths of the sides are different. If two triangles are similar, the sides come in the same ratio. For example, a 9-12-15 triangle is similar to a 6-8-10 triangle because the sides 9, 12, and 15 are each 1.5 times the corresponding sides 6, 8, and 10.
- The diameter of a circle is twice the radius: $D = 2R$.
- The circumference of a circle is $2\pi R$, where R is the radius.
- The length of an arc along a circle is $R\theta$, where R is the radius and θ is the angle of the arc in **radians** as measured from the center of the circle. Note: You can't use degrees in this formula; you need to use radians. To convert from degrees to radians, multiply by $\frac{\pi}{180}$. For example, $60°$ equates $60 \times \frac{\pi}{180} = \frac{\pi}{3}$ radians.
- According to **Thales's theorem**, if one side of a triangle is the diameter of a circle, it is a right triangle (so the Pythagorean theorem applies to it).
- The volume of a cube is L^3, where L is the length of one edge.
- The volume of a rectangular prism (boxes commonly have this shape; all of the sides are rectangles and meet at right angles) is LWH, where L, W, and H are the dimensions of the prism.
- The volume inside of a sphere is $\frac{4\pi R^3}{3}$, where R is the radius.
- The volume of a right-circular cylinder is $\pi R^2 H$, where R is the radius and H is the height of the cylinder.
- The surface area of a cube is $6L^2$, where L is the length of an edge.
- The surface area of a sphere is $4\pi R^2$, where R is the radius.

Example 1. In the figure below, a circle is inscribed in a square. (This means that the diameter of the circle is the same as the length of an edge of the square.) If a point is chosen at random inside of the square, what is the probability that the point will lie in the circle?

Compare the area of the circle to the area of the square. The area of a circle is πR^2. The area of a square is L^2. To find the probability that a point lies in the circle, divide the area of the circle by that of the square.

$$P(\text{point lies in circle}) = \frac{\text{area of circle}}{\text{area of square}} = \frac{\pi R^2}{L^2}$$

The numerator includes R squared, whereas the denominator includes L squared. In order to make progress, we need to know how R relates to L. Look at the picture. The diameter of the circle is $2R$, and the diameter of the circle equals the length of the square, such that $L = 2R$. Plug $L = 2R$ into the equation above. Be careful here; L is squared. Recall from algebra that $(ab)^c = a^c b^c$, such that $L^2 = (2R)^2 = 2^2 R^2 = 4R^2$.

$$P(\text{point lies in circle}) = \frac{\pi R^2}{(2R)^2} = \frac{\pi R^2}{4R^2} = \frac{\pi}{4}$$

Note that R^2 cancels out since $\frac{R^2}{R^2} = 1$. The probability that a point randomly selected inside the square will lie in the circle is $\frac{\pi}{4}$ (which is approximately 0.785 or 78.5%).

Example 2. A small mark is randomly placed on a rod. The rod is then cut into two pieces; one piece is twice as long as the other. What is the probability that the mark will be on the longer piece?

Compare the length of the longer piece to the length of the original rod. (In previous chapters, we found the number of outcomes for a specific event and divided by the total number of outcomes. Here, the original length of the rod corresponds to the total number of outcomes, while the length of the longer piece corresponds to the event of a mark lying on the longer piece.)

$$P(\text{mark is on longer piece}) = \frac{\text{length of longer piece}}{\text{original length of rod}}$$

The longer piece is twice as long as the shorter piece. Let x be the length of the shorter piece. Then the length of the longer piece is $2x$. The original length of the rod is the sum of these two pieces: $x + 2x = 3x$. Plug these into the formula above.

$$P(\text{mark is on longer piece}) = \frac{2x}{3x} = \frac{2}{3}$$

Note that x cancels out since $\frac{x}{x} = 1$. The probability that the mark will be on the longer piece is $\frac{2}{3}$ (which is approximately 0.667 or 66.7%).

Example 3. If a point is chosen at random inside of triangle ABC below, what is the probability that it will be closer to vertex A than to the base BC?

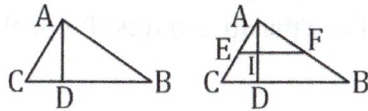

Consider triangle ABC above. The vertical line segment AD shows the height; the base is BC. The horizontal line segment EF marks half the height; that is, AI = DI is one-half of the height AD. Triangles AFI and ABD are **similar**. (Since FI is parallel to BD, their interior angles are congruent.) For similar triangles, the sides come in the same ratio. This means that AI:FI = AD:BD. Since AI is one-half of AD, FI is one-half of BD. It can similarly be shown that EI is one-half of CD. Since EI + IF = EF and CD + BD = BC, it follows that EF is one-half of BC. (Since triangles AFE and ABC are similar, you might have realized that EF is one-half of BC with less work than we have shown here.) Once you know that EF and AI are each one-half of BC and AD, respectively, you are ready to find the probability. Find the ratio of the areas of AFE to ABC. Plug in BC = 2 EF and AD = 2 AI. Note that the ½'s cancel out. In the last step, EF and AI also cancel out.

$$P(\text{point lies above EF}) = \frac{\text{area of AFE}}{\text{area of ABC}} = \frac{\frac{1}{2}(EF)(AI)}{\frac{1}{2}(BC)(AD)} = \frac{(EF)(AI)}{(BC)(AD)} = \frac{(EF)(AI)}{(2EF)(2AI)} = \frac{1}{4}$$

The probability that the point is closer to the top than the base is $\frac{1}{4}$ (or 0.25 or 25%).

Example 4. If a point is chosen at random inside of square ABCD below, what is the probability that the point will be closer to A than to any other corner?

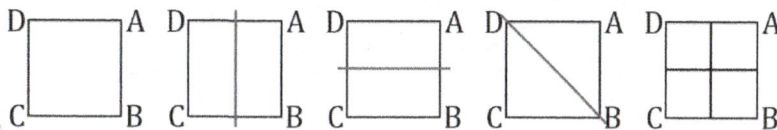

The second figure from the left adds a vertical bisector; any point right of this line is closer to A than to D. The center figure adds a horizontal bisector; any point above this line is closer to A than to B. The fourth figure from the left adds a diagonal; any point to the right of this diagonal is closer to A than to C. Combine these three results to get the right figure: Any point in the top right square is closer to A than it is to B, C, or D. Since this square has one-fourth the area of ABCD, the probability that a random point inside ABCD will be closer to A than any other corner is $\frac{1}{4}$ (or 0.25 or 25%).

Example 5. A cube with a width of 3 units is centered about a rectangular prism with dimensions of 3 units by 4 units by 5 units such that their faces are parallel. If a point is chosen at random inside of the prism, what is the probability that the point will lie inside of the cube?

This is similar to Example 1. Since this problem is three-dimensional, we need to find the ratio of the volumes.

$$\text{P(point lies in cube)} = \frac{\text{volume of cube}}{\text{volume of prism}} = \frac{L^3}{LWH} = \frac{3^3}{(3)(4)(5)} = \frac{27}{60} = \frac{9}{20}$$

The probability that a point randomly selected inside the prism will lie in the cube is $\frac{9}{20}$ (or 0.45 or 45%).

Chapter 12 Problems

Directions: Find the indicated probabilities, assuming that the selection is <u>**random**</u>.

(1) A square is inscribed in a circle. A point is chosen at random inside of the circle.

P(point lies inside of the square)

(2) A mark is randomly placed on a rod. The rod is cut into three pieces. The ratio of the lengths of the pieces is 1:2:3.

P(mark lies on the shortest piece)

(3) A triangle is inscribed in a semicircle as shown below. A point is chosen at random inside of the semicircle.

P(point lies inside of the triangle)

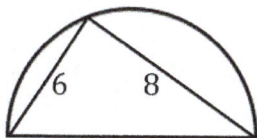

(4) A sphere is inscribed in a cube. A point is chosen at random inside of the cube.

P(point doesn't lie inside of the sphere)

(5) A quarter circle is inscribed in a square as shown below. A point is chosen at random inside of the square.

P(point lies inside of the ¼-circle)

(6) A and B lie on the circumference. The angle below is from the center. A third point on the circumference is chosen at random.

P(point lies on the shortest arc from A to B)

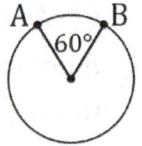

(7) The corners of a cube are labeled A, B, C, D, E, F, G, and H. A point is chosen at random inside of the cube.

P(point is closer to A than any of B-H)

(8) A sphere is centered about a cylinder. The diameter and height of the cylinder both equal the diameter of the sphere. A point is chosen at random inside of the cylinder.

P(point lies inside of the sphere)

(9) A small mark is randomly placed on a disc. A circular hole is cut out from the center of the disc. The radius of the hole is half the radius of the disc.

P(mark doesn't get cut out)

(10) A rectangular prism has dimensions of 2 units by 3 units by 4 units. A point is chosen at random on its surface.

P(point lies on either face that is 3 by 4)

(11) A triangle is inscribed in a quarter circle as shown below. A point is chosen at random inside of the quarter circle.

P(point lies inside of the triangle)

(12) A point is chosen at random inside of triangle ABC below, where DF is parallel to BC.

P(point lies inside of triangle DEF)

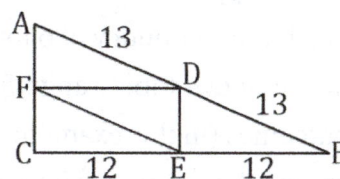

13 Data Analysis

In this chapter, we will present some basic skills for analyzing a set of data. Suppose that we obtain a list of numerical values in one of the following ways.

- We could measure a physical quantity like distance or temperature.
- We could have a set of a outcomes for a random event like rolling dice.

The first step is to tabulate the data. For example, the table below lists the possible outcomes when two standard, fair 6-sided dice are rolled.

1+1=2	1+2=3	1+3=4	1+4=5	1+5=6	1+6=7
2+1=3	2+2=4	2+3=5	2+4=6	2+5=7	2+6=8
3+1=4	3+2=5	3+3=6	3+4=7	3+5=8	3+6=9
4+1=5	4+2=6	4+3=7	4+4=8	4+5=9	4+6=10
5+1=6	5+2=7	5+3=8	5+4=9	5+5=10	5+6=11
6+1=7	6+2=8	6+3=9	6+4=10	6+5=11	6+6=12

If the quantity of interest in the above table is the sum of two dice, note that most of the sums occur multiple times. For example, a sum of 5 appears four times: 1+4, 2+3, 3+2, and 4+1. When a table of data has repeated values like this, it is more efficient to make a **frequency table**. The **frequency** indicates the number of times a particular values appears in a data set. For example, a sum of 5 has a frequency of 4 and a sum of 7 has a frequency of 6 for the table above. Note that the possible values for the sum in the above table range from 2 to 12. To make a frequency table, list the possible outcomes (in this example, the outcomes for the sum of the dice vary from 2 to 12) and record the frequency for each outcome (the number of times each outcome appears). For example, the frequency table below corresponds to the table above.

Sum of 2 Dice	2	3	4	5	6	7	8	9	10	11	12
Frequency	1	2	3	4	5	6	5	4	3	2	1

For example, this frequency table indicates that a sum of 8 appears 5 times. These are 2+6, 3+5, 4+4, 5+3, and 6+2.

When there are several different data values, the data values are often organized into intervals called **bins**. For example, for a set of integer values ranging from 50 to 79, rather than working with 30 different data values (51, 52, 53, to 79), the data might be grouped into 6 different intervals: 50 to 54, 55 to 59, 60-64, 65-69, 70-74, and 75-79. In this case, frequency indicates how many data values lie in a particular interval. When doing this, each interval should be the same size.

A **histogram** helps to visualize the data in a frequency table. The data values (or the intervals) are placed on the horizontal axis and the corresponding frequency is placed on the vertical axis. Vertical bars are drawn such that the height of the bar represents the **frequency** for the data value (or interval). For example, the histogram below was made for the frequency table on the previous page.

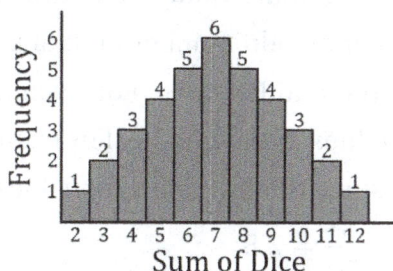

The histogram above makes it visually clear that the most probable sum is 7, since it has the highest frequency (6), and makes it easy to read off the frequencies for each sum. However, if we're interested in probabilities, we can go a step further. Rather than put frequency on the vertical axis, we can put probability on the vertical axis. For the sum of two dice, divide the frequency by 36 to get the corresponding probability. For example, for a sum of 10, the frequency is 3 because there are 3 ways to make a sum of 10: 4+6, 5+5, and 6+4. There are $6^2 = 36$ ways to roll two dice. Divide the frequency 3 by 36 to find the probability that the sum is 10: $\frac{3}{36} = \frac{1}{12}$. The figure below shows the **probability distribution** for the sum of two dice; this makes it easy to read probability. For example, the probability that the sum will be 5 is $\frac{1}{9}$.

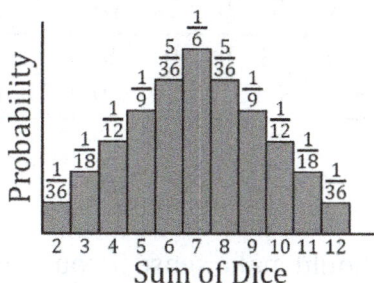

There are a few different quantities that are like an "average," so it is important to distinguish between them.

- The **mean** value (or **arithmetic mean**) is the kind of average that students are most familiar with. Given a set of data points, to find the mean value, add up all of the values and divide by the total number of values (N).

$$\text{mean} = \frac{x_1 + x_2 + x_3 + \cdots + x_N}{N}$$

  For example, the mean value of 2.7, 3.1, 2.9, and 2.3 is $\frac{2.7+3.1+2.9+2.3}{4} = \frac{11}{4} = 2.75$.

- The **median** refers to the middle value; there are just as many values below it as there are above it. For an odd number of data points, simply put the values in order and identify the middle value. For even number of data points, find the mean of the two values in the middle. For example, to find the median for 2.7, 3.1, 2.9, and 2.3, since there are 4 data values, find the mean of the two middle values: $\frac{2.7+2.9}{2} = \frac{5.6}{2} = 2.8$.

- If we are working with probabilities (such as a probability distribution), the "average" that we will find is the **expected value**. We will use the symbol E for the expected value. To find the **expected value**, first multiply each value by the corresponding probability and then add these together.

$$E = x_1 p_1 + x_2 p_2 + x_3 p_3 + \cdots + x_N p_N$$

  For example, for the probability distribution for the sum of two dice shown on the previous page, the expected value is

$$E = 2\left(\frac{1}{36}\right) + 3\left(\frac{1}{18}\right) + 4\left(\frac{1}{12}\right) + 5\left(\frac{1}{9}\right) + 6\left(\frac{5}{36}\right) + 7\left(\frac{1}{6}\right)$$
$$+ 8\left(\frac{5}{36}\right) + 9\left(\frac{1}{9}\right) + 10\left(\frac{1}{12}\right) + 11\left(\frac{1}{18}\right) + 12\left(\frac{1}{36}\right)$$
$$E = \frac{1}{18} + \frac{1}{6} + \frac{1}{3} + \frac{5}{9} + \frac{5}{6} + \frac{7}{6} + \frac{10}{9} + 1 + \frac{5}{6} + \frac{11}{18} + \frac{1}{3}$$
$$E = \frac{1 + 3 + 6 + 10 + 15 + 21 + 20 + 18 + 15 + 11 + 6}{18}$$
$$E = \frac{126}{18} = 7$$

  The answer ($E = 7$) should make sense if you look at the previous graph.

In addition to average, it's desirable to quantify the "spread." This means, is the data spread out or is it concentrated, and how much so? There are a few common ways to quantify the amount of spread in data.

- The **range** is the difference between the greatest value and the least value. For example, for 2.7, 3.1, 2.9, and 2.3, the range is $3.1 - 2.3 = 0.8$. The range is the simplest measure of spread, but also the least relevant statistically.

- Given a set of data points, to find the **standard deviation**, use the formula below (where $N - 1$ is inside of the square root).

$$\text{std. dev.} = \sqrt{\frac{(x_1 - \text{mean})^2 + (x_2 - \text{mean})^2 + (x_3 - \text{mean})^2 + \cdots + (x_N - \text{mean})^2}{N - 1}}$$

For example, for 2.7, 3.1, 2.9, and 2.3, recall that we previously found the mean to be 2.75. Plug these values into the standard deviation formula.

$$\text{std. dev.} = \sqrt{\frac{(2.7 - 2.75)^2 + (3.1 - 2.75)^2 + (2.9 - 2.75)^2 + (2.3 - 2.75)^2}{4 - 1}}$$

$$\text{std. dev.} = \sqrt{\frac{0.0025 + 0.1225 + 0.0225 + 0.2025}{3}} = \sqrt{\frac{0.35}{3}} \approx 0.34$$

Note that this value (0.34) is somewhat less than half the range.

- If we are working with probabilities (such as a probability distribution), we will first find the **variance** using the formula below, where the x's are the values, the p's are the corresponding probabilities, and E is the expected value. The **standard deviation** is the square root of the variance: $\text{std. dev.} = \sqrt{\text{Var.}}$

$$\text{Var.} = p_1(x_1 - E)^2 + p_2(x_2 - E)^2 + p_3(x_3 - E)^2 + \cdots + p_N(x_N - E)^2$$

For example, for the sum of two dice probability distribution, we get:

$$\text{Var.} = \left(\frac{1}{36}\right)(2 - 7)^2 + \left(\frac{1}{18}\right)(3 - 7)^2 + \left(\frac{1}{12}\right)(4 - 7)^2 + \left(\frac{1}{9}\right)(5 - 7)^2$$

$$+ \left(\frac{5}{36}\right)(6 - 7)^2 + \left(\frac{1}{6}\right)(7 - 7)^2 + \left(\frac{5}{36}\right)(8 - 7)^2 + \left(\frac{1}{9}\right)(9 - 7)^2$$

$$+ \left(\frac{1}{12}\right)(10 - 7)^2 + \left(\frac{1}{18}\right)(11 - 7)^2 + \left(\frac{1}{36}\right)(12 - 7)^2$$

$$\text{Var.} = \frac{25}{36} + \frac{16}{18} + \frac{9}{12} + \frac{4}{9} + \frac{5}{36} + 0 + \frac{5}{36} + \frac{4}{9} + \frac{9}{12} + \frac{16}{18} + \frac{25}{36}$$

$$\text{Var.} = \frac{25}{36} + \frac{32}{36} + \frac{27}{36} + \frac{16}{36} + \frac{5}{36} + \frac{5}{36} + \frac{16}{36} + \frac{27}{36} + \frac{32}{36} + \frac{25}{36}$$

$$\text{Var.} = \frac{210}{36} = \frac{35}{6} \approx 5.83$$

$$\text{std. dev.} = \sqrt{\text{Var.}} = \sqrt{5.83} \approx 2.4$$

Note that there is an alternate formula for the variance:

$$\text{Var.} = p_1 x_1^2 + p_2 x_2^2 + p_3 x_3^2 + \cdots + p_N x_N^2 - E^2$$

For the sum of two dice probability distribution, this method gives:

$$\text{Var.} = \left(\frac{1}{36}\right) 2^2 + \left(\frac{1}{18}\right) 3^2 + \left(\frac{1}{12}\right) 4^2 + \left(\frac{1}{9}\right) 5^2 + \left(\frac{5}{36}\right) 6^2 + \left(\frac{1}{6}\right) 7^2$$

$$+ \left(\frac{5}{36}\right) 8^2 + \left(\frac{1}{9}\right) 9^2 + \left(\frac{1}{12}\right) 10^2 + \left(\frac{1}{18}\right) 11^2 + \left(\frac{1}{36}\right) 12^2 - 7^2$$

$$\text{Var.} = \frac{4}{36} + \frac{9}{18} + \frac{16}{12} + \frac{25}{9} + \frac{180}{36} + \frac{49}{6} + \frac{320}{36} + \frac{81}{9} + \frac{100}{12} + \frac{121}{18} + \frac{144}{36} - 49$$

$$\text{Var.} = \frac{4}{36} + \frac{18}{36} + \frac{48}{36} + \frac{100}{36} + \frac{180}{36} + \frac{294}{36} + \frac{320}{36} + \frac{324}{36} + \frac{300}{36} + \frac{242}{36} + \frac{144}{36} - \frac{1764}{36}$$

$$\text{Var.} = \frac{1974}{36} - \frac{1764}{36} = \frac{210}{6} = \frac{35}{6} \approx 5.83$$

$$\text{std. dev.} = \sqrt{\text{Var.}} = \sqrt{5.83} \approx 2.4$$

As you can see, this alternate method leads to the same answer. (In either case, it's easy to make an arithmetic or calculator mistake if you're carrying out the calculation by hand. Some calculators have built-in probability and statistics functions, or you might use data analysis software, a spreadsheet, or an app.)

Example 1. For the set of data listed below, (A) find the mean, (B) find the median, (C) find the standard deviation, (D) make a frequency table, and (E) draw a histogram.

$$8, 10, 10, 7, 9, 8, 10, 9, 8, 11, 11, 7, 10, 11, 10, 9$$

(A) To find the mean, add the values and divide by the total number of values. Note that there are two 7's, three 8's, three 9's, five 10's, and three 11's.

$$\text{mean} = \frac{8 + 10 + 10 + 7 + 9 + 8 + 10 + 9 + 8 + 11 + 11 + 7 + 10 + 11 + 10 + 9}{16}$$

$$\text{mean} = \frac{2(7) + 3(8) + 3(9) + 5(10) + 3(11)}{16} = \frac{14 + 24 + 27 + 50 + 33}{16}$$

$$\text{mean} = \frac{148}{16} = 9.25$$

(B) To find the median, put the values in order.

$$7, 7, 8, 8, 8, 9, 9, 9, 10, 10, 10, 10, 10, 11, 11, 11$$

There are 16 values. Since 16 is an even number, there are two middle values. The eighth value is a 9 and the ninth value is a 10. Find the mean of these two values: $\frac{9+10}{2}$ $= \frac{19}{2} = 9.5$. (If there had been an odd number of values, the median would simply be the middle value; in that case, we wouldn't find a mean in the last step.)

(C) Use the formula for the standard deviation. The formula would appear very long with 16 values, so we will begin by doing one step at a time in a table.

$$\text{std. dev.} = \sqrt{\frac{(x_1 - \text{mean})^2 + (x_2 - \text{mean})^2 + (x_3 - \text{mean})^2 + \cdots + (x_N - \text{mean})^2}{N - 1}}$$

List all 16 data values. Put them in order from least to greatest. Since each value is repeated, this will save time.

7	7	8	8	8	9	9	9
10	10	10	10	10	11	11	11

Subtract the mean, 9.25, from each value.

−2.25	−2.25	−1.25	−1.25	−1.25	−0.25	−0.25	−0.25
0.75	0.75	0.75	0.75	0.75	1.75	1.75	1.75

Square each difference. The values in the table are rounded.

5.0625	5.0625	1.5625	1.5625	1.5625	0.0625	0.0625	0.0625
0.5625	0.5625	0.5625	0.5625	0.5625	3.0625	3.0625	3.0625

Add these values together.

$$2(5.0625) + 3(1.5625) + 3(0.0625) + 5(0.5625) + 3(3.0625) = 27$$

Finally, divide by $N - 1$ and then take the square root.

$$\text{std. dev.} = \sqrt{\frac{27}{16 - 1}} = \sqrt{\frac{27}{15}} = \sqrt{\frac{9}{5}} = \sqrt{1.8} \approx 1.3$$

(D) Count how many times each value occurs.

Data Value	7	8	9	10	11
Frequency	2	3	3	5	3

(E) Use the frequency table to determine the height of each vertical bar.

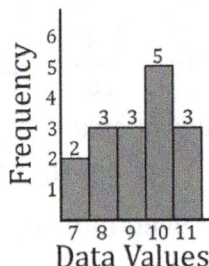

Example 2. Four fair coins are flipped at once. We are interested in the number of coins that show heads. (A) Make a frequency table. (B) Graph the probability distribution. (C) Find the expected value. (D) Find the variance and standard deviation.

(A) First find how many ways there are for zero to four heads to show on four coins. We will use the strategy from "another alternate solution" to Example 2 in Chapter 6.

- There is $\binom{4}{0} = \frac{4!}{0!4!} = 1$ way to choose 0 out of 4 heads: TTTT.

- There are $\binom{4}{1} = \frac{4!}{1!3!} = 4$ ways to choose 1 out of 4 heads: HTTT, THTT, TTHT, and TTTH.

- There are $\binom{4}{2} = \frac{4!}{2!2!} = 6$ ways to choose 2 out of 4 heads: HHTT, HTHT, HTTH, THHT, THTH, and TTHH.

- There are $\binom{4}{3} = \frac{4!}{3!1!} = 4$ ways to choose 3 out of 4 heads: HHHT, HHTH, HTHH, and THHH.

- There is $\binom{4}{4} = \frac{4!}{4!0!} = 1$ way to choose all 4 heads: HHHH.

Number of Heads	0	1	2	3	4
Frequency	1	4	6	4	1

(B) Find the probability for zero to four heads to show. There are $2^4 = 16$ possible outcomes. Divide each frequency from Part A by 16: $P(0) = \frac{1}{16}$, $P(1) = \frac{4}{16} = \frac{1}{4}$, $P(2) = \frac{6}{16} = \frac{3}{8}$, $P(3) = \frac{4}{16} = \frac{1}{4}$, and $P(4) = \frac{1}{16}$. Check: $\frac{1}{16} + \frac{1}{4} + \frac{3}{8} + \frac{1}{4} + \frac{1}{16} = \frac{1+4+6+4+1}{16} = \frac{16}{16} = 1$.

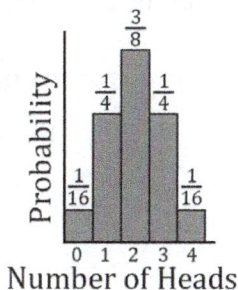

(C) Use the formula for the expected value. The values are the number of heads.

$$E = x_1 p_1 + x_2 p_2 + x_3 p_3 + \cdots + x_N p_N$$

$$E = 0\left(\frac{1}{16}\right) + 1\left(\frac{1}{4}\right) + 2\left(\frac{3}{8}\right) + 3\left(\frac{1}{4}\right) + 4\left(\frac{1}{16}\right)$$

$$E = 0 + \frac{1}{4} + \frac{3}{4} + \frac{3}{4} + \frac{1}{4} = \frac{1+3+3+1}{4} = \frac{8}{4} = 2$$

Looking at the graph above, the answer ($E = 2$) should make sense.

(D) Use one of the two methods for finding the variance and standard deviation.

$$\text{Var.} = p_1(x_1 - E)^2 + p_2(x_2 - E)^2 + p_3(x_3 - E)^2 + \cdots + p_N(x_N - E)^2$$

$$\text{Var.} = \left(\frac{1}{16}\right)(0-2)^2 + \left(\frac{1}{4}\right)(1-2)^2 + \left(\frac{3}{8}\right)(2-2)^2 + \left(\frac{1}{4}\right)(3-2)^2 + \left(\frac{1}{16}\right)(4-2)^2$$

$$\text{Var.} = \frac{4}{16} + \frac{1}{4} + 0 + \frac{1}{4} + \frac{4}{16} = \frac{1}{4} + \frac{1}{4} + \frac{1}{4} + \frac{1}{4} = \frac{4}{4} = 1$$

$$\text{std. dev.} = \sqrt{\text{Var.}} = \sqrt{1} = 1$$

Note that the alternate method gives the same answer:

$$\text{Var.} = p_1 x_1^2 + p_2 x_2^2 + p_3 x_3^2 + \cdots + p_N x_N^2 - E^2$$

$$\text{Var.} = \left(\frac{1}{16}\right)0^2 + \left(\frac{1}{4}\right)1^2 + \left(\frac{3}{8}\right)2^2 + \left(\frac{1}{4}\right)3^2 + \left(\frac{1}{16}\right)4^2 - 2^2$$

$$\text{Var.} = 0 + \frac{1}{4} + \frac{12}{8} + \frac{9}{4} + \frac{16}{16} - 4 = \frac{1}{4} + \frac{6}{4} + \frac{9}{4} + \frac{4}{4} - \frac{16}{4} = \frac{4}{4} = 1$$

$$\text{std. dev.} = \sqrt{\text{Var.}} = \sqrt{1} = 1$$

Chapter 13 Problems

Directions: For each list of numbers, find the mean, find the median, find the standard deviation, make a frequency table, and draw a histogram.

(1) 33, 27, 33, 27, 39, 21, 27, 27, 39, 45, 33

(2) 75, 80, 95, 85, 70, 75, 80, 85, 90, 100 80, 75, 85, 90, 90, 70, 95, 80, 85, 70

Directions: For each situation, make a frequency table, graph the probability distribution, and find the expected value, variance, and standard deviation.

(3) A bag contains 6 blue balls and 4 red balls. 6 balls are randomly selected without replacement. We're interested in the number of blue balls.

(4) Two fair 4-sided dice with sides numbered 1, 2, 3, and 4 are rolled once. We're interested in the product of the two numbers.

14 Probability Distributions

When an experiment (such as rolling dice or flipping coins) involves chance, we can't predict exactly which outcome will occur when, but we can determine probabilities for the different possible outcomes. The set of possible outcomes is referred to as the **sample space**. For example, if three coins are flipped, the sample space consists of 8 possible outcomes: HHH, HHT, HTH, THH, HTT, THT, TTH, and TTT. Many problems are concerned with a **random variable** that is a function defined on the sample space. For example, if we wish to find the probability that a specific number of coins show heads, the random variable is the number of heads showing on three coins. As another example, if we wish to find the probability that two dice add up to a particular value, the random variable is the sum of the dice.

In math, a **function** is written in the form $y(x)$ where y is a function of x. The argument (x) is the input; the function produces a single output value (y) for each value of x. We refer to $y(x)$ as a function of x. A function may depend on more than one variable. The function $z(w, x)$ depends on both w and x. To learn more about what exactly a function is in mathematics, consult a precalculus text. In probability, what you need to know about it is that a random variable is a function of the sample space, meaning that we can find the value of a random variable (like the number of heads showing on 3 coins) by looking at the sample space (HHH, HHT, HTH, etc.), and that a random variable is single-valued. If the random variable Y is the number of heads showing on 3 coins, then Y(HHH) = 3 and Y(THT) = 1, for example. The random variable Y is single-valued in the sense that Y(HHT) is definitely equal to 2 or that Y(TTT) is zero; if you count the number of H's, you get one definite value for Y. That is, for each single input (like HTH or like TTH), Y has exactly one output.

A random variable may be discrete or continuous. A **discrete** random variable has separate entities that can be counted, whereas a **continuous** random variable does not. The number of heads showing on coins or the sum of the dots showing on dice are examples of **discrete** random variables. Geometric random variables, like how far a point is from the edge of a rod or from the center of a disc, are often **continuous**.

We will now explore a variety of discrete random variables and their corresponding probability distributions. The simplest kind of random variable is a Bernoulli random variable. A **Bernoulli** random variable can only take on two possible values; it equals 1 for a successful outcome and it equals 0 for failure. For example, if a single coin is flipped once, the number of heads shown is a Bernoulli variable. In this case, 1 is a success, while 0 is a failure. Let k be the random variable. In this example, k is the number of heads. Let p represent the probability for the successful outcome and let $q = 1 - p$ represent the probability for the failure. The **Bernoulli distribution** is $P(k)$, where $P(0) = q = 1 - p$ and $P(1) = p$. To find the expected value and variance, note that the outcomes are the values of k (that is, $x_1 = 0$ and $x_2 = 1$) and $P(0)$ and $P(1)$ are the corresponding probabilities (we referred to these as p_1 and p_2 in Chapter 13).

$$E = x_1 p_1 + x_2 p_2 = 0(1 - p) + (1)p = p$$
$$\text{Var.} = p_1(x_1 - E)^2 + p_2(x_2 - E)^2 = (1 - p)(0 - p)^2 + p(1 - p)^2$$
$$\text{Var.} = (1 - p)p^2 + p(1 - 2p + p^2) = p^2 - p^3 + p - 2p^2 + p^3 = p - p^2 = p(1 - p)$$

We used the foil method from algebra: $(x - y)^2 = x^2 - 2xy + y^2$. For a fair coin, $p = \frac{1}{2}$ such that $E = \frac{1}{2}$ and $\text{Var.} = \left(\frac{1}{2}\right)\left(1 - \frac{1}{2}\right) = \left(\frac{1}{2}\right)\left(\frac{1}{2}\right) = \frac{1}{4}$.

A **binomial** random variable is like a Bernoulli random variable, except that the trials are repeated n times instead of just once. For example, if a coin is flipped n times, the number of heads showing is a binomial random variable. If k is the number of heads, then $0 \le k \le n$. As with the Bernoulli distribution, p represents the probability of a successful outcome for a single trial, and $q = 1 - p$ represents the probability that the trial is a failure. The **binomial distribution** is $P(k)$, where $0 \le k \le n$ and where:

$$P(k) = \binom{n}{k} p^k q^{n-k} = \frac{n!}{k!\,(n-k)!} p^k (1 - p)^{n-k}$$

This is a handy formula. For example, suppose that 5 fair coins are flipped at once and we want to find the probability that 3 of the coins show heads. In this example, $n = 5$, $k = 3$, $p = \frac{1}{2}$, and $q = 1 - p = 1 - \frac{1}{2} = \frac{1}{2}$. The above formula gives:

$$P(3) = \frac{5!}{3!\,2!} \left(\frac{1}{2}\right)^3 \left(\frac{1}{2}\right)^2 = 10\left(\frac{1}{8}\right)\left(\frac{1}{4}\right) = \frac{10}{32} = \frac{5}{16}$$

Now let's check the answer. Following the method from Chapter 6, there are $2^5 = 32$ ways to flip 5 coins. There are 10 ways for 3 of the 5 coins to show heads: HHHTT,

HHTHT, HHTTH, HTHHT, HTHTH, HTTHH, THHHT, THHTH, THTHH, and TTHHH. The probability that 3 of the coins show heads is $\frac{10}{32} = \frac{5}{16}$.

The expected value for a binomial distribution turns out to be $E = np$, and the variance is $np(1 - p)$. For example, if 4 fair coins are flipped at once and k is the number of heads showing, we get $E = 4p = 4\left(\frac{1}{2}\right) = 2$ and Var. $= (4)\left(\frac{1}{2}\right)\left(1 - \frac{1}{2}\right) = (4)\left(\frac{1}{2}\right)\left(\frac{1}{2}\right) = 1$ (which agrees with the answers to Example 2 in Chapter 13).

The formula for $P(k)$ for the binomial distribution gives the probability that there will be exactly k successes (like k heads out of n coins). If you want to find the probability that there will be $\leq k$ successes (or "at most" k successes), you need to find the **cumulative** probability distribution. For the binomial distribution, the cumulative probability distribution is:

$$P(\leq k) = P(0) + P(1) + P(2) + \cdots + P(k)$$

For example, if you flip 5 fair coins at once and want the probability that there are 3 **or fewer** heads (or, equivalently, at least 2 tails), you want $P(\leq 3) = P(0) + P(1) + P(2) + P(3)$.

The binomial distribution doesn't have to be used just for counting heads or just for flipping coins. There are many other applications. The following conditions must hold in order to use the binomial distribution:

- The process needs to be random. The number of trials must be finite.
- You need a random variable that can only be 0 or 1 for a single trial. (Then k represents the total number of successes out of all n trials.)
- Each trial must have the same value of p.
- The trials must be independent. (For example, if balls are selected from a bag, each ball needs to be put back in the bag before selecting the next ball.)

Consider the examples below:

- 6 fair coins are flipped at once. We're interested in the number of tails. Let k represent the number of tails. The formula will still work. (Alternatively, work with the number of heads and use the complement rule.)

- If the coins are unfair, the formula still works if all of the coins have the same value of p.

- Rolling n dice where p will be the same for each die, and asking a question that has an answer of 0 or 1 for each die. For example, rolling 5 standard, fair 6-sided dice at once, the probability that 3 dice will show four's is given by $P(3)$ with $n = 5$ and $p = \frac{1}{6}$. The probability that 3 dice will show five or higher is also given by $P(3)$, but this time with $p = \frac{2}{6} = \frac{1}{3}$. (However, if some dice are 6-sided and others are 10-sided, the binomial distribution wouldn't apply.)

- If a bag contains balls of two colors, if each ball is **placed back in the bag** before selecting the next ball, you may still use the binomial distribution. (However, if the balls are selected without replacement, then the value of p is different for each selection. For selections **without replacement**, see the **hypergeometric distribution**.) If a bag contains balls of three or more colors, but you just want to know how many balls of one color are selected, with replacement, the binomial distribution still applies; k is the number of balls of the desired color.

- If you define random variable so that it either equals -1 or $+1$ for each trial, for example, you will need to modify the formula since the binomial distribution is set up for a random variable that either equals 0 or 1 for each trial.

The **uniform distribution** is very simple; each value of $P(k)$ is the same. For a discrete uniform probability distribution where k is an integer from 1 to n, for example, then $P(k) = \frac{1}{n}$ for each value of k. In this case, each outcome is equally likely to occur. A simple example of a discrete uniform distribution is a fair die that is rolled once, where the random variable equals the number of dots showing. Note that in this case, the quantity k has a different meaning. Here, k is the number showing on a single die for a single throw, whereas for our coin-flipping example for the binomial distribution k was the number of heads showing when n coins were flipped. For a standard, fair 6-sided die, $P(k) = \frac{1}{6}$ and k is an integer from 1-6. Note that $P(1) + P(2) + P(3) + P(4) + P(5) + P(6) = 1$. The reason that $P(k) = \frac{1}{n}$ is that the sum of the probabilities must be one. More generally, suppose that k varies from a to b in steps of 1. For example, if k can be 5, 6, 7, 8, 9, or 10, then $a = 5$ and $b = 10$; or if k varies from 1-8 then $a = 1$ and $b = 8$. In such cases, the expected value is $\frac{a+b}{2}$ (the average value of k) and the variance is $\frac{n^2-1}{12}$. For example, if k can be 5, 6, 7, 8, 9, or 10, the expected value is $\frac{5+10}{2} = \frac{15}{2} = 7.5$ and the variance is $\frac{6^2-1}{12} = \frac{35}{12}$ since there are $n = 6$ values of k.

For a **<u>continuous</u>** uniform distribution, $P(x) = \frac{1}{b-a}$ over the interval from a to b and is zero elsewhere. (If you make a graph with $P(x)$ on the vertical axis and x on the horizontal axis, the graph is a horizontal line segment from a to b. The area between this line and the horizontal axis is a rectangle with an area of 1. For a continuous distribution, the area under part of a curve represents the probability of an event occurring in that region, so the area under the entire curve must be 1 for the same reason that the sum of the probabilities for a discrete probability distribution has to be one.) The continuous uniform distribution has an expected value of $\frac{a+b}{2}$ and the variance is $\frac{b^2-a^2}{12}$ (which is different from the discrete answer of $\frac{n^2-1}{12}$).

The **<u>multinomial distribution</u>** is a generalization of the binomial distribution. With the binomial distribution, we ask as single yes-no question, like "Did the coin show heads?" With the multinomial distribution, we ask more than one question, but we have to ask the questions so that every possibility is covered. For example, if a standard, fair 6-sided die is rolled n times, the questions might be if the outcome is 1, if the outcome is 2, if the outcomes is 3, etc. up to if the outcome is 6 (this question is asked for each trial); one outcome is guaranteed to be correct. This forms a **<u>partition</u>** of the sample space. Recall from Case 5 of Chapter 2 that a partition is formed when a set of distinct elements is divided into subsets where every element of the set is placed into one of the subsets. In our example with the die, the set is the numbers 1-6; we placed all 6 numbers into one of 6 different subsets. For the multinomial distribution:

- n is the total number of trials.
- We divide the sample space into a **<u>partition</u>** using yes-no questions (like we did in the example with the die above) where yes is 1 and no is 0 (like the Bernoulli trial). Every possible outcome needs to be accounted for. Let $Q_1, Q_2,$

$Q_3, \dots, Q_m$ be the questions, where m is the number of questions, and let $p_1, p_2,$ $p_3, \dots, p_m$ be the corresponding probabilities (p's may be different for different questions, but for a single question, p must be the same for each trial.) Note that $p_1 + p_2 + p_3 + \cdots + p_m = 1$. The partition effectively creates m random variables: one for each question. (The case $m = 2$ is the binomial distribution.)

- Let k_1 be the number of yes's for Q_1, k_2 be the number of yes's for Q_2, etc. Note that $k_1 + k_2 + k_3 + \cdots + k_m = n$. Why? For a single trial, exactly one of the Q's will have an answer of yes, so that exactly one of the k's will increase by one. After n trials, there will be exactly n answers of yes, so the sum of the k's must equal n. In the example below, $k_1 + k_2 + k_3 + k_4 + k_5 + k_6 = 0 + 1 + 0 + 3 + 1 + 0 = 5 = n$ (not to be confused with m, which is 6).

- For a given set of values for the k's, the probability is:

$$\frac{n!}{k_1!\,k_2!\,k_3! \cdots k_m!} p_1^{k_1} p_2^{k_2} p_3^{k_3} \cdots p_m^{k_m}$$

For example, suppose that a standard, fair 6-sided die is rolled 5 times, and we want the probability that it shows two 1 time, four 3 times, and five 1 time. In this case, $n = 5$, $k_1 = k_3 = k_6 = 0$, $k_2 = k_5 = 1$, $k_4 = 3$, $m = 6$, and $p_1 = p_2 = p_3 = p_4 = p_5 = p_6 = \frac{1}{6}$. Recall from Chapter 1 that $0! = 1$ and from algebra that $x^0 = 1$. The probability is:

$$P = \frac{5!}{0!\,1!\,0!\,3!\,1!\,0!}\left(\frac{1}{6}\right)^0\left(\frac{1}{6}\right)^1\left(\frac{1}{6}\right)^0\left(\frac{1}{6}\right)^3\left(\frac{1}{6}\right)^1\left(\frac{1}{6}\right)^0$$

$$P = \frac{120}{6}(1)\left(\frac{1}{6}\right)(1)\left(\frac{1}{216}\right)\left(\frac{1}{6}\right)(1) = \frac{20}{7776} = \frac{5}{1944}$$

Check the answer using a technique from Chapter 6. There are 20 permutations with one 2, three 4's, and one 5: 24445, 24454, 24544, 25444, 42445, 42454, 42544, 44245, 44254, 44425, 44454, 44524, 44542, 45244, 45424, 45442, 52444, 54244, 54424, and 54442. There are $6^5 = 7776$ permutations in total. The probability is $\frac{20}{7776} = \frac{5}{1944}$.

The **hypergeometric distribution** modifies the binomial distribution so that each trial is made **without replacement**. Each trial thus reduces the number of outcomes that are available for the next trial. For example, suppose that a bag contains M blue balls out of a total of N balls, where n balls are selected **without replacement**. The formula below gives the probability that k of the n selected balls will be blue. (If instead each ball were placed back in the bag before selecting the next ball, you need to use the binomial distribution instead of the hypergeometric distribution.)

$$P(k) = \frac{\binom{M}{k}\binom{N-M}{n-k}}{\binom{N}{n}}$$

This formula works because the numerator is the number of ways to choose k out of M blue balls and also choose $n - k$ non-blue balls out of the remaining $N - M$ balls, and the denominator is the total number of ways to choose n out of N balls. (You have basically used this formula in previous chapters without realizing it.) Note that k can't exceed M (the number of blue balls, in this case) or n (the number of balls selected).

As an example, suppose that a bag contains 5 blue balls and 7 red balls, 4 balls are selected without replacement, and we want the probability of selecting 2 blue balls. Here, $M = 5$, $N = 5 + 7 = 12$, $k = 2$, and $n = 4$. (Check these carefully. It's very easy to make a mistake identifying these values and plugging them in.) The probability is:

$$P(2) = \frac{\binom{5}{2}\binom{12-5}{4-2}}{\binom{12}{4}} = \frac{\binom{5}{2}\binom{7}{2}}{\binom{12}{4}} = \frac{(10)(21)}{495} = \frac{210}{495} = \frac{14}{33}$$

In this example, there are $\binom{5}{2} = 10$ ways to choose 2 out of 5 blue balls and $\binom{7}{2} = 21$ ways to choose 2 out of 7 red balls for a total of 210 ways to choose 2 blue balls and 2 red balls, and there are $\binom{12}{4} = 495$ ways to choose 4 balls out of 12.

The **geometric distribution** repeats trials until there is a successful outcome. If k is the total number of trials, then there are $k - 1$ failures followed by 1 success; the last trial is always the success in the geometric distribution. The probability that the kth trial will be the first success is

$$P(k) = pq^{k-1} = p(1-p)^{k-1}$$

where, as usual, p is the probability of success and $q = 1 - p$ is the probability of a failure for a single trial. (This distribution gets its name because the infinite geometric series is $1 + q + q^2 + q^3 + \cdots = \frac{1}{1-q}$ provided that $|q| < 1$. If we multiply this series by p, we get $p + pq + pq^2 + pq^3 + \cdots = \frac{p}{1-q} = 1$; it equals 1 because $p = 1 - q$. Note that $p = 1 - q$, $q = 1 - p$, and $p + q = 1$ are all equivalent. The left-hand side is the sum of the possible values of $P(k)$. The sum is one because it is the sum of all of the possible probabilities.) For the geometric distribution, the expected value is $E = \frac{1}{p}$ and the variance is Var. $= \frac{q}{p^2}$.

As an example, suppose that a standard, fair 6-sided die is rolled. The probability that a 3 will be rolled for the first time on the 5th roll is $P(5) = \left(\frac{1}{6}\right)\left(\frac{5}{6}\right)^{5-1} = \frac{1}{6}\left(\frac{5}{6}\right)^4 = \frac{1\cdot 5^4}{6\cdot 6^4} = \frac{625}{7776}$ since $p = \frac{1}{6}$ and $q = 1 - p = 1 - \frac{1}{6} = \frac{5}{6}$.

For the geometric distribution, the **cumulative** distribution is given below. (Recall that we introduced the concept of a cumulative distribution when we discussed the binomial distribution.) Here, $P(\leq k)$ is the probability that a success will occur **no later** than the kth trial. (Note that for the cumulative geometric distribution, there isn't a $P(0)$ since there can't be a success in zero trials. In contrast, there is a $P(0)$ in the cumulative binomial distribution because there can be zero heads in n flipped coins.)
$$P(\leq k) = P(1) + P(2) + \cdots + P(k)$$
$$P(\leq k) = p + pq + pq^2 + \cdots + pq^{k-1} = 1 - q^k$$
Why? The sum of a finite geometric series is $1 + q + q^2 + q^3 + \cdots + q^{k-1} = \frac{1-q^k}{1-q}$ if $|q| < 1$. Multiply by p on both sides to get $p + pq + pq^2 + \cdots + pq^{k-1} = 1 - q^k$. The right-hand side is $1 - q^k$ because the $1 - q$ cancels out when you multiply by p since $p = 1 - q$, as mentioned in a prior paragraph.

As an example, suppose that a standard, fair 6-sided die is rolled. The probability that a three will occur in **5 rolls or less** is $P(\leq 5) = 1 - \left(\frac{5}{6}\right)^5 = 1 - \frac{5^5}{6^5} = 1 - \frac{3125}{7776} = \frac{4651}{7776}$. Observe that this agrees with
$$P(1) + P(2) + P(3) + P(4) + P(5) = \frac{1}{6} + \frac{1}{6}\left(\frac{5}{6}\right) + \frac{1}{6}\left(\frac{5}{6}\right)^2 + \frac{1}{6}\left(\frac{5}{6}\right)^3 + \frac{1}{6}\left(\frac{5}{6}\right)^4$$
$$= \frac{1}{6} + \frac{5}{36} + \frac{25}{216} + \frac{125}{1296} + \frac{625}{7776} = \frac{1296 + 1080 + 900 + 750 + 625}{7776} = \frac{4651}{7776}$$

If $\lambda > 0$ (which is the lowercase Greek letter lambda) for a process that has a **Poisson distribution**, the probability that there will be $k \geq 0$ successes is

$$P(k) = \frac{\lambda^k e^{-\lambda}}{k!}$$

Note that $e \approx 2.71828183$ is **Euler's constant**. The expression $e^{-\lambda}$ is referred to as an **exponential**. Note that $e^{-\lambda} = \frac{1}{e^\lambda}$ for the same reason that $x^{-1} = \frac{1}{x}$ in algebra. To find the value of $e^{-\lambda}$ on a scientific calculator, look for an e^x or exp button (or check the instruction manual). Get out your calculator and try to find e^{-3}; if you do this correctly, you will get approximately 0.04978707.

Examples of when the Poisson distribution applies include the number of particles emitted by a radioactive material and the number of defects produced by a machine.

For example, suppose that $\lambda = 0.4$ for a process that follows the Poisson distribution. The probability that there will be 3 successes is

$$P(3) = \frac{0.4^3 e^{-0.4}}{3!} \approx \frac{(0.064)(0.67032)}{6} \approx 0.0072 = 0.72\%$$

In practice, when the Poisson distribution applies, it is generally as an **approximation** to the binomial distribution for small k and small p with $\lambda = np$. This is particularly useful when n is a large number. Most calculators overflow if you try to enter 100! (one hundred factorial). Just imagine trying to work with a sample size of a million or Avogadro's number. Replace λ with np in the Poisson distribution in order to obtain the Poisson approximation to the binomial distribution. Here, n is the total number of trials and p is the probability of a successful outcome for a single trial. When k and p are each relatively small, the approximation works well.

$$P(k) \approx \frac{(np)^k e^{-np}}{k!}$$

For example, consider a machine that produces defective products at a rate of 3%. If the machine makes 50 products, to find the probability that exactly 2 of the products will be defective, set $n = 50$, $p = \frac{3}{100} = 0.03$, $\lambda = np = (50)(0.03) = 1.5$, and $k = 2$.

$$P(2) \approx \frac{1.5^2 e^{-1.5}}{2!} \approx \frac{(2.25)(0.22313)}{2} \approx 0.251 = 25.1\%$$

We divided the defect rate (3%) by 100 to convert it from a percent to a decimal. To find the exact answer, use the binomial distribution with $n = 50, k = 2, p = 0.03$, and $q = 1 - p = 1 - 0.03 = 0.97$.

$$P(2) = \binom{50}{2} 0.03^2 0.97^{50-2} \approx (1225)(0.0009)(0.23176) \approx 0.256 = 25.6\%$$

Compare the answer for the Poisson approximation (25.1%) to the answer for the binomial distribution (25.6%) to see that the approximation works fairly well for this example. The advantage of the Poisson approximation is that if the number of products made were in the thousands or millions (which is the case for many companies), the binomial distribution would have the challenge of calculating factorials like 1000! or like 1,000,000! (Try these on your calculator.)

(The most important probability distribution for statistical analysis is arguably the **normal distribution**. The normal distribution and its analysis involve calculus, which is beyond the scope of this book. If interested, you might read a book on statistics.)

If you want to make a **graph** of a discrete probability distribution, make a histogram where each vertical bar has a height equal to $P(k)$, like we did in Chapter 13.

Following is a quick summary of the **discrete** probability distributions in this chapter:
- Bernoulli: A single trial has a yes-no question where yes = 1 and no = 0.
$$P(0) = q = 1 - p \quad \text{and} \quad P(1) = p$$
- Binomial: n independent trials have the same yes-no question where yes = 1 and no = 0. For each trial, the probability of success is p and the probability of failure is $q = 1 - p$. The probability that there will be k successes is
$$P(k) = \binom{n}{k} p^k q^{n-k} = \frac{n!}{k! \, (n-k)!} p^k (1-p)^{n-k}$$
- Uniform (discrete): $P(k) = \frac{1}{n}$ for each value of k; each outcome is equally likely.
- Multinomial: m yes-no questions where yes = 1 and no = 0 with probabilities $p_1, p_2, \ldots, p_m$ divide the sample space into a partition where every outcome is covered; $k_1, k_2, \ldots, k_m$ are the number of yes's; n is the number of trials.
$$\frac{n!}{k_1! \, k_2! \, k_3! \cdots k_m!} p_1^{k_1} p_2^{k_2} p_3^{k_3} \cdots p_m^{k_m}$$

- Hypergeometric: A sample contains M objects with a particular attribute out of a total of N objects; the probability that k out of n objects selected **without replacement** will have the attribute characteristic of the M objects. (For example, the M objects might be blue balls.)

$$P(k) = \frac{\binom{M}{k}\binom{N-M}{n-k}}{\binom{N}{n}}$$

- Geometric: Repeated trials have the same yes-no question where yes = 1 and no = 0. For each trial, the probability of success is p and the probability of failure is $q = 1 - p$. The probability that the first $k - 1$ trials will all be no and that the first yes will occur with the kth trial is

$$P(k) = pq^{k-1} = p(1-p)^{k-1}$$

(For the cumulative geometric distribution, see the last bullet point.)

- Poisson: For a Poisson process with parameter $\lambda > 0$, the probability that there will be $k \geq 0$ successes is

$$P(k) = \frac{\lambda^k e^{-\lambda}}{k!}$$

The Poisson distribution is often used as an approximation to the binomial distribution when n is large with $\lambda = np$, provided that k and p are small:

$$P(k) \approx \frac{(np)^k e^{-np}}{k!}$$

- Cumulative: The probability that there will be $\leq k$ successes (or "at most" k successes or "no more than" k successes or k "or fewer" successes) is

$$P(\leq k) = P(0) + P(1) + P(2) + \cdots + P(k)$$

Specifically, for the **geometric** distribution, the cumulative probability is:

$$P(\leq k) = 1 - q^k$$

Example 1. Ten fair coins are flipped at once. Find the probability that (A) six coins will show heads and (B) no more than two coins will show heads.

(A) Let heads = 1 and tails = 0. For each coin, $p = \frac{1}{2}$ and $q = 1 - p = 1 - \frac{1}{2} = \frac{1}{2}$. Use the binomial distribution with $k = 6$ and $n = 10$.

$$P(6) = \binom{n}{k} p^k q^{n-k} = \binom{10}{6} \left(\frac{1}{2}\right)^6 \left(\frac{1}{2}\right)^{10-6} = \frac{10!}{6! \, 4!} \frac{1}{2^6} \frac{1}{2^4} = (210) \left(\frac{1}{64}\right) \left(\frac{1}{16}\right)$$

$$P(6) = \frac{210}{1024} = \frac{105}{512} \approx 0.205 \approx 20.5\%$$

(B) For "no more than" two heads, use the cumulative probability formula.

$$P(\leq 2) = P(0) + P(1) + P(2) = \binom{10}{0} \left(\frac{1}{2}\right)^0 \left(\frac{1}{2}\right)^{10} + \binom{10}{1} \left(\frac{1}{2}\right)^1 \left(\frac{1}{2}\right)^9 + \binom{10}{2} \left(\frac{1}{2}\right)^2 \left(\frac{1}{2}\right)^8$$

$$P(\leq 2) = \frac{1}{1024} + \frac{10}{1024} + \frac{45}{1024} = \frac{56}{1024} = \frac{7}{128} \approx 0.0547 \approx 5.47\%$$

Tip: For a fair coin, $p = q = \frac{1}{2}$ such that $p^k q^{n-k} = p^n$ regardless of k. That's how we knew the denominator would be 1024 in each term. For an unfair coin, or any other case where $p \neq \frac{1}{2}$, this shortcut won't work.

Example 2. Seven standard, fair 6-sided dice are rolled at once. Find the probability that (A) four 3's, two 1's, and one 4 are rolled and (B) exactly four of the dice show a 5 or higher.

(A) Ask $m = 6$ questions where yes = 1 and no = 0: one question for each possible outcome of one die (1-6). This makes a partition with $p_1 = p_2 = \cdots = p_6 = \frac{1}{6}$. Use the multinomial distribution with $n = 7$, $k_1 = 2$, $k_2 = k_5 = k_6 = 0$, $k_3 = 4$, and $k_4 = 1$.

$$\frac{n!}{k_1! \, k_2! \, k_3! \, k_4! \, k_5! \, k_6!} p_1^{k_1} p_2^{k_2} p_3^{k_3} p_4^{k_4} p_5^{k_5} p_6^{k_6} = \frac{7!}{2! \, 0! \, 4! \, 1! \, 0! \, 0!} \left(\frac{1}{6}\right)^2 \left(\frac{1}{6}\right)^0 \left(\frac{1}{6}\right)^4 \left(\frac{1}{6}\right)^1 \left(\frac{1}{6}\right)^0 \left(\frac{1}{6}\right)^0$$

$$= \frac{5040}{(2)(1)(24)(1)(1)(1)} \left(\frac{1}{36}\right) (1) \left(\frac{1}{1296}\right) \left(\frac{1}{6}\right) (1)(1) = \frac{5040}{48} \frac{1}{279{,}936}$$

$$= \frac{105}{279{,}936} = \frac{35}{93{,}312} \approx 0.000375 \approx 0.0375\%$$

Recall from Chapter 1 that $0! = 1$ and from algebra that $x^0 = 1$. **Tip**: Since the p's are equal and $k_1 + k_2 + k_3 + k_4 + k_5 + k_6 = n = 7$, $p_1^{k_1} p_2^{k_2} p_3^{k_3} p_4^{k_4} p_5^{k_5} p_6^{k_6} = p^n = \left(\frac{1}{6}\right)^7$.

(B) Don't use the multinomial distribution; it will require additional work since we don't know how many of which dice are which values. Ask the question "Does the die show a 5 or higher?" Let yes = 1 and no = 0. For each die, $p = \frac{2}{6} = \frac{1}{3}$ (since a 5 or a 6 is a success) and $q = 1 - p = 1 - \frac{1}{3} = \frac{2}{3}$. Since this same question and same p applies to each die, we may use the binomial distribution with $k = 4$ and $n = 7$. (Note that we couldn't use the binomial distribution in Part A.)

$$P(4) = \binom{n}{k} p^k q^{n-k} = \binom{7}{4} \left(\frac{1}{3}\right)^4 \left(\frac{2}{3}\right)^{7-4} = \frac{7!}{4!\,3!} \frac{1}{3^4} \frac{2^3}{3^3} = (35) \left(\frac{1}{81}\right) \left(\frac{8}{27}\right)$$

$$P(4) = \frac{280}{2187} \approx 0.128 \approx 12.8\%$$

Example 3. A bag contains 6 blue balls and 9 red balls. Find the probability that exactly 3 of the balls will be blue if 5 balls are selected (A) without replacement and (B) so that each ball is placed back in the bag before making the next selection.

(A) $n = 5$ balls are selected **without replacement**. There are $M = 6$ blue balls out of $N = 6 + 9 = 15$ total balls. Use the hypergeometric distribution with $k = 3$.

$$P(3) = \frac{\binom{M}{k} \binom{N-M}{n-k}}{\binom{N}{n}} = \frac{\binom{6}{3} \binom{15-6}{5-3}}{\binom{15}{5}} = \frac{\binom{6}{3} \binom{9}{2}}{\binom{15}{5}} = \frac{(20)(36)}{3003}$$

$$P(3) = \frac{720}{3003} = \frac{240}{1001} \approx 0.240 \approx 24.0\%$$

There are $\binom{6}{3} = 20$ ways to choose 3 out of 6 blue balls and $\binom{9}{2} = 36$ ways to choose 2 out of 9 red balls for a total of $(20)(36) = 720$ ways to choose 3 blue balls and 2 red balls. There are $\binom{15}{5} = 3003$ ways to choose 5 out of 15 balls.

(B) The hypergeometric distribution **doesn't** apply since this involves **replacement**. Ask the question "Is the balls blue?" Let yes = 1 and no = 0. For each selection, $p = \frac{6}{15} = \frac{2}{5}$ (since 6 out of 15 balls are blue for each selection; with replacement, all 15 balls are in the bag for each selection) and $q = 1 - p = 1 - \frac{2}{5} = \frac{3}{5}$. Since this same question and same p applies to each ball, we may use the binomial distribution with $k = 3$ and $n = 5$. (We couldn't use the binomial distribution in Part A because each p was different.)

$$P(3) = \binom{n}{k} p^k q^{n-k} = \binom{5}{3} \left(\frac{2}{5}\right)^3 \left(\frac{3}{5}\right)^{5-3} = \frac{5!}{3!\,2!} \frac{2^3\,3^2}{5^3\,5^2} = (10) \frac{8}{125} \frac{9}{25} = \frac{720}{3125} = 0.2304 = 23.04\%$$

The answer to Part A (24.0%), without replacement, is larger than the answer to Part B (23.0%), with replacement. To try to understand this, we'll work out each answer again using a different method that makes it easier to compare the two cases:

- In Part A, without replacement, since there are fewer balls in the bag after each selection, the probability of selecting 3 blue balls first and 2 red balls second is $\frac{6}{15} \frac{5}{14} \frac{4}{13} \frac{9}{12} \frac{8}{11} \approx 0.0240$. The probability of selecting the balls in a different order is the same since the same numerators and denominators are involved; for example, BRBRB is $\frac{6}{15} \frac{9}{14} \frac{5}{13} \frac{8}{12} \frac{4}{11} \approx 0.0240$. There are $\frac{5!}{3!2!} = \frac{120}{(6)(2)} = 10$ permutations of BBBRR. This gives a probability of $\approx 0.240 \approx 24.0\%$.

- In Part B, with replacement, since there are always 6 blue balls and 9 red balls in the bag, the probability of selecting 3 blue balls first and 2 red balls second is $\frac{6}{15} \frac{6}{15} \frac{6}{15} \frac{9}{15} \frac{9}{15} = 0.02304$. There are $\frac{5!}{3!2!} = \frac{120}{(6)(2)} = 10$ permutations of BBBRR. This gives a probability of $0.2304 = 23.04\%$.

What is the important difference in these two examples? In Part A, the numerators and denominators both decrease; the last denominator is 11. In Part B, the fractions for each color remain unchanged. In Part A, the much smaller denominator for the final selections is more significant than the decreasing numerator for each color, and this makes the answer slightly larger overall **without** replacement.

Example 4. A fair 8-sided die with sides numbered 1-8 is rolled. Find the probability that a 6 or higher (A) will first occur on the fourth roll and (B) will occur on the fourth roll or sooner.

(A) Ask the question "Does the die show a 6 or higher?" Let yes $= 1$ and tails $= 0$. For each die, $p = \frac{3}{8}$ (since 6, 7, and 8 are 3 of the 8 possible values of one 8-sided die) and $q = 1 - p = 1 - \frac{3}{8} = \frac{5}{8}$. Since the first 3 trials will be no and the 4th trial will be yes, use the geometric distribution with $k = 4$.

$$P(4) = pq^{k-1} = \left(\frac{3}{8}\right) \left(\frac{5}{8}\right)^{4-1} = \left(\frac{3}{8}\right) \left(\frac{5^3}{8^3}\right) = \frac{(3)(125)}{(8)(512)} = \frac{375}{4096} \approx 0.0916 \approx 9.16\%$$

(B) This time, we want yes to occur in 4 rolls or less. Use the cumulative probability for the geometric distribution.

$$P(\leq 4) = 1 - q^k = 1 - \left(\frac{5}{8}\right)^4 = 1 - \frac{625}{4096} = \frac{4096 - 625}{4096} = \frac{3471}{4096} \approx 0.847 \approx 84.7\%$$

Check: $P(1) + P(2) + P(3) + P(4) = \left(\frac{3}{8}\right) + \left(\frac{3}{8}\right)\left(\frac{5}{8}\right) + \left(\frac{3}{8}\right)\left(\frac{5}{8}\right)^2 + \left(\frac{3}{8}\right)\left(\frac{5}{8}\right)^3 = \frac{3}{8} + \frac{15}{64} +$

$\frac{75}{512} + \frac{375}{4096} = \frac{1536+960+600+375}{4096} = \frac{3471}{4096}.$

Example 5. Given that $\lambda = 2$ for a process that follows the Poisson distribution, find the probability there will be exactly four successes.

Use the Poisson distribution with $\lambda = 2$ and $k = 4$.

$$P(2) = \frac{\lambda^k e^{-\lambda}}{k!} = \frac{2^4 e^{-2}}{4!} \approx \frac{(16)(0.13534)}{24} \approx 0.0902 \approx 9.02\%$$

Example 6. A radioactive sample contains n atoms, where n is huge. The probability that a single atom will decay and release an alpha particle during a 1-second interval is $\frac{5}{n}$. Find the probability that exactly 3 alpha particles will be emitted over a 1-second interval.

Ask the question "Did the atom decay and release an alpha particle during the one-second interval?" Let yes $= 1$ and no $= 0$. For each atom, $p = \frac{5}{n}$ and $q = 1 - p = 1 - \frac{5}{n} = \frac{n-5}{n}$. Since this same question and same p applies to each atom, we may use the binomial distribution. However, we have a problem; we don't know n. Recall that the Poisson distribution is often used as an approximation to the binomial distribution. Since n is large, $p = \frac{5}{n}$ is small. Also, $k = 3$ is a small number. For small p and k, the Poisson distribution makes a good approximation to the binomial distribution. Use the Poisson distribution with $\lambda = np = n\left(\frac{5}{n}\right) = 5$. (We're not merely using the Poisson distribution for its approximation; n canceled out in the formula for λ. We would have been stuck without the Poisson distribution.)

$$P(k) \approx \frac{(np)^k e^{-np}}{k!} = \frac{5^3 e^{-5}}{3!} \approx \frac{(125)(0.0067379)}{6} \approx 0.14 = 14\%$$

Chapter 14 Problems

Directions: Find the indicated probabilities **using formulas from this chapter**, assuming that the selection is **random**.

(1) 12 fair coins are flipped at once.
P(8H), P(6H), P(7T)

(2) 15 fair coins are flipped at once.
P($\leq$3H), P($\geq$11T)

(3) A fair coin is flipped until it shows heads.
P(exactly 5 flips), P($\leq$5 flips)

(4) An unfair coin shows heads 2/3 of the time. It is flipped 8 times.
P(4H), P(6H)

(5) A fair, 4-sided die with sides numbered 1-4 is rolled until 3 occurs.

P(exactly 4 rolls), P(≤4 rolls), P(≥5 rolls)

(6) 10 standard, fair 6-sided dice are rolled at once.

P(4 sixes, 3 twos, 2 fives, 1 three, any order), P(exactly 7 dice show less than 3)

(7) An unfair die has P(1)=P(2)=P(3)= 1/9 and P(4)=P(5)=P(6)=2/9. It is rolled 5 times.

P(3 fives, 2 twos, any order), P(5 sixes)

(8) 5 standard, fair 6-sided dice are rolled at once. This is repeated (rolling all 5 dice) until all 5 dice show 4's.

P(exactly 3 rolls), P(≤1000 rolls)

(9) A bag contains 8 blue balls and 4 red balls. 4 balls are selected without replacement.
P(4B), P(2B), P(3R)

(10) A bag contains 8 blue balls and 4 red balls. 4 balls are selected one at a time, and each ball is placed back in the bag before the next ball is selected.
P(4B), P(2B), P(≤1B)

(11) A bag contains 5 blue balls, 4 green balls, and 3 red balls. 4 balls are selected without replacement.
P(4B), P(3B), P(≤2G)

(12) A bag contains 6 blue balls and 4 red balls. A ball is selected and put back in the bag. This is repeated until a red ball is selected.
P(exactly 4 grabs), P(≤4 grabs)

(13) 5 cards are drawn from a standard, fair 52-card deck without replacement. P(all cards are clubs)

(14) 5 cards are drawn from a standard, fair 52-card deck without replacement. P(4 aces), P(4 of a kind)

(15) A machine has a 0.5% defect rate. The machine makes 500 products. P(exactly 4 defects), P($\geq$4 defects)

(16) When a man tells a particular joke, 1 out of 50 random people don't get it. The man tells the joke to 800 random people. P(exactly 12 won't get it)

Answers

Chapter 1

(1) Case 1. $3! = 6$: ACR, ARC, CAR, CRA, RAC, RCA.

(2) Case 2. $\frac{4!}{2!} = 12$: OORT, OOTR, OROT, ORTO, OTOR, OTRO, ROOT, ROTO, RTOO, TOOR, TORO, TROO.

(3) Case 1. $6! = 720$.   (4) Case 2. $\frac{3!}{2!} = 3$: 225, 252, 522.

(5) Case 1. $5! = 120$.

(6) Case 2. $\frac{5!}{3!2!} = 10$: 77,888; 78,788; 78,878; 78,887; 87,788; 87,878; 87,887; 88,778; 88,787; 88,877.

(7) Case 2. $\frac{8!}{3!2!} = 3360$.   (8) Case 2. $\frac{9!}{4!2!} = 7560$.

(9) Case 2. $\frac{9!}{3!2!} = 30{,}240$.   (10) Case 2. $\frac{6!}{2!2!2!} = 90$.

(11) Case 2. $\frac{7!}{4!3!} = 35$: 2,228,888; 2,282,888; 2,288,288; 2,288,828; 2,288,882; 2,822,888; 2,828,288; 2,828,828; 2,828,882; 2,882,288; 2,882,828; 2,882,882; 2,888,228; 2,888,282; 2,888,822; 8,222,888; 8,228,288; 8,228,828; 8,228,882; 8,282,288; 8,282,828; 8,282,882; 8,288,228; 8,288,282; 8,288,822; 8,822,288; 8,822,828; 8,822,882; 8,828,228; 8,828,282; 8,828,822; 8,882,228; 8,882,282; 8,882,822; 8,888,222.

(12) Case 2. $\frac{8!}{3!2!2!} = 1680$.

(13) Case 3. $\frac{5!}{(5-2)!} = \frac{5!}{3!} = 20$: EH, EI, EL, EX, HE, HI, HL, HX, IE, IH, IL, IX, LE, LH, LI, LX, XE, XH, XI, XL.

(14) Case 3. $\frac{6!}{(6-4)!} = \frac{6!}{2!} = 360$.

(15) Case 4. $\frac{7!}{(7-3)!} + 18 = \frac{7!}{4!} + 18 = 210 + 18 = 228$.

Notes: Ignoring the second A, there would be 210 permutations. There are also 18 permutations involving two A's: AAD, AAN, AAQ, AAR, AAT, AAU, ADA, ANA, AQA, ARA, ATA, AUA, DAA, NAA, QAA, RAA, TAA, UAA.

(16) Case 3. $\frac{4!}{(4-3)!} = \frac{4!}{1!} = 24$: 127, 128, 172, 178, 182, 187, 217, 218, 271, 278, 281, 287, 712, 718, 721, 728, 781, 782, 812, 817, 821, 827, 871, 872.

(17) Case 4. It's easy to list the 7 permutations: 45, 49, 54, 55, 59, 94, 95.

(18) Case 3. $\frac{6!}{(6-5)!} = \frac{6!}{1!} = 720$.

(19) Case 4. $3! + 6 = 6 + 6 = 12$: ENN, ENV, EVN, NEN, NEV, NNE, NNV, NVE, NVN, VEN, VNE, VNN.

Notes: Ignoring the second N, there would be 6 permutations: ENV, EVN, NEV, NVE, VEN, VNE. There are also 6 permutations involving two N's: ENN, NEN, NNE, NNV, NVN, VNN.

(20) Case 4. $\frac{4!}{(4-2)!} + 1 = \frac{4!}{2!} + 1 = 12 + 1 = 13$: IN, IO, IU, NI, NN, NO, NU, OI, ON, OU, UI, UN, UO.

Notes: Ignoring the second N, there would be 12 permutations: IN, IO, IU, NI, NO, NU, OI, ON, OU, UI, UN, UO. There is also one permutation involving two N's: NN.

(21) $\frac{5!}{(5-4)!} + 72 + 72 + 6 = \frac{5!}{1!} + 150 = 120 + 150 = 270$.

Notes: Ignoring the second E and the second L, there would be 120 permutations. There are 72 permutations involving two E's that don't also have two L's (12 of the form EExy, 12 of the form ExEy, 12 of the form ExyE, 12 of the form xEEy, 12 of the form xEyE, and 12 of the form xyEE; for example, EExy includes EEIL, EEIP, EEIS, EELI, EELP, EELS, EEPI, EEPL, EEPS, EESI, EESL, and EESP), there are 72 permutations involving two L's that don't also have two E's (12 of the form LLxy, 12 of the form LxLy, 12 of the form LxyL, 12 of the form xLLy, 12 of the form xLyL, and 12 of the form xyLL; for example, LLxy includes LLEI, LLEP, LLES, LLIE, LLIP, LLIS, LLPE, LLPI, LLPS, LLSE, LLSI, and LLSP), and there are 6 permutations involving two E's and two L's (EELL, ELEL, ELLE, LEEL, LELE, LLEE).

(22) Case 4. It's easy to list the 3 permutations: 47, 74, 77.

(23) Case 4. $3! + 3 + 3 + 1 = 6 + 7 = 13$: 222, 224, 226, 242, 246, 262, 264, 422, 426, 462, 622, 624, 642.

Notes: Ignoring the extra 2's, there would be 6 permutations (246, 264, 426, 462, 624, 642). There are also 6 permutations involving exactly two 2's (224, 226, 242, 262, 422, 622) and one permutation involving three 2's (222).

(24) Case 4. $3! + 18 = 6 + 18 = 24$: 114, 119, 141, 144, 149, 191, 194, 199, 411, 414, 419, 441, 449, 491, 494, 499, 911, 914, 919, 941, 944, 949, 991, 994.

Notes: Ignoring the second 1, second 4, and second 9, there would be 6 permutations. There are also 6 permutations involving two 1's (114, 119, 141, 191, 411, 911), 6 permutations involving two 4's (144, 414, 441, 449, 494, 944), and 6 permutations involving two 9's (199, 499, 919, 949, 991, 991).

(25) Case 5. $\frac{4!4!}{(4-2)!(4-3)!} = \frac{4!4!}{2!1!} = \frac{(24)(24)}{2} = 288$.

Notes: There are 12 permutations of 2 letters of CUBE: BC, BE, BU, CB, CE, CU, EB, EC, EU, UB, UC, UE. There are 24 permutations of 3 digits of 5491: 145, 149, 154, 159, 194, 195, 415, 419, 451, 459, 491, 495, 514, 519, 541, 549, 591, 594, 914, 915, 941, 945, 951, 954. According to the directions, the letters must come before the digits. Examples: BC145, CE594, UB951.

(26) Case 6. $12 \times \frac{3!}{(3-2)!} = 12 \times \frac{3!}{1!} = 12 \times 6 = 72$.

Notes: There are 12 permutations of 3 letters of AREA (Case 4 gives $3! = 6$ permutations of AER and there are also 6 permutations with two A's): AAE, AAR, AEA, AER, ARA, ARE, EAA, EAR, ERA, RAA, RAE, REA. There are 6 permutations of 2 digits of 345: 34, 35, 43, 45, 53, 54. Multiply 12 by 6 to get 72. Examples: AAE34, RAE45, ERA54.

(27) Case 6. $\frac{5!}{(5-3)!} \times 3 = \frac{5!}{2!} \times 3 = \frac{120}{2} \times 3 = 60 \times 3 = 180$.

Notes: There are 60 permutations of 3 letters of PRISM. There are 3 permutations of 2 digits of 818: 18, 81, 88. Multiply 60 by 3 to get 180. Examples: IMP18, SIP88, MRI81.

(28) Case 6. $(120 + 72) \times \frac{5!}{(5-3)!} = 192 \times \frac{5!}{2!} = 192 \times \frac{120}{2} = 192 \times 60 = 11{,}520$.

Notes: There are 192 permutations of 4 letters of ORIGIN. There are 60 permutations of 3 digits of 72,156. Multiply 192 by 60 to get 11,520. Use Case 4 to find the permutations of 4 letters of ORIGIN. Ignoring the second I, there are $\frac{5!}{(5-4)!} = \frac{5!}{1!} = 120$ permutations of 4 letters of GINRO. When there are two I's, the structure will have the form IIxy, IxIy, IxyI, xIIy, xIyI, or xyII (where x is one of G, N, R, and O, and where y is also one of these letters but not the same as x). Each of these structures has 12 permutations. For example, for the structure IIxy, the permutations include: IIGN, IIGO, IIGR, IING, IINO, IINR, IIOG, IION, IIOR, IIRG, IIRN, IIRO. Multiply 6 by 12 to get 72 and add 72 to 120 to get 192. Examples: GINR125, RONG276, GIRI765.

(29) Case 6: $\frac{6!}{(6-1)!} \times 13 = \frac{6!}{5!} \times 13 = 6 \times 13 = 78$.

Notes: There are 6 permutations of 1 letter of MATRIX: A, I, M, R, T, X. There are 13 permutations of 3 digits of 93,699: 369, 396, 399, 639, 693, 699, 936, 939, 963, 969, 993, 996, 999. Use Case 4 to find the permutations of 3 digits of 93,699. Ignoring the extra 9's, there are $3! = 6$ permutations of 369: 369, 396, 639, 693, 936, 963. There are 6 permutations with exactly two 9's: 399, 939, 993, 699, 969, 996. There is 1 permutation with three 9's: 999. Add 6 plus 6 plus 1 to get 13. Examples: A369, X999, M699.

(30) Case 6: $(24 + 9 + 1) \times \frac{3!}{(3-2)!} = 34 \times \frac{3!}{1!} = 34 \times 6 = 204$.

Notes: There are 34 permutations of 3 letters of DEGREE. There are 6 permutations of 2 digits of 602: 02, 06, 20, 26, 60, 62. Multiply 34 by 6 to get 204. Use Case 4 to find the permutations of 3 letters of DEGREE. Ignoring the extra E's, there are $\frac{4!}{(4-3)!} = \frac{4!}{1!} = 24$ permutations of 3 letters of DEGR. There are 9 permutations with two E's: DEE, EDE, EGE, ERE, EED, EEG, EER, GEE, REE. There is one permutation with three E's: EEE. Add 24 (where all four letters are different) plus 9 (with exactly two E's) plus 1 (with three E's) to get 34. Examples: DEE02, GER62, EEE06.

(31) Case 6: $(360 + 120) \times 3 = 480 \times 3 = 1440$.

Notes: There are 480 permutations of 4 letters of FRACTAL. There are 3 permutations of 2 digits of 5000: 00, 05, 50. Multiply 480 by 3 to get 1440. Use Case 4 to find the permutations of 4 letters of FRACTAL. Ignoring the second A, there are $\frac{6!}{(6-4)!} = \frac{6!}{2!} = 360$ permutations of 4 letters of ACFLRT. When there are two A's, the structure will have the form AAxy, AxAy, AxyA, xAAy, xAyA, or xyAA (where x is one of CFLRT, and where y is also one of these letters but not the same as x). Each of these structures has 20 permutations. For example, for the structure AAxy, the permutations include: AACF, AACL, AACR, AACT, AAFC, AAFL, AAFR, AAFT, AALC, AALF, AALR, AALT, AARC, AARF, AARL, AART, AATC, AATF, AATL, AATR. There are thus $6(20) = 120$ permutations with two A's. Add 360 to 120 to get 480. Examples: ACFLOO, CARAO5, TRFC50.

(32) Case 6. $\left(\frac{7!}{3!} + \frac{7!}{3!2!} + \frac{7!}{3!2!} + \frac{7!}{3!2!} + \frac{7!}{2!2!}\right) \times 6 = (840 + 420 + 420 + 420 + 1260) \times 6$

$= 3360 \times 6 = 20{,}160$.

Notes: There are 3360 permutations of 7 letters of ABSCISSA. There are 6 permutations of 3 digits of 2244: 224, 242, 244, 422, 424, 442. Multiply 3360 by 6 to get 20,160. Use Case 4 to find the permutations of 7 letters of ABSCISSA. Ignore one of the A's to find that there are $\frac{7!}{3!} = 840$ permutations of ABCISSS. (Use the Case 2 formula to determine this.) Ignore the B to find that there are $\frac{7!}{3!2!} = 420$ permutations of AACISSS. Ignore the C to find that there are $\frac{7!}{3!2!} = 420$ permutations of AABISSS. Ignore the I to find that there are $\frac{7!}{3!2!} = 420$ permutations of AABCSSS. Ignore one of the S's to find that there are $\frac{7!}{2!2!} = 1260$ permutations of AABCISS. Add 840 plus 420 plus 420 plus 420 plus 1260 to get 3360. Examples: ABCISSS224, SCABIAS442, CASSABS424.

(33) Case 7. It's easy to list the 4 permutations: 26, 62, 72, 76.

Note: Of the $\frac{3!}{(3-2)!} = \frac{3!}{1!} = 6$ permutations (Case 3), 27 and 67 are odd numbers.

(34) Case 7. The 12 permutations are 5238, 5283, 5328, 5382, 5823, 5832, 8235, 8253, 8325, 8352, 8523, 8532.

Note: Of the $4! = 24$ permutations (Case 1) of 3582, the ones that are greater than 5000 either begin with a 5 or an 8.

(35) Case 7. $\frac{6!}{(6-3)!} + \frac{6!}{(6-3)!} = \frac{6!}{3!} + \frac{6!}{3!} = 120 + 120 = 240$.

Notes: For the 4-letter permutations of COMPLEX that end with E, 3 of the letters CLMPOX come before the E. Use the Case 3 formula to find that there are $\frac{6!}{(6-3)!} = \frac{6!}{3!} = 120$ permutations of 3 letters of CLMPOX. For the 4-letter permutations of COMPLEX that end with O, 3 of the letters CELMPX come before the O. Use the Case 3 formula to find that there are $\frac{6!}{(6-3)!} = \frac{6!}{3!} = 120$ permutations of 3 letters of CELMPX. Add 120 plus 120 to get 240. Examples: CLME, EXPO, LCXE.

(36) Case 7. The 21 permutations include: EEIR, EEIS, EERI, EERS, EESI, EESR, EESS, IEER, IEES, IREE, ISEE, REEI, REES, RIEE, RSEE, SEEI, SEER, SEES, SIEE, SREE, SSEE.

(37) Case 7. $\frac{4!}{2!} + \frac{4!}{2!} + \frac{4!}{2!} = \frac{24}{2} + \frac{24}{2} + \frac{24}{2} = 12 + 12 + 12 = 36$: 40,089; 40,098; 40,809; 40,890; 40,908; 40,980; 48,009; 48,090; 48,900; 49,008; 49,080; 49,800; 80,049; 80,094; 80,409; 80,490; 80,904; 80,940; 84,009; 84,090; 84,900; 89,004; 89,040; 89,400; 90,048; 90,084; 90,408; 90,480; 90,804; 90,840; 94,008; 94,080; 94,800; 98,004; 98,040; 98,400.

Notes: The 5-digit numbers beginning with 4 are followed by the digits 0089. There are $\frac{4!}{2!} = \frac{24}{2} = 12$ permutations of 0089 (Case 2). The 5-digit numbers beginning with 8 are followed by the digits 0049. There are $\frac{4!}{2!} = \frac{24}{2} = 12$ permutations of 0049 (Case 2). The 5-digit numbers beginning with 9 are followed by the digits 0048. There are $\frac{4!}{2!} = \frac{24}{2} = 12$ permutations of 0048 (Case 2). Add 12 plus 12 plus 12 to get 36.

(38) Case 7. $\frac{3!}{(3-2)!} = \frac{3!}{1!} = 6$: 366, 396, 636, 696, 936, 966.

Notes: To be evenly divisible by 6, the digits must add up to a multiple of 3 (like 3, 6, 9, 12, 15, 18, or 21) and the final digit must be even. For a subset of 63,965, the digits will add up to a multiple of 3 if they do not contain the 5, and the final digit will be even if it is a 6. So we need to exclude the 5 and require the final digit to be a 6. This means that we need to pick 3 digits from 3, 6, 6, and 9 such that the final digit is a 6. Since the final digit is one of the 6's, we are left to pick 2 digits from 3, 6, and 9 to be the first two digits. Use Case 3 to get $\frac{3!}{(3-2)!} = \frac{3!}{1!} = 6$.

(39) Case 7. $\frac{5!}{(5-3)!} = \frac{5!}{2!} = \frac{120}{2} = 60$.

Notes: The permutations will have the structure ExyzE, where x, y, and z are three different letters of the set CNPRT. Use Case 3 to get $\frac{5!}{(5-3)!} = \frac{5!}{2!} = \frac{120}{2} = 60$.

(40) Case 7. $6 \times 12 = 72$.

Notes: The permutations will have the structure AIxy, IAxy, xAIy, xIAy, xyAI, or xyIA, where x is one of L, P, R, or S and y is also one of these letters provided that y is different from x. For each structure, there are 12 permutations. For example, for the structure AIxy, the permutations include: AILP, AILR, AILS, AIPL, AIPR, AIPS, AIRL, AIRP, AIRS, AISL, AISP, AISR. Multiply 6 by 12 to get 72.

Chapter 2

(1) Case 1. $\binom{6}{2} = \frac{6!}{2!4!} = 15$: AD, AE, AI, AM, AN, DE, DI, DM, DN, EI, EM, EN, IM, IN, MN.

Note: Since these are combinations (not permutations), order doesn't matter. For example, AD is the same combination as DA.

(2) Case 1. $\binom{7}{5} = \frac{7!}{5!2!} = 21$: AGIRT, AGIRV, AGIRY, AGITV, AGITY, AGIVY, AGRTV, AGRTY, AGRVY, AGTVY, AIRTV, AIRTY, AIRVY, AITVY, ARTVY, GIRTV, GIRTY, GIRVY, GITVY, GRTVY, IRTVY.

(3) Case 3. $\binom{5}{3} + 12 = \frac{5!}{3!2!} + 12 = 10 + 12 = 22$: ACC, ACL, ACS, ACU, ALL, ALS, ALU, ASU, AUU, CCL, CCS, CCU, CLL, CLS, CLU, CSU, CUU, LLS, LLU, LSU, LUU, SUU.

Notes: Ignoring the repeated letters, there would be 10 combinations (choosing 3 letters from ACLSU): ACL, ACS, ACU, ALS, ALU, ASU, CLS, CLU, CSU, LSU. There are also 12 combinations involving repeated letters: ACC, ALL, AUU, CCL, CCS, CCU, CLL, CUU, LLS, LLU, LUU, SUU.

(4) Case 1. $\binom{4}{2} = \frac{4!}{2!2!} = 6$: 01, 06, 09, 16, 19, 69.

(5) Case 1. $\binom{8}{4} = \frac{8!}{4!4!} = 70$.

(6) Case 2. $\binom{7+3-1}{3} = \binom{9}{3} = \frac{9!}{3!6!} = 84$.

(7) Case 2. $\binom{6+4-1}{4} = \binom{9}{4} = \frac{9!}{4!5!} = 126$.

(8) Case 3. $\binom{6}{3} + 11 = \frac{6!}{3!3!} + 11 = 20 + 11 = 31$.

Notes: Ignoring the repeated letters, there would be 20 combinations (choosing 3 letters from CEILOS): CEI, CEL, CEO, CES, CIL, CIO, CIS, CLO, CLS, COS, EIL, EIO, EIS, ELO, ELS, EOS, ILO, ILS, IOS, LOS. There are also 11 combinations involving repeated letters: CEE, CSS, EEI, EEL, EEO, EES, ESS, ISS, LSS, OSS, SSS.

(9) Case 2. $\binom{8+5-1}{5} = \binom{12}{5} = \frac{12!}{5!7!} = 792$.

(10) Case 3. It's easy to list the 6 combinations: 225, 226, 255, 256, 555, 556.

(11) Case 3. $\binom{6}{4} + 16 = \frac{6!}{4!2!} + 16 = 15 + 16 = 31$.

Notes: Ignoring the extra 4's, there would be 15 combinations (choosing 4 digits from 013469): 0134, 0136, 0139, 0146, 0149, 0169, 0346, 0349, 0369, 0469, 1346, 1349, 1369, 1469, 3469. There are also 16 combinations involving multiple 4's: 0144, 0344, 0444, 0446, 0449, 1344, 1444, 1446, 1449, 3444, 3446, 3449, 4444, 4446, 4449, 4469.

(12) Case 2. $\binom{10 + 7 - 1}{7} = \binom{16}{7} = \frac{16!}{7!9!} = 11{,}440.$

(13) Case 4. $\binom{3}{2}\binom{5}{3} = \frac{3!}{2!1!}\frac{5!}{3!2!} = \frac{5!}{2!2!1!} = \frac{(5)(4)(3)(2)}{(2)(2)} = (5)(3)(2) = 30$: EIACH, EIACR, EIACT, EIAHR, EIAHT, EIART, EICHR, EICHT, EICRT, EIHRT, EPACH, EPACR, EPACT, EPAHR, EPAHT, EPART, EPCHR, EPCHT, EPCRT, EPHRT, IPACH, IPACR, IPACT, IPAHR, IPAHT, IPART, IPCHR, IPCHT, IPCRT, IPHRT.

(14) Case 6. $\binom{8}{4}\binom{4}{2} = \frac{8!}{4!4!}\frac{4!}{2!2!} = \frac{8!}{4!2!2!} = \frac{(8)(7)(6)(5)}{(2)(2)} = (2)(7)(6)(5) = 420.$

Alternate solution: $\frac{8!}{4!2!2!} = 420.$ This works since $\binom{2}{2} = 1$ for the 2 left behind.

(15) Case 5. $\frac{9!}{4!3!2!} = 1260.$

Note: You could alternatively use Case 6 with $\binom{9}{4}\binom{5}{3}\binom{2}{2}.$

(16) Case 4. $\binom{7}{5}\binom{3}{2} = \frac{7!}{5!2!}\frac{3!}{2!1!} = (21)(3) = 63.$

(17) Case 4. $\binom{4}{2}\binom{8}{6} = \frac{4!}{2!2!}\frac{8!}{6!2!} = (6)(28) = 168.$

(18) Case 4. $\binom{6}{1}\binom{4}{2}\binom{6}{4} = \frac{6!}{1!5!}\frac{4!}{2!2!}\frac{6!}{4!2!} = (6)(6)(15) = 540.$

(19) Case 4. $\left[\binom{6}{4} + 10\right](2) = \left(\frac{6!}{4!2!} + 10\right)(2) = (15 + 10)(2) = (25)(2) = 50.$

Notes: Ignoring the extra A, there would be 15 ways to choose 4 letters from ACFLRT: ACFL, ACFR, ACFT, ACLR, ACLT, ACRT, AFLR, AFLT, AFRT, ALRT, CFLR, CFLT, CFRT, CLRT, FLRT. There are also 10 combinations involving two A's: AACF, AACL, AACR, AACT, AAFL, AAFR, AAFT, AALR, AALT, AART. There are 2 ways to choose 2 digits from 5000: 00 and 05 (since 05 and 50 are the same). Multiply 25 by 2 to make 50.

(20) Case 5. $\frac{10!}{4!4!2!} = 3150.$

Note: You could alternatively use Case 6 with $\binom{10}{4}\binom{6}{4}\binom{2}{2}.$

(21) Case 1. $\binom{12}{4} = \frac{12!}{4!8!} = 495.$

(22) Case 6. $\binom{11}{6}\binom{5}{3} = \frac{11!}{6!5!}\frac{5!}{3!2!} = \frac{11!}{6!3!2!} = 4620.$

Alternate solution: $\frac{11!}{6!3!2!} = 4620.$ This works since $\binom{2}{2} = 1$ for the 2 left behind.

(23) Case 4. $\binom{9}{6}\binom{7}{5} = \frac{9!}{6!3!}\frac{7!}{5!2!} = (84)(21) = 1764.$

Note: If you're wondering whether all of the balls of the same color are distinct, see the note in Example 4.

(24) Case 4. $\binom{8}{4}\binom{11}{5}\binom{9}{6} = \frac{8!}{4!4!}\frac{11!}{5!6!}\frac{9!}{6!3!} = (70)(462)(84) = 2,716,560.$

(25) Case 6. $\binom{24}{8}\binom{16}{6}\binom{10}{4} = \frac{24!}{8!16!}\frac{16!}{6!10!}\frac{10!}{4!6!} = \frac{24!}{8!6!4!6!} = 1,236,826,871,280.$

Alternate solution: $\frac{24!}{8!6!4!6!}.$ This works since $\binom{6}{6} = 1$ for the 6 left behind.

Notes: The answer can alternatively be expressed as $1.23682687128 \times 10^{12}$. (If you use a calculator with less precision, you won't get as many decimals, but out of a trillion, the digits at the end aren't really all that significant.)

(26) Case 5. $\frac{20!}{12!5!3!} = 7,054,320.$

Note: You could alternatively use Case 6 with $\binom{20}{12}\binom{8}{5}\binom{3}{3}.$

(27) Case 7. $\binom{8}{2} + \binom{4}{2} = \frac{8!}{2!6!} + \frac{4!}{2!2!} = 28 + 6 = 34.$

Notes: For both balls to be the same color, we must either select 2 blue balls or 2 red balls. There are $\binom{8}{2} = 28$ ways to select 2 blue balls and $\binom{4}{2} = 6$ ways to select 2 red balls, for a total of $28 + 6 = 34$ combinations.

(28) Case 7. $\binom{9}{3} + \binom{8}{3} + \binom{7}{3} = \frac{9!}{3!6!} + \frac{8!}{3!5!} + \frac{7!}{3!4!} = 84 + 56 + 35 = 175.$

Notes: For all 3 balls to be the same color, we must either select 3 blue balls, 3 green balls, or 3 red balls. There are $\binom{9}{3} = 84$ ways to select 3 blue balls, $\binom{8}{3} = 56$ ways to select 3 green balls, and $\binom{7}{3} = 35$ ways to select 3 red balls.

(29) Case 7. $3\binom{3}{2} = 3\left(\frac{3!}{2!1!}\right) = 3(3) = 9$: 014, 016, 034, 036, 049, 069, 146, 346, 469.

Notes: To make a three-digit number with exactly one odd digit, the other two digits must be even. There are $\binom{3}{2} = 3$ ways to choose 2 even digits out of 0, 4, and 6. Multiply by 3 because the remaining digit is either a 1, 3, or 9.

(30) Case 7. $\binom{9}{6} - 4 = \frac{9!}{6!3!} - 4 = 84 - 4 = 80$.

Notes: There are $\binom{9}{6} = 84$ ways to choose 6 letters from LONGITUDE. Only 4 of these combinations have fewer than 2 vowels: EDLNGT, IDLNGT, ODLNGT, UDLNGT.

(31) Case 7. $\binom{16}{1}\binom{15}{3} = \frac{16!}{1!15!}\frac{15!}{3!12!} = (16)(455) = 7280$.

Notes: There are $\binom{16}{1} = 16$ ways to choose one team captain and $\binom{15}{3} = 455$ ways to choose 3 additional team members.

Alternate solution: There are $\binom{16}{4} = 1820$ ways to choose a team of 4 people and 4 ways for each team to have one captain: $4(1820) = 7280$.

(32) Case 7. $\binom{5}{3} = \frac{5!}{3!2!} = 10$: BELMO, BELMP, BELMR, BELOP, BELOR, BELPR, BEMOP, BEMOR, BEMPR, BEOPR.

Notes: Since 2 of the 7 letters are the B and E, we need to choose 3 of the 5 remaining letters: LMOPR.

(33) Case 7. $\binom{5}{2}\binom{6}{2} + \binom{5}{2}\binom{4}{2} + \binom{6}{2}\binom{4}{2} = \frac{5!}{2!3!}\frac{6!}{2!4!} + \frac{5!}{2!3!}\frac{4!}{2!2!} + \frac{6!}{2!4!}\frac{4!}{2!2!} =$
$(10)(15) + (10)(6) + (15)(6) = 150 + 60 + 90 = 300$.

Notes: There are $\binom{5}{2}\binom{6}{2} = 150$ ways to choose 2 blue balls and 2 green balls, there are $\binom{5}{2}\binom{4}{2} = 60$ ways to choose 2 blue balls and 2 red balls, and there are $\binom{6}{2}\binom{4}{2} = (15)(6) = 90$ ways to choose 2 green balls and 2 red balls.

(34) Case 7. $\binom{6}{3} + 1 = \frac{6!}{3!3!} + 1 = 20 + 1 = 21$: AIO, GHL, GHM, GHR, GHT, GLM, GLR, GLT, GMR, GMT, GRT, HLM, HLR, HLT, HMR, HMT, HRT, LMR, LMT, LRT, MRT.

Notes: There are $\binom{6}{3} = 20$ ways to choose 3 of the 6 consonants. There is just 1 way to choose 3 vowels: AIO.

(35) Case 7. $\binom{15}{5}\binom{5}{0} + \binom{15}{4}\binom{5}{1} + \binom{15}{3}\binom{5}{2} = \frac{15!}{5!10!}\frac{5!}{0!5!} + \frac{15!}{4!11!}\frac{5!}{1!4!} + \frac{15!}{3!12!}\frac{5!}{2!3!}$

$= (3003)(1) + (1365)(5) + (455)(10) = 3003 + 6825 + 4550 = 14{,}378$

Notes: There are $\binom{15}{5}\binom{5}{0} = 3003$ ways to choose 5 out of 15 blue/green balls and

0 red balls, there are $\binom{15}{4}\binom{5}{1} = 6825$ ways to choose 4 out of 15 blue/green balls

and 1 red ball, and there are $\binom{15}{3}\binom{5}{2} = 4550$ ways to choose 3 out of 15

blue/green balls and 2 red balls, using the Case 4 formula to choose r_1 elements

from a set of 15 blue/green balls and r_2 elements from a set of 5 red balls.

Alternate solution: There are $\binom{20}{5} = \frac{20!}{5!15!} = 15{,}504$ ways to choose 5 out of 20 balls

regardless of color. There is 1 way to choose 5 red balls, there are $\binom{5}{4}\binom{15}{1} =$

$\frac{5!}{4!1!}\frac{15!}{1!14!} = (5)(15) = 75$ ways to choose 4 red balls and 1 blue or green ball, and

there are $\binom{5}{3}\binom{15}{2} = \frac{5!}{3!2!}\frac{15!}{2!13!} = (10)(105) = 1050$ ways to choose 3 red balls and 2

blue/green balls. Subtract 1, 75, and 1050 from 15,504 to get 14,378.

(36) Case 7. $\binom{7}{5}\binom{3}{0} + \binom{7}{4}\binom{3}{1} + \binom{7}{3}\binom{3}{2} = \frac{7!}{5!2!}\frac{3!}{0!3!} + \frac{7!}{4!3!}\frac{3!}{1!2!} + \frac{7!}{3!4!}\frac{3!}{2!1!}$

$= (21)(1) + (35)(3) + (35)(3) = 21 + 105 + 105 = 231.$

Notes: There are $\binom{7}{5}\binom{3}{0} = 21$ ways to choose 5 letters and 0 digits, there are

$\binom{7}{4}\binom{3}{1} = 105$ ways to choose 4 letters and 1 digit, and there are $\binom{7}{3}\binom{3}{2} = 105$

ways to choose 3 letters and 2 digits. (You can't choose 2 letters and 3 digits because

then there would be more digits than letters, which would violate the condition.)

Alternate solution: There are $\binom{10}{5} = \frac{10!}{5!5!} = 252$ ways to choose 5 out of 10

characters (letters or numbers). There are $\binom{7}{2}\binom{3}{3} = (21)(1) = 21$ ways to choose

2 letters and all 3 numbers. Subtract 21 from 252 to get 231.

Chapter 3

(1) $(200 - 164 + 1) + (312 - 256 + 1) = 37 + 57 = 94$.

Note: Add 1 to each section because both endpoints are included.

(2) $(58 - 32 + 1) + (82 - 65 + 1) + (121 - 97 + 1) = 27 + 18 + 25 = 70$.

(3) $\$52 - \$17 = \$35$.

Note: Since the person already has \$17, this endpoint is not included; don't add one.

(4) $33 - 19 + 1 = 15$.

(5) $200 - 100 + 1 = 101$.

(6) $199 - 101 + 1 = 99$. Note: Count 101-199 with both endpoints.

(7) $\$16 - (-\$9) = \$16 + \$9 = \$25$.

Note: \$9 are needed to get to zero, then an additional \$16 are needed.

(8) $18 - 7 = 11$. Note: The person was already on the 7th floor, so this endpoint is not included; don't add one. The flights are: 7 to 8, 8 to 9, 9 to 10, 10 to 11, 11 to 12, 12 to 13, 13 to 14, 14 to 15, 15 to 16, 16 to 17, and 17 to 18.

(9) $\frac{200}{8} - \frac{40}{8} + 1 = 25 - 5 + 1 = 21$. The multiples include: 40, 48, 56, 64, 72, 80, 88, 96, 104, 112, 120, 128, 136, 144, 152, 160, 168, 176, 184, 192, 200.

(10) $\frac{96}{12} - \frac{12}{12} + 1 = 8 - 1 + 1 = 8$. The multiples include: 12, 24, 36, 48, 60, 72, 84, 96.

(11) $\frac{693}{7} - \frac{77}{7} + 1 = 99 - 11 + 1 = 89$. Notes: 77 is the smallest multiple of 7 that is greater than 70 and 693 is the greatest multiple of 7 that is less than 700.

(12) $\frac{792}{9} - \frac{306}{9} + 1 = 88 - 34 + 1 = 55$. Notes: 306 is the smallest multiple of 9 that is greater than 300 and 792 is the greatest multiple of 9 that is less than 800.

(13) $\frac{2200}{11} - \frac{1100}{11} + 1 = 200 - 100 + 1 = 101$.

(14) $\frac{996}{6} - \frac{102}{6} + 1 = 166 - 17 + 1 = 150$. Notes: A number that is evenly divisible by both 2 and 3 must be evenly divisible by 6; 102 is the smallest three-digit multiple of 6 and 996 is the greatest three-digit multiple of 6.

(15) $\frac{9990}{15} - \frac{1005}{15} + 1 = 666 - 67 + 1 = 600$. Notes: A number that is evenly divisible by both 3 and 5 must be evenly divisible by 15; 1005 is the smallest four-digit multiple of 15 and 9990 is the greatest four-digit multiple of 15.

(16) $\frac{30}{2} - \frac{6}{2} + 1 = 15 - 3 + 1 = 13$. Notes: The even numbers are whole numbers that are even multiples of 2/3. If you multiply 2/3 by 9, you get 6; if you multiply 2/3 by 12, you get 8; if you multiply 2/3 by 15, you get 10; if you multiply 2/3 by 18, you get 12; etc. (Alternatively, if you divide 6, 8, 10, etc. by 2/3, you get a whole number.) Here is another way to look at it. The multiples of 2/3 include: $\frac{2}{3}, \frac{4}{3}, 2, \frac{8}{3}, \frac{10}{3}, 4, \frac{14}{3}, \frac{16}{3}, 6$, etc. Of these, the numbers 2, 4, 6, etc. are whole numbers. The even numbers in the range 6-30 include 6, 8, 10, 12, 14, 16, 18, 20, 22, 24, 26, 28, and 30.

(17) $\frac{12}{3} - \frac{6}{3} + 1 = 4 - 2 + 1 = 3$. The multiples include: 6, 9, and 12.

Notes: Multiples of 3 are whole numbers that are even multiples of 0.75. If you multiply 0.75 by 8, you get 6; if you multiply 0.75 by 12, you get 9; if you multiply 0.75 by 16, you get 12. (Alternatively, if you divide 6, 9, 12, etc. by 0.75, you get a whole number.) Here is another way to look at it. The multiples of 0.75 include: 0.75, 1.5, 2.25, 3, 3.75, 4.5, 5.25, 6, 6.75, 7.5, 8.25, 9, etc. Of these, the numbers 3, 6, 9, etc. are whole numbers. The multiples also need to be greater than 3 and less than 15.

(18) Sum rule: $15 + 20 = 35$. Note: Choose a pen **or** a pencil.

(19) Product rule: $(4)(9) = 36$. Note: Choose **both** a lunch **and** a dinner.

(20) Product rule: $(6)(9) = 54$. Note: Choose **both** a math class **and** a science class.

(21) $(7)(4 + 3) = (7)(7) = 49$. Notes: Use the sum rule for the soup or salad, where a soup **or** salad is selected. Then use the product rule with the entrée.

(22) $\binom{8}{3}\binom{5}{2} = \frac{8!}{3!5!}\frac{5!}{2!3!} = \frac{8!}{3!2!3!} = 560$. Note: This is Case 6 from Chapter 2.

(23) Sum rule: $8 + 5 = 13$. Note: Choose a boy **or** a girl.

(24) $(3)(12)(8)(25) = 7200$. Note: This is the total number of salespeople.

(25) $(5)(10)(60)(4) = 12,000$. Note: This is the total number of items.

(26) (A) 59 ate pizza. (B) 49 ate tacos. (C) 26 ate tacos, but didn't eat pizza. Notes: 36 ate pizza, but didn't eat tacos; $36 + 23 + 26 = 85$ people.

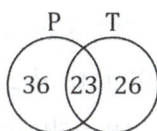

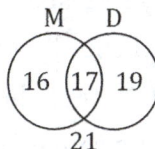

(27) (A) 16 went to a movie, but not a dance. (B) 19 went to a dance, but not a movie. Notes: $16 + 17 + 19 + 21 = 73$ students; 21 didn't go to a movie or a dance.

(28) (A) 80 campers. (B) 18 did both. (C) 38 went swimming, but not boating.

Notes: 24 campers went boating, but not swimming; $24 + 18 + 38 = 80$ campers.

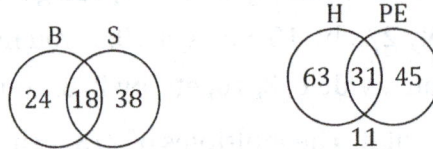

B   S

24 (18) 38

H   PE

63 (31) 45

11

(29) (A) 31 took both. (B) 63 took health, but not PE. (C) 45 took PE, but not health.

Note: $63 + 31 + 45 + 11 = 150$.

(30) $601 - 406 = 195$. Notes: There are $800 - 200 + 1 = 601$ numbers all together (because both of the endpoints, 200 and 800, are included). There are 406 numbers that don't contain any 3's. Why? If the first digit is a 2, 4, 5, 6, or a 7, then there are 5 choices for the first digit and 9 choices for each of the other digits (0, 1, 2, 4, 5, 6, 7, 8, or 9). Multiply to get $(5)(9)(9) = 405$. There is also one number in the range that begins with an 8: 800. Add 405 to 1 to make 406.

Alternate solution: Let's check the answer with a method that doesn't use complementary counting. There are 100 numbers that begin with a 3: 300-399. There are 50 numbers that have 3 as the middle digit (which don't begin with a 3): 230-239, 430-439, 530-539, 630-639, and 730-739. There are 45 numbers that end with a 3 (which don't have a 3 as the first or second digit): 203, 213, 223, 243, 253, 263, 273, 283, 293, and the similar numbers in the 400's, 500's, 600's, and 700's. Add 100, 50, and 45 to make 195.

(31) $900 - 150 = 750$. Notes: There are $999 - 100 + 1 = 900$ three-digit numbers all together (where both endpoints of the range 100-999 are included). The first multiple of 6 in this range is 102 and the last multiple of 6 in this range is 996. To find how many multiples of 6 lie in the range 102-996, use the formula from earlier in this chapter: $\frac{996}{6} - \frac{102}{6} + 1 = 166 - 17 + 1 = 150$. It should make sense that the final answer, 750, is exactly five-sixths of the total number of three-digit numbers (since the total number of three-digit numbers, 900, is evenly divisible by six).

(32) $9000 - 6561 = 2439$. Notes: There are 9000 four-digit numbers all together (where both endpoints of the range 1000-9999 are included). There are 6561 numbers that don't contain any 0's. Why? There are 9 choices for each digit (1-9). Multiply to get $(9)(9)(9)(9) = 6561$.

Alternate solution: Let's check the answer with a method that doesn't use complementary counting. No four-digit numbers begin with a 0. There are 900 numbers with a 0 as the second digit: 1000-1099, 2000-2099, 3000-3099, thru 9000-9099. There are 810 numbers with a 0 as the third digit (where the second digit isn't a 0): 1100-1109, 1200-1209, 1300-1309, thru 1900-1909, and the similar numbers in the 2000's, 3000's, 4000's, thru 9000's. There are 729 numbers with a 0 as the final digit (where the second and third digits aren't 0): 1110, 1120, 1130, thru 1190, and the similar numbers in the 1200's, 1300's, 1400's thru 1900's, and the similar numbers in the 2000's, 3000's, 4000's, thru 9000's. Add 900, 810, and 729 to make 2439.

(33) $90,000 - 52,488 = 37,512$. Notes: There are 90,000 five-digit numbers all together (where both endpoints of the range 10,000-99,999 are included). There are 52,488 numbers that don't contain any 1's. Why? There are 8 choices for the first digit (2-9) and 9 choices for each of the remaining digits (0 and 2-9). Multiply to get $(8)(9)(9)(9)(9) = 52,488$.

(34) $(500 - 324) + (501 - 406) = 176 + 95 = 271$. Notes: There are 500 numbers in the range 500-999 and 501 numbers in the range 1000-1500. In the range 500-999, there are 324 numbers that don't contain a 7, since there are 4 choices for the first digit (5, 6, 8, or 9) and 9 choices for each of the other digits (0, 1, 2, 3, 4, 5, 6, 8, or 9). Multiply to get $(4)(9)(9) = 324$. In the range 1000-1499, there are 405 numbers that don't contain a 7, since the first digit has to be a 1, there are 5 choices for the second digit (0, 1, 2, 3, or 4), and there are 9 choices for each of remaining digits (0, 1, 2, 3, 4, 5, 6, 8, or 9). Multiply to get $(5)(9)(9) = 405$. Now add 1 for the number 1500 (the only four-digit number with a 5 as the second digit) to get 406. Alternate solution: Let's check the answer with a method that doesn't use complementary counting. There are 100 numbers that begin with a 7: 700-799. There are 90 numbers with a 7 as the second-to-last digit (which don't begin with a 7): 570-579, 670-679, 870-879, 970-979, 1070-1079, 1170-1179, 1270-1279, 1370-1379, and 1470-1479. There are 81 numbers that end with a 7 (which don't have a 7 as any of the previous digits): 507, 517, 527, 537, 547, 557, 567, 587, 597, and the similar numbers in the 600's, 800's, 900's, 1000's, 1100's, 1200's, 1300's, and 1400's. Add 100, 90, and 81 to make 271.

(35) $448 - 294 = 154$. Notes: There are 448 three-digit numbers that don't contain any 8's or 9's. Why? There are 7 choices for the first digit (1-7) and 8 choices for each of the remaining digits (0-7). Multiply to get $(7)(8)(8) = 448$. Out of these 448 numbers, there are 294 that don't contain any 2's. Why? There are 6 choices for the first digit (1 or 3-7) and 7 choices for each of the remaining digits (0-1 or 3-7). Multiply to get $(6)(7)(7) = 294$. Subtract 294 from 448 to get 154.

Alternate solution: Let's check the answer with a method that doesn't use complementary counting. There are 64 numbers that begin with a 2: 200-207, 210-217, 220-227, 230-237, 240-247, 250-257, 260-267, and 270-277. There are 48 numbers with a 2 as the middle digit (where the first digit isn't a 2): 120-127, 320-327, 420-427, 520-527, 620-627, and 720-727. There are 42 numbers with a 2 as the final digit (which don't have a 2 as the first or second digit): 102, 112, 132, 142, 152, 162, 172, and the similar numbers in the 300's, 400's, 500's, 600's, and 700's. Add 64, 48, and 42 to make 154.

(36) $9000 - 1000 = 8000$. Notes: There are 9000 four-digit numbers all together (where both endpoints of the range 1000-9999 are included). The first multiple of 9 in this range is 1008 and the last multiple of 9 in this range is 9999. To find how many multiples of 9 lie in the range 1008-9999, use the formula from earlier in this chapter: $\frac{9999}{9} - \frac{1008}{9} + 1 = 1111 - 112 + 1 = 1000$. It should make sense that the final answer, 8000, is exactly 8/9 of the total number of four-digit numbers (since the total number of four-digit numbers, 9000, is evenly divisible by nine).

(37) $787 - 65 = 722$. Notes: There are $863 - 77 + 1 = 787$ numbers all together (because both of the endpoints, 77 and 863, are included). The first multiple of 12 in this range is 84 and the last multiple of 12 in this range is 852. To find how many multiples of 12 lie in the range 84-852, use the formula from earlier in this chapter: $\frac{852}{12} - \frac{84}{12} + 1 = 71 - 7 + 1 = 65$.

Alternate solution: Let's check the answer with a method that doesn't use complementary counting. The largest whole number less than 787 that is evenly divisible by 12 is 780. Take 11/12 of 780 to get 715. Add 7 to 715 to get 722 (because $787 - 780 = 7$).

(38) $\frac{9(8)}{2} = 36$. Note: See Part A of Example 10.

(39) $(8)(6) = 48$. Note: See Part B of Example 10.

(40) $\frac{(7)(6)}{2} + \frac{(10)(9)}{2} = 21 + 45 = 66$.

Alternate solution: If everybody shook hands, there would be $\frac{(17)(16)}{2} = 136$

handshakes. If every boy shook hands with every girl, there would be $(7)(10) = 70$

handshakes. Subtract to get $136 - 70 = 66$.

(41) $\frac{(8)(7)}{2} - 8 = 28 - 8 = 20$. Notes: If every pair of corners were connected, there

would be $\frac{(8)(7)}{2} = 28$ lines. Since 8 lines would connect adjacent corners, subtract 8.

Alternate solution: Every corner connects to 5 other corners. Divide by 2 since each

line connects one pair of corners (to avoid double counting): $\frac{(8)(5)}{2} = 20$.

Chapter 4

(1) $P(1B) = 1/6 \approx 0.167 \approx 16.7\%$, $P(1G) = 1/3 \approx 0.333 \approx 33.3\%$, $P(1R) = 1/2 = 0.5 = 50\%$. Notes: The total number of balls equals $4 + 8 + 12 = 24$. Simply divide 4, 8, or 12 by 24. Check: $\frac{1}{6} + \frac{1}{3} + \frac{1}{2} = 1$.

(2) $P(2B) = 1/12 \approx 0.0833 \approx 8.33\%$, $P(2R) = 5/12 \approx 0.417 \approx 41.7\%$. Notes: Using combinations, there are $\binom{9}{2} = \frac{9!}{2!7!} = 36$ ways to choose 2 balls out of 9, $\binom{3}{2} = \frac{3!}{2!1!} = 3$ ways to choose 2 blue balls out of 3, and $\binom{6}{2} = \frac{6!}{2!4!} = 15$ ways to choose 2 red balls out of 6. This gives $P(2B) = \frac{3}{36} = \frac{1}{12}$ and $P(2R) = \frac{15}{36} = \frac{5}{12}$. Alternatively, using permutations, there are $(9)(8) = 72$ ways to select 2 balls (9 for the first ball and 8 for the second ball), $(3)(2) = 6$ ways to select 2 blue balls, and $(6)(5) = 30$ ways to select 2 red balls. This gives $P(2B) = \frac{6}{72} = \frac{1}{12}$ and $P(2R) = \frac{30}{72} = \frac{5}{12}$.

(3) $P(1B,1R, \text{any order}) = 35/72 \approx 0.486 \approx 48.6\%$, $P(2B) = 25/144 \approx 0.174 \approx 17.4\%$, $P(2R) = 49/144 \approx 0.340 \approx 34.0\%$. Notes: Since the first ball is placed back in the bag, this problem involves replacement. See Part C of Example 1. **With replacement**, using permutations, there are $(12)(12) = 144$ ways to choose 2 balls, there are $(5)(5) = 25$ ways to select 2 blue balls, there are $(7)(7) = 49$ ways to select 2 red balls, there are $(5)(7) = 35$ ways to select 1 blue and then 1 red, and there are $(7)(5) = 35$ ways to select 1 red and then blue. This gives $P(1B,1R, \text{any order}) = \frac{35+35}{144} = \frac{70}{144} = \frac{35}{72}$, $P(2B) = \frac{25}{144}$, and $P(2R) = \frac{49}{144}$. Check: $\frac{35}{72} + \frac{25}{144} + \frac{49}{144} = 1$. With replacement, you need to work with permutations instead of combinations (see the note in the chapter before the first example).

(4) $P(1B,1W, \text{any order}) = 16/33 \approx 0.485 \approx 48.5\%$, $P(2 \text{ match}) = 17/33 \approx 0.515 \approx 51.5\%$. Notes: Using permutations, there are $(12)(11) = 132$ ways to select 2 socks (12 for the first sock and 11 for the second sock). There are $(4)(8) = 32$ ways to select a black sock and then a white sock and $(8)(4) = 32$ ways to select a white stock and then a black sock; there are therefore $32 + 32 = 64$ ways to select one black sock and one white sock in any order. This gives $P(1B,1W, \text{any order}) = \frac{64}{132} =$

$\frac{16}{33}$. There are $(4)(3) = 12$ ways to select 2 black socks and $(8)(7) = 56$ ways to select two white socks; there are therefore $12 + 56 = 68$ ways to select two matching socks. This gives P(2 match) $= \frac{68}{132} = \frac{17}{33}$. Check: $\frac{16}{33} + \frac{17}{33} = 1$. Alternatively, using combinations, there are $\binom{12}{2} = \frac{12!}{2!10!} = 66$ ways to choose 2 socks out of 12, $\binom{4}{2} = \frac{4!}{2!2!} = 6$ ways to choose 2 black socks out of 4, $\binom{8}{2} = \frac{8!}{2!6!} = 28$ ways to choose 2 white socks out of 8, $\binom{4}{1} = \frac{4!}{1!3!} = 4$ ways to choose 1 black sock out of 4, and $\binom{8}{1} = \frac{8!}{1!7!} = 8$ ways to choose 1 white sock out of 8. There are $(4)(8) = 32$ ways to choose 1 black sock and 1 white sock (in any order, since these are combinations). This gives P(1B,1W, any order) $= \frac{32}{66} = \frac{16}{33}$. There are $6 + 28 = 34$ ways to choose 2 matching socks (2 black or 2 white). This gives P(2 match) $= \frac{34}{66} = \frac{17}{33}$.

(5) P(1T,1G, any order) $= 4/33 \approx 0.121 \approx 12.1\%$, P(2 match) $= 1/3 \approx 0.333 \approx$ 33.3%. Notes: Using permutations, there are $(12)(11) = 132$ ways to select 2 socks (12 for the first sock and 11 for the second sock). There are $(2)(4) = 8$ ways to select a tan sock and then a gray sock and $(4)(2) = 8$ ways to select a gray stock and then a tan sock; there are therefore $8 + 8 = 16$ ways to select one tan sock and one gray sock in any order. This gives P(1T,1G, any order) $= \frac{16}{132} = \frac{4}{33}$. There are $(2)(1) = 2$ ways to select 2 tan socks, $(4)(3) = 12$ ways to select 2 gray socks, and $(6)(5) = 30$ ways to select two white socks; there are therefore $2 + 12 + 30 = 44$ ways to select two matching socks. This gives P(2 match) $= \frac{44}{132} = \frac{1}{3}$. Alternatively, using combinations, there are $\binom{12}{2} = \frac{12!}{2!10!} = 66$ ways to choose 2 socks out of 12, $\binom{2}{2} = \frac{2!}{2!0!} = 1$ way to choose 2 tan socks out of 2, $\binom{4}{2} = \frac{4!}{2!2!} = 6$ ways to choose 2 gray socks out of 4, $\binom{6}{2} = \frac{6!}{2!4!} = 15$ ways to choose 2 white socks out of 6, $\binom{2}{1} = \frac{2!}{1!1!} = 2$ ways to choose 1 tan sock out of 2, and $\binom{4}{1} = \frac{4!}{1!3!} = 4$ ways to choose 1 gray sock out of 4. There are $(2)(4) = 8$ ways to choose 1 tan sock and 1 gray sock (in any order). This gives P(1T,1G, any order) $= \frac{8}{66} = \frac{4}{33}$. There are $1 + 6 + 15 = 22$ ways to choose 2

matching socks (2 tan, 2 gray, or 2 white). This gives P(2 match) $= \frac{22}{66} = \frac{1}{3}$.

(6) P(2G) = 1/20 = 0.05 = 5%, P(1B first and then 1R) = 7/48 ≈ 0.146 ≈ 14.6%. Notes: Using permutations, there are (16)(15) = 240 ways to select 2 balls (16 for the first ball and 15 for the second ball). There are (7)(5) = 35 ways to select a blue ball first and a red ball second. This gives P(1B first and then 1R) $= \frac{35}{240} = \frac{7}{48}$. There are (4)(3) = 12 ways to select 2 green balls. This gives P(2G) $= \frac{12}{240} = \frac{1}{20}$. Since the mixed case gives a specific order, use permutations for that. If you use combinations for the other case, there are $\binom{16}{2} = \frac{16!}{2!14!} = 120$ ways to choose 2 balls out of 16 and $\binom{4}{2} = \frac{4!}{2!2!} = 6$ ways to choose 2 green balls out of 4. This gives P(2G) $= \frac{6}{120} = \frac{1}{20}$.

(7) P(1B,1G,1R, any order) = 3/13 ≈ 0.231 ≈ 23.1%, P(3 match) = 46/455 ≈ 0.101 ≈ 10.1%. Notes: Using combinations, there are $\binom{15}{3} = \frac{15!}{3!12!} = 455$ ways to choose 3 balls out of 15, $\binom{5}{3} = \frac{5!}{3!2!} = 10$ ways to choose 3 blue balls out of 5, $\binom{3}{3} = \frac{3!}{3!0!} = 1$ way to choose 3 green balls out of 3, $\binom{7}{3} = \frac{7!}{3!4!} = 35$ ways to choose 3 red balls out of 7, $\binom{5}{1} = \frac{5!}{1!4!} = 5$ ways to choose 1 blue ball out of 5, $\binom{3}{1} = \frac{3!}{1!2!} = 3$ ways to choose 1 green ball out of 3, and $\binom{7}{1} = \frac{7!}{1!6!} = 7$ ways to choose 1 red ball out of 7. There are (5)(3)(7) = 105 ways to choose 1 blue ball, 1 green ball, and 1 red ball (in any order, since these are combinations). This gives P(1B,1G,1R) $= \frac{105}{455} = \frac{3}{13}$. There are 10 + 1 + 35 = 46 ways to choose 3 matching balls (3 blue, 3 green, or 3 red). This gives P(3 match) $= \frac{46}{455}$. Alternatively, using permutations, there are (15)(14)(13) = 2730 ways to select 3 balls (15 for the first ball, 14 for the second ball, and 13 for the third ball). There are (5)(3)(7) = 105 ways to select BGR (a blue ball first, a green ball second, and a red ball third), (5)(7)(3) = 105 ways to select BRG (blue first, red second, green third), (3)(5)(7) = 105 ways to select GBR, (3)(7)(5) = 105 ways to select GRB, (7)(5)(3) = 105 ways to select RBG, and (7)(3)(5) = 105 ways to select RGB. Therefore, there are 105 + 105 + 105 + 105 + 105 + 105 = 630 ways to select three socks that are all different colors. This gives

$P(1B, 1G, 1R, \text{any order}) = \frac{630}{2730} = \frac{3}{13}$. There are $(5)(4)(3) = 60$ ways to select 3 blue balls, $(3)(2)(1) = 6$ ways to select 3 green balls, and $(7)(6)(5) = 210$ ways to select 3 red balls. Therefore, there are $60 + 6 + 210 = 276$ ways to select 3 balls that are the same color. This gives $P(3 \text{ match}) = \frac{276}{2730} = \frac{46}{455}$.

(8) $P(4W) = 7/306 \approx 0.0229 \approx 2.29\%$, $P(2 \text{ matching pairs}) = 191/765 \approx 0.250 \approx 25.0\%$. Notes: Using combinations, there are $\binom{18}{4} = \frac{18!}{4!14!} = 3060$ ways to choose 4 socks out of 18, $\binom{6}{4} = \frac{6!}{4!2!} = 15$ ways to choose 4 black socks out of 6, $\binom{4}{4} = \frac{4!}{4!0!} = 1$ way to choose 4 tan socks out of 4, $\binom{8}{4} = \frac{8!}{4!4!} = 70$ ways to choose 4 white socks out of 8, $\binom{6}{2} = \frac{6!}{2!4!} = 15$ ways to choose 2 black socks out of 6, $\binom{4}{2} = \frac{4!}{2!2!} = 6$ ways to choose 2 tan socks out of 4, and $\binom{8}{2} = \frac{8!}{2!6!} = 28$ ways to choose 2 white socks out of 8. Since there are 70 ways to choose 4 white socks out of 8, this gives $P(4W) = \frac{70}{3060} = \frac{7}{306}$. To have two matching pairs, all 4 socks could be the same color or there could be 2 of one color and 2 of another color. There are 15 ways to choose 4 black socks, 1 way to choose 4 tan socks, and 70 ways to choose 4 white socks. There are $(15)(6) = 90$ ways to choose 2 black socks and 2 tan socks, $(15)(28) = 420$ ways to choose 2 black socks and 2 white socks, and $(6)(28) = 168$ ways to choose 2 tan socks and 2 white socks. Therefore, there are $15 + 1 + 70 + 90 + 420 + 168 = 764$ ways to choose 2 matching pairs. This gives $P(2 \text{ matching pairs}) = \frac{764}{3060} = \frac{191}{765}$. Alternatively, using permutations, there are $(18)(17)(16)(15) = 73{,}440$ ways to select 4 socks. There are $(8)(7)(6)(5) = 1680$ ways to select 4 white socks. This gives $P(4W) = \frac{1680}{73{,}440} = \frac{7}{306}$. The second part of this problem is more complicated in terms of permutations, as there are several cases to consider:

- There are $(6)(5)(4)(3) = 360$ ways to select 4 black socks, $(4)(3)(2)(1) = 24$ ways to select 4 tan socks, and $(8)(7)(6)(5) = 1680$ ways to select 4 white socks. Therefore, there are $360 + 24 + 1680 = 2064$ ways to select 4 socks of the same color.
- To select 2 black socks and 2 tan socks, they could be selected as BBTT, BTBT,

BTTB, TBBT, TBTB, or TTBB. There are $(6)(5)(4)(3) = 360$ ways to select BBTT, and 360 ways for each of the other permutations, giving $360 + 360 + 360 + 360 + 360 + 360 = 2160$ ways to select 2 black socks and 2 tan socks.

- To select 2 black socks and 2 white socks, they could be selected as BBWW, BWBW, BWWB, WBBW, WBWB, or WWBB. There are $(6)(5)(8)(7) = 1680$ ways to select BBWW, and 1680 ways for each of the other permutations, giving $1680 + 1680 + 1680 + 1680 + 1680 + 1680 = 10,080$ ways to select 2 black socks and 2 white socks.

- To select 2 tan socks and 2 white socks, they could be selected as TTWW, TWTW, TWWT, WTTW, WTWT, or WWTT. There are $(4)(3)(8)(7) = 672$ ways to select BBTT, and 672 ways for each of the other permutations, giving $672 + 672 + 672 + 672 + 672 + 672 = 4032$ ways to select 2 tan socks and 2 white socks.

- There are $2160 + 10,080 + 4032 = 16,272$ ways to select 2 pairs of 2 different colors. Add this to the 2064 ways to select 4 socks of the same color: $16,272 + 2064 = 18,336$. There are 18,336 ways to select 2 matching pairs.

- This gives $P(2 \text{ matching pairs}) = \frac{18,336}{73,440} = \frac{191}{765}$.

(9) $P(3B) = 24/91 \approx 0.264 \approx 26.4\%$, $P(3R) = 2/91 \approx 0.0220 \approx 2.20\%$, $P(2B,1R,$ any order$) = 45/91 \approx 0.495 \approx 49.5\%$. Notes: Using combinations, there are $\binom{15}{3} = \frac{15!}{3!12!} = 455$ ways to choose 3 balls out of 15, $\binom{10}{3} = \frac{10!}{3!7!} = 120$ ways to choose 3 blue balls out of 10, $\binom{5}{3} = \frac{5!}{3!2!} = 10$ ways to choose 3 red balls out of 5, and $\binom{10}{2}\binom{5}{1} = \frac{10!}{2!8!}\frac{5!}{1!4!} = (45)(5) = 225$ ways to choose 2 blue balls and 1 red ball (recall Case 4 from Chapter 2). This gives $P(3B) = \frac{120}{455} = \frac{24}{91}$, $P(3R) = \frac{10}{455} = \frac{2}{91}$, and $P(2B,1R,$ any order$) = \frac{45}{91}$. Check: The other possible outcome is 1 blue ball and 2 red balls (in any order). For this, $\binom{10}{1}\binom{5}{2} = \frac{10!}{1!9!}\frac{5!}{2!3!} = (10)(10) = 100$, such that the probability of selecting 1 blue ball and 2 red balls is $\frac{100}{455} = \frac{20}{91}$. Observe that $\frac{24}{91} + \frac{2}{91} + \frac{45}{91} + \frac{20}{91} = 1$. Using permutations, there are $(15)(14)(13) = 2730$ ways to select 3 balls out of 15.

There are $(10)(9)(8) = 720$ ways to select 3 blue balls out of 10 and $(5)(4)(3) = 60$ ways to select 3 red balls out of 5. This gives $P(3B) = \frac{720}{2730} = \frac{24}{91}$ and $P(3R) = \frac{60}{2730} = \frac{2}{91}$. There are $(10)(9)(5) = 450$ ways to select BBR (blue first, blue second, and red third), $(10)(5)(9) = 450$ ways to select BRB, and $(5)(10)(9) = 450$ ways to select RBB, for a total of $450 + 450 + 450 = 1350$ ways to select 2 blue and 1 red in any order. This gives $P(\text{2B,1R, any order}) = \frac{1350}{2730} = \frac{45}{91}$.

(10) $P(3T) = 27/512 \approx 0.0527 \approx 5.27\%$, $P(3W) = 125/512 \approx 0.244 \approx 24.4\%$, $P(\text{2T first and then 1W}) = 45/512 \approx 0.0879 \approx 8.79\%$. Notes: Since each sock is placed back in the drawer, this problem involves replacement. See Part C of Example 1. **With replacement**, using permutations, there are $(16)(16)(16) = 4096$ ways to select 3 socks out of 16, $(6)(6)(6) = 216$ ways to select 3 tan socks out of 6, $(10)(10)(10) = 1000$ ways to select 3 white socks out of 10, and $(6)(6)(10) = 360$ ways to select 2 tan socks first and then 1 white sock. This gives $P(3T) = \frac{216}{4096} = \frac{27}{512}$, $P(3W) = \frac{1000}{4096} = \frac{125}{512}$, and $P(\text{2T first and then 1W}) = \frac{360}{4096} = \frac{45}{512}$. With replacement, you need to work with permutations instead of combinations (see the note in the chapter before the first example).

(11) $P(\text{2 consecutive vowels}) = 1/3 \approx 0.333 \approx 33.3\%$, $P(\text{begin and end with a vowel}) = 1/15 \approx 0.0667 \approx 6.67\%$. Notes: Each arrangement is a permutation. There are $6! = 720$ arrangements of all 6 letters of the word NUMBER. When a permutation has 2 consecutive vowels, it will have one of the following structures: EUwxyz, UEwxyz, wEUxyz, wUExyz, wxEUyz, wxUEyz, wxyEUz, wxyUEz, wxyzEU, wxyzUE. For example, for the structure EUwxyz, E and U are the two vowels with the E before the U while wxyz represent the four consonants in unknown order. Each of these 10 structures has $4! = 24$ permutations (these are the ways to permute the 4 consonants). Therefore, $(10)(24) = 240$ permutations have 2 consecutive vowels. This gives $P(\text{2 consecutive vowels}) = \frac{240}{720} = \frac{1}{3}$. There are $4! = 24$ permutations of the form EwxyzU and $4! = 24$ permutations of the form UwxyzE. Therefore, $24 + 24 = 48$ permutations begin and end with a vowel. This gives $P(\text{begin and end with a vowel}) = \frac{48}{720} = \frac{1}{15}$.

Alternate solutions: There are other ways to obtain these same answers. For example, the probability of the first letter being a vowel is 1/3 (since 2 of the 6 letters are vowels). If the first letter is a vowel, the probability that the second letter will be a vowel is 1/5 (since there are 5 letters remaining to select). This makes the probability that the first 2 letters will both be vowels $\frac{1}{3}\frac{1}{5} = \frac{1}{15}$. The probability that the 2nd and 3rd letters will both be vowels is similarly 1/15. It's the same for the 3rd and 4th letters, the 4th and 5th letters, and the 5th and 6th letters. All 5 pairs of consecutive letters have a probability of 1/15 of both being vowels, so P(2 consecutive vowels) $= \frac{5}{15} = \frac{1}{3}$. Similarly, the probability that the 1st and 6th letters will both be vowels is $\frac{1}{15}$.

(12) P(even number) = 2/5 = 0.4 = 40%, P(digits add up to 13) = 1/5 = 0.2 = 20%, P(doesn't include a 7) = 2/5 = 0.4 = 40%. Notes: There are $\frac{5!}{(5-3)!} = \frac{5!}{2!} = 5(4)(3) = 60$ ways to form a 3-letter permutation of the digits 42,175. (See Case 3 in Chapter 1.) The probability that the last digit is a 2 or a 4 is 2/5 because there are 5 digits to select from: P(even number) $= \frac{2}{5}$. For the 3 digits to add up to 13, they must be the 2, 4, and 7 or the 1, 5, and 7. There are 3! = 6 permutations of 247 and 3! = 6 permutations of 157. Therefore, there are 6 + 6 = 12 permutations where the digits add up to 13. This gives P(digits add up to 13) $= \frac{12}{60} = \frac{1}{5}$. If the 7 is excluded, there are $\frac{4!}{(4-3)!} = \frac{4!}{1!} = 24$ ways to form a 3-letter permutation of the digits 1245. This gives P(doesn't include a 7) $= \frac{24}{60} = \frac{2}{5}$.

(13) P(a multiple of 2) = 1/2 = 0.5 = 50%, P(a multiple of 5) = 1/5 = 0.2 = 20%, P(a multiple of 10) = 1/10 = 0.1 = 10%. Notes: There are 99 − 10 + 1 = 90 two-digit numbers: 10 thru 99. (As discussed in Chapter 3, we add one after subtracting because both endpoints, 10 and 99, are included.) One-half are even and one-half are odd. Therefore, P(a multiple of 2) $= \frac{1}{2}$. The multiples of 5 include 10, 15, 20, etc., thru 95. Similar to Example 3 in Chapter 3, we divide 10 and 95 (the first and last multiples) each by 5 to get 2 and 19, subtract to get 17, and add one to get 18 because both endpoints are included. This gives P(a multiple of 5) $= \frac{18}{90} = \frac{1}{5}$. It

should be no surprise that one-fifth of the numbers in this range are evenly divisible by five. The multiples of 10 include 10, 20, 30, etc., thru 90. There are 9 multiples of 10. This gives P(a multiple of 5) $= \frac{9}{90} = \frac{1}{10}$.

(14) P(no vowels) $= 8/45 \approx 0.178 \approx 17.8\%$, P(at least 2 vowels) $= 13/45 \approx 0.289 \approx 28.9\%$. Notes: This is Case 4 of Chapter 1. First, ignore the second A and find the three-letter subsets of ABEGLR. There are $\frac{6!}{(6-3)!} = \frac{6!}{3!} = 6(5)(4) = 120$ ways to form a three-letter permutation of the letters ABEGLR. Next, count the three-letter permutations that have two A's: AAB, AAE, AAG, AAL, AAR, ABA, AEA, AGA, ALA, ARA, BAA, EAA, GAA, LAA, RAA. There are 15 three-letter permutations with two A's. Therefore, there are $120 + 15 = 135$ three-letter permutations of ALGEBRA. There are $\frac{4!}{(4-3)!} = \frac{4!}{1!} = 24$ three-letter permutations of BGLR (the case with no vowels). This gives P(no vowels) $= \frac{24}{135} = \frac{8}{45}$. The three-letter permutations with at least two vowels include the 15 permutations previously listed with two A's in addition to 24 permutations that have one E and exactly one A (because AAE, AEA, and EAA were already counted in the 15 with two A's): ABE, AEB, AEG, AEL, AER, AGE, ALE, ARE, BAE, BEA, EAB, EAG, EAL, EAR, EBA, EGA, ELA, ERA, GAE, GEA, LAE, LEA, RAE, REA. Therefore, there are $15 + 24 = 39$ permutations with at least two vowels. This gives P(at least 2 vowels) $= \frac{39}{135} = \frac{13}{45}$.

Note: **If you randomly select 3 letters from the word ALGEBRA, you actually get a different answer**. In this problem, we made tiles for each possible 3-letter arrangement, such that each tile is equally likely. If instead you select 3 random letters from the word ALGEBRA, each of the 135 permutations discussed previously is no longer equally likely. For example, in that case, the probability of getting no vowels is $\left(\frac{4}{7}\right)\left(\frac{3}{6}\right)\left(\frac{2}{5}\right) = \frac{4}{35}$, since 4 out of 7 letters are initially consonants, then 3 out of 6 are consonants when the second letter is selected, and 2 out of 5 are consonants for the last selection. For example, AGR is more likely in this case, since there are two A's to choose from. (We will encounter a similar issue in Chapter 10.)

(15) P(3 boys) $= 1/22 \approx 0.0455 \approx 4.55\%$, P(3 girls) $= 7/44 \approx 0.159 \approx 15.9\%$, P(1 boy, 2 girls, any order) $= 21/44 \approx 0.477 \approx 47.7\%$. Notes: Using combinations, there

are $\binom{12}{3} = \frac{12!}{3!9!} = 220$ ways to choose 3 students out of 12, $\binom{5}{3} = \frac{5!}{3!2!} = 10$ ways to

choose 3 boys out of 5, $\binom{7}{3} = \frac{7!}{3!4!} = 35$ ways to choose 3 girls out of 7, and $\binom{5}{1}\binom{7}{2} =$

$\frac{5!}{1!4!}\frac{7!}{2!5!} = (5)(21) = 105$ ways to choose 2 boys and 1 girl (recall Case 4 from

Chapter 2). This gives P(3 boys) $= \frac{10}{220} = \frac{1}{22}$, P(3 girls) $= \frac{35}{220} = \frac{7}{44}$, and P(1 boy, 2

girls, any order) $= \frac{105}{220} = \frac{21}{44}$. Check: The other possible outcome is 2 boys and 1 girl

(in any order). For this, $\binom{5}{2}\binom{7}{1} = \frac{5!}{2!3!}\frac{7!}{1!6!} = (10)(7) = 70$, such that the probability

of selecting 2 boys and 1 girl is $\frac{70}{220} = \frac{7}{22}$. Observe that $\frac{1}{22} + \frac{7}{44} + \frac{21}{44} + \frac{7}{22} = 1$. Using

permutations, there are $(12)(11)(10) = 1320$ ways to select 3 students out of 12.

There are $(5)(4)(3) = 60$ ways to select 3 boys out of 5 and $(7)(6)(5) = 210$ ways

to select 3 girls out of 7. This gives P(3 boys) $= \frac{60}{1320} = \frac{1}{22}$ and P(3 girls) $= \frac{210}{1320} = \frac{7}{44}$.

There are $(5)(7)(6) = 210$ ways to select BGG (boy first, girl second, and girl third),

$(7)(5)(6) = 210$ ways to select GBG, and $(7)(6)(5) = 210$ ways to select GGB, for a

total of $210 + 210 + 210 = 630$ ways to select 1 boy and 2 girls in any order. This

gives P(1 boy, 2 girls, any order) $= \frac{630}{1320} = \frac{21}{44}$.

(16) P(3 markers) $= 4/91 \approx 0.0440 \approx 4.40\%$, P(2 pencils, 1 pen, any order) $= 6/91$

$\approx 0.0659 \approx 6.59\%$. Notes: Using combinations, there are $\binom{15}{3} = \frac{15!}{3!12!} = 455$ ways to

choose 3 objects out of 15, $\binom{6}{3} = \frac{6!}{3!3!} = 20$ ways to choose 3 markers out of 6, and

$\binom{4}{2}\binom{5}{1} = \frac{4!}{2!2!}\frac{5!}{1!4!} = (6)(5) = 30$ ways to choose 2 pencils and 1 pen (recall Case 4

from Chapter 2). This gives P(3 markers) $= \frac{20}{455} = \frac{4}{91}$ and P(2 pencils, 1 pen, any

order) $= \frac{30}{455} = \frac{6}{91}$. Using permutations, there are $(15)(14)(13) = 2730$ ways to select

3 objects out of 15. There are $(6)(5)(4) = 120$ ways to select 3 markers out of 6. This

gives P(3 markers) $= \frac{120}{2730} = \frac{4}{91}$. There are $(4)(3)(5) = 60$ ways to select pencil-pencil-

pen, $(4)(5)(3) = 60$ ways to select pencil-pen-pencil, and $(5)(4)(3) = 60$ ways to

select pen-pencil-pencil, for a total of $60 + 60 + 60 = 180$ ways to select 2 pencils and

1 pen in any order. This gives P(2 pencils, 1 pen, any order) $= \frac{180}{2730} = \frac{6}{91}$.

Chapter 5

(1) P(B or G) = 7/9 ≈ 0.778 ≈ 77.8%, P(B or R) = 2/3 ≈ 0.667 ≈ 66.7%, P(G or R) = 5/9 ≈ 0.556 ≈ 55.6%. Notes: Since we want one color or another, find the union. For a single ball to be one of two colors, the events are mutually exclusive. $P(B) = \frac{4}{9}$, $P(G) = \frac{3}{9} = \frac{1}{3}$, $P(R) = \frac{2}{9}$; there are $4 + 3 + 2 = 9$ balls. $P(B \cup G) = P(B) + P(G) = \frac{4}{9} + \frac{3}{9} = \frac{7}{9}$, $P(B \cup R) = P(B) + P(R) = \frac{4}{9} + \frac{2}{9} = \frac{6}{9} = \frac{2}{3}$, $P(G \cup R) = P(G) + P(R) = \frac{3}{9} + \frac{2}{9} = \frac{5}{9}$.

Note: Even though these problems can be solved without using concepts from Chapter 5, the instructions specifically state to use a **technique from this chapter**.

(2) P(B or 3) = 5/8 = 0.625 = 62.5%, P(odd number) = 1/2 = 0.5 = 50%, P(not a 4) = 3/4 = 0.75 = 75%. Notes: Since we want one event or another, find the union. $P(B) = P(R) = \frac{4}{8} = \frac{1}{2}$, $P(1) = P(2) = P(3) = P(4) = \frac{2}{8} = \frac{1}{4}$; there are $4 + 4 = 8$ balls. The events blue or 3 aren't mutually exclusive since one event doesn't prevent the other event (the same ball could be blue or 3). First find the intersection $P(B \cap 3) = P(B)P(3) = \left(\frac{1}{2}\right)\left(\frac{1}{4}\right) = \frac{1}{8}$; these events are independent since an outcome of blue doesn't affect the chances that it will be a 3 and vice-versa. Use the modified sum formula: $P(B \cup 3) = P(B) + P(3) - P(B \cap 3) = \frac{4}{8} + \frac{2}{8} - \frac{1}{8} = \frac{5}{8}$. For a single ball to be one of two numbers, the events are mutually exclusive. $P(1 \cup 3) = P(1) + P(3) = \frac{1}{4} + \frac{1}{4} = \frac{2}{4} = \frac{1}{2}$ and $P(1 \cup 2 \cup 3) = P(1) + P(2) + P(3) = \frac{1}{4} + \frac{1}{4} + \frac{1}{4} = \frac{3}{4}$.

(3) P(B or G) = 2/3 ≈ 0.667 ≈ 66.7%, P(G or R) = 8/15 ≈ 0.533 ≈ 53.3%, P(B, G, or Y) = 4/5 = 0.8 = 80%. Notes: Since we want one color or another, find the union. For a single ball to be one of two colors, the events are mutually exclusive. $P(B) = \frac{5}{15} = \frac{1}{3}$, $P(G) = \frac{5}{15} = \frac{1}{3}$, $P(R) = \frac{3}{15} = \frac{1}{5}$, $P(Y) = \frac{2}{15}$; there are $5 + 5 + 3 + 2 = 15$ balls. $P(B \cup G) = P(B) + P(G) = \frac{1}{3} + \frac{1}{3} = \frac{2}{3}$, $P(G \cup R) = P(G) + P(R) = \frac{5}{15} + \frac{3}{15} = \frac{8}{15}$, $P(R^c) = 1 - P(R) = 1 - \frac{1}{5} = \frac{4}{5}$. Note that P(B, G, or Y) is the complement to P(R) since blue, green, or yellow includes every color except for red.

(4) P(B or 2) = 3/4 = 0.75 = 75%, P(R or 1) = 1/2 = 0.5 = 50%, P(1, 3, or 4) = 5/8 = 0.625 = 62.5%. Notes: Since we want one event or another, find

the union. $P(B) = \frac{5}{8}$, $P(R) = \frac{3}{8}$, $P(1) = P(2) = P(3) = \frac{2}{8} = \frac{1}{4}$, $P(4) = P(5) = \frac{1}{8}$; there are $5 + 3 = 8$ balls. The events blue or 2 aren't mutually exclusive since one event doesn't prevent the other event (the same ball could be blue or 2). First find the intersections $P(B \cap 2)$ and $P(R \cap 1)$. Unlike Problem 2, these intersections **aren't** independent; one way to see this is to note that the probability that a ball is a 2 depends on whether or not the ball is blue or red. If a ball is blue, the chance that it will be a 2 is 1/5, but if a ball is red, the chance that it will be a 2 is 1/3. Therefore, we need to use conditional probabilities to find the intersections: $P(B \cap 2) = P(B)P(2|B) = \left(\frac{5}{8}\right)\left(\frac{1}{5}\right) = \frac{1}{8}$ and $P(R \cap 1) = P(R)P(1|R) = \left(\frac{3}{8}\right)\left(\frac{1}{3}\right) = \frac{1}{8}$. These should make sense; for example, 1 out of the 8 balls is both blue and number 2. Use the modified sum formula: $P(B \cup 2) =$ $P(B) + P(2) - P(B \cap 2) = \frac{5}{8} + \frac{2}{8} - \frac{1}{8} = \frac{6}{8} = \frac{3}{4}$ and $P(R \cup 1) = P(R) + P(1) - P(R \cap 1)$ $= \frac{3}{8} + \frac{2}{8} - \frac{1}{8} = \frac{4}{8} = \frac{1}{2}$. For a single ball to be one of three numbers, the events are mutually exclusive: $P(1 \cup 3 \cup 4) = P(1) + P(3) + P(4) = \frac{1}{4} + \frac{1}{4} + \frac{1}{8} = \frac{5}{8}$.

Note: $P(B \cup 2)$ and $P(R \cup 1)$ could alternatively be found using the complement rule. For example, the complement of $P(B \cup 2)$ is $P(R \cap 1) \cup P(R \cap 3)$; that is, the balls that are red 1 and red 3 are neither blue nor 2.

(5) P(1B first then 1W) $= 1/4 = 0.25 = 25\%$, P(2 match) $= 1/2 = 0.5 = 50\%$. Notes: Since the first sock is placed back in the drawer, $P(B) = P(W) = \frac{1}{2}$ for each selection. $P(B \cap W) = P(B)P(W) = \left(\frac{1}{2}\right)\left(\frac{1}{2}\right) = \frac{1}{4}$, $P(B \cap B) = P(B)P(B) = \left(\frac{1}{2}\right)\left(\frac{1}{2}\right)$ $= \frac{1}{4}$, $P(W \cap W) = P(W)P(W) = \left(\frac{1}{2}\right)\left(\frac{1}{2}\right) = \frac{1}{4}$, $P(2$ match$) = P(2B \cup 2W) =$ $P(2B) + P(2W) = \frac{1}{4} + \frac{1}{4} = \frac{1}{2}$. Alternatively, $P(1W$ first then $1B) = \frac{1}{4}$, $P(1B, 1W,$ any order$) = \frac{1}{4} + \frac{1}{4} = \frac{1}{2}$, and $P(2$ match$)$ is its complement.

(6) P(1B,1W, any order) $= 2/3 \approx 0.667 \approx 66.7\%$, P(2 match) $= 1/3 \approx 0.333 \approx$ 33.3%. Notes: After the first sock is selected, only 3 socks remain in the drawer. Use the conditional probability formulas. $P(B \cap W) = P(B)P(W|B) = \left(\frac{1}{2}\right)\left(\frac{2}{3}\right) = \frac{1}{3}$, $P(W \cap B) = P(W)P(B|W) = \left(\frac{1}{2}\right)\left(\frac{2}{3}\right) = \frac{1}{3}$, $P(1B, 1W,$ any order$) = P(B \cap W) \cup$

$P(W \cap B) = P(B \cap W) + P(W \cap B) = \frac{1}{3} + \frac{1}{3} = \frac{2}{3}$, $P(2B) = P(B_1 \cap B_2) =$

$P(B_1)P(B_2|B_1) = \left(\frac{1}{2}\right)\left(\frac{1}{3}\right) = \frac{1}{6}$, $P(2W) = P(W_1 \cap W_2) = P(W_1)P(W_2|W_1) = \left(\frac{1}{2}\right)\left(\frac{1}{3}\right) =$

$\frac{1}{6}$, $P(2 \text{ match}) = P(2B) \cup P(2W) = P(2B) + P(2W) = \frac{1}{6} + \frac{1}{6} = \frac{1}{3}$. Alternatively,

$P(2 \text{ match}) = 1 - P(1B, 1W, \text{any order}) = 1 - \frac{2}{3} = \frac{1}{3}$ since they are complements.

Alternate solution: There are $\binom{2}{1}\binom{2}{1} = \frac{2!}{1!1!}\frac{2!}{1!1!} = (2)(2) = 4$ ways to choose 1 black

and 1 white sock from 2 black socks and 2 white socks, $\binom{2}{2} = \frac{2!}{0!2!} = 1$ way to choose

2 black socks from 2 black socks (or 2 white socks from 2 white socks), $1 + 1 = 2$

ways to choose 2 matching socks from 2 black socks and 2 white socks, and $\binom{4}{2} =$

$\frac{4!}{2!2!} = \frac{(4)(3)}{(2)(1)} = 6$ ways to choose 2 socks out of 4. Divide 4 by 6 to get

$P(1B, 1W, \text{any order}) = \frac{4}{6} = \frac{2}{3}$ and divide 2 by 6 to get $P(2 \text{ match}) = \frac{2}{6} = \frac{1}{3}$.

(7) P(1B first then 1W) = 3/16 = 0.1875 = 18.75%, P(2 match) = 5/8 = 0.625 =

62.5%. Notes: Since the first sock is placed back in the drawer, $P(B) = \frac{3}{4}$ and

$P(W) = \frac{1}{4}$ for each selection. $P(B \cap W) = P(B)P(W) = \left(\frac{3}{4}\right)\left(\frac{1}{4}\right) = \frac{3}{16}$, $P(B \cap B) =$

$P(B)P(B) = \left(\frac{3}{4}\right)\left(\frac{3}{4}\right) = \frac{9}{16}$, $P(W \cap W) = P(W)P(W) = \left(\frac{1}{4}\right)\left(\frac{1}{4}\right) = \frac{1}{16}$, $P(2 \text{ match}) =$

$P(2B \cup 2W) = P(2B) + P(2W) = \frac{9}{16} + \frac{1}{16} = \frac{10}{16} = \frac{5}{8}$. Alternatively,

$P(1W \text{ first then } 1B) = \frac{3}{16}$, $P(1B, 1W, \text{any order}) = \frac{3}{16} + \frac{3}{16} = \frac{3}{8}$, and $P(2 \text{ match})$ is its

complement: $P(2 \text{ match}) = 1 - \frac{3}{8} = \frac{5}{8}$.

(8) P(1B first then 1W) = 1/4 = 0.25 = 25%, P(2B) = 1/2 = 0.5 = 50%. Notes:

After the first sock is selected, only 3 socks remain in the drawer. Use the

conditional probability formulas. $P(B \cap W) = P(B)P(W|B) = \left(\frac{3}{4}\right)\left(\frac{1}{3}\right) = \frac{1}{4}$ (since 1

out of 3 socks are white after 1 black sock has already been selected), $P(2B) =$

$P(B_1 \cap B_2) = P(B_1)P(B_2|B_1) = \left(\frac{3}{4}\right)\left(\frac{2}{3}\right) = \frac{1}{2}$.

Alternate solution: There are $\binom{3}{2} = \frac{3!}{2!1!} = 3$ ways to choose 2 black socks from 3

black socks and $\binom{4}{2} = \frac{4!}{2!2!} = \frac{(4)(3)}{(2)(1)} = 6$ ways to choose 2 black socks out of 4 socks.

Divide 3 by 6 to get $P(2B) = \frac{3}{6} = \frac{1}{2}$.

(9) P(1B,1R, any order) = 12/25 = 0.48 = 48%, P(2 match) = 13/25 = 0.52 = 52%.

Notes: Since the first ball is placed back in the bag, $P(B) = \frac{6}{10} = \frac{3}{5}$ and $P(R) = \frac{4}{10} = \frac{2}{5}$

for each selection. $P(B \cap R) = P(R \cap B) = P(B)P(R) = \left(\frac{3}{5}\right)\left(\frac{2}{5}\right) = \frac{6}{25}$,

$P(1B,1R,\text{ any order}) = P(B \cap R) \cup P(R \cap B) = P(B \cap R) + P(R \cap B) = \frac{6}{25} + \frac{6}{25} = \frac{12}{25}$,

$P(B \cap B) = P(B)P(B) = \left(\frac{3}{5}\right)\left(\frac{3}{5}\right) = \frac{9}{25}$, $P(R \cap R) = P(R)P(R) = \left(\frac{2}{5}\right)\left(\frac{2}{5}\right) = \frac{4}{25}$,

$P(2 \text{ match}) = P(2B \cup 2R) = P(2B) + P(2R) = \frac{9}{25} + \frac{4}{25} = \frac{13}{25}$. Alternatively, the two

answers are complements: $P(2 \text{ match}) = 1 - \frac{12}{25} = \frac{13}{25}$.

(10) P(2B,1R, any order) = 216/455 ≈ 0.475 ≈ 47.5%, P(3B) = 12/65 ≈ 0.185 ≈

18.5%, P(at least 1 red) = 53/65 ≈ 0.815 ≈ 81.5%. Notes: After each ball is

selected, fewer balls remain in the bag. Use the conditional probability formulas.

$P(B_1 \cap B_2 \cap R) = P(B_1)P(B_2|B_1)P(R|B_1 \cap B_2) = \left(\frac{9}{15}\right)\left(\frac{8}{14}\right)\left(\frac{6}{13}\right) = \frac{432}{2730} = \frac{72}{455}$.

Similarly, $P(B_1 \cap R \cap B_2) = P(R \cap B_1 \cap B_2) = \frac{72}{455}$. $P(2B,1R, \text{ any order}) =$

$P(B_1 \cap B_2 \cap R) + P(B_1 \cap R \cap B_2) + P(R \cap B_1 \cap B_2) = 3\left(\frac{72}{455}\right) = \frac{216}{455}$.

$P(B_1 \cap B_2 \cap B_3) = P(B_1)P(B_2|B_1)P(B_3|B_1 \cap B_2) = \left(\frac{9}{15}\right)\left(\frac{8}{14}\right)\left(\frac{7}{13}\right) = \frac{504}{2730} = \frac{12}{65}$. B_1, B_2,

and B_3 **don't** refer to specific balls (unlike Chapter 4, where we did use subscripts to

refer to specific balls); with the conditional probability formula, when the same

color ball is to be selected in different events, we are using the subscripts to indicate

that a ball of that color is being selected first, second, third, etc. P(at least 1 red) =

$1 - \frac{12}{65} = \frac{53}{65}$ because it is the complement to selecting three blue balls.

Alternate solution: There are $\binom{9}{2}\binom{6}{1} = \frac{9!}{2!7!}\frac{6!}{1!5!} = (36)(6) = 216$ ways to choose 2

blue balls and 1 red ball from 9 blue balls and 6 red balls, $\binom{9}{3} = \frac{9!}{3!6!} = \frac{(9)(8)(7)}{(3)(2)(1)} = 84$

ways to choose 3 blue balls from 9 blue balls, and $\binom{15}{3} = \frac{15!}{3!12!} = \frac{(15)(14)(13)}{(3)(2)(1)} = 455$

ways to choose 3 balls out of 15. Divide 216 by 455 to get P(2B,1R, any order) $= \frac{216}{455}$

and divide 84 by 455 to get $P(3B) = \frac{84}{455} = \frac{12}{65}$.

(11) $P(2B) = 4/15 \approx 0.267 \approx 26.7\%$, $P(2R) = 2/35 \approx 0.0571 \approx 5.71\%$, P(at least 1 green) $= 13/35 \approx 0.371 \approx 37.1\%$. Notes: There are $8 + 3 + 4 = 15$ balls initially; after the first ball is selected, only 14 balls remain in the bag. Use the conditional probability formulas. $P(2B) = P(B_1 \cap B_2) = P(B_1)P(B_2|B_1) = \left(\frac{8}{15}\right)\left(\frac{7}{14}\right) = \frac{4}{15}$,

$P(2R) = P(R_1 \cap R_2) = P(R_1)P(R_2|R_1) = \left(\frac{4}{15}\right)\left(\frac{3}{14}\right) = \frac{2}{35}$, $P(B \cap R) = P(B)P(R|B) = \left(\frac{8}{15}\right)\left(\frac{4}{14}\right) = \frac{16}{105}$, $P(R \cap B) = P(R)P(B|R) = \left(\frac{4}{15}\right)\left(\frac{8}{14}\right) = \frac{16}{105}$. The complement to at

least one green is $P(2B) + P(2R) + P(B \cap R) + P(R \cap B) = \frac{4}{15} + \frac{2}{35} + \frac{16}{105} + \frac{16}{105} =$

$\frac{28}{105} + \frac{6}{105} + \frac{32}{105} = \frac{66}{105} = \frac{22}{35}$. (These are all the cases where no green balls are

selected.) Therefore, P(at least 1 green) $= 1 - \frac{22}{35} = \frac{13}{35}$.

<u>Alternate solution</u> for P(at least 1 green): There are $\binom{8}{2} = \frac{8!}{2!6!} = \frac{(8)(7)}{(2)(1)} = 28$ ways to

choose 2 blue balls from 8 blue balls, $\binom{4}{2} = \frac{4!}{2!2!} = \frac{(4)(3)}{(2)(1)} = 6$ ways to choose 2 red balls

from 4 red balls, and $\binom{15}{2} = \frac{15!}{2!13!} = \frac{(15)(14)}{(2)(1)} = 105$ ways to choose 2 balls out of 15.

Divide 28 by 105 to get $P(2B) = \frac{28}{105} = \frac{4}{15}$ and divide 6 by 105 to get $P(2R) = \frac{6}{105} = \frac{2}{35}$.

(12) $P(3B) = 1/13 \approx 0.0769 \approx 7.69\%$, $P(3G) = 2/91 \approx 0.0220 \approx 2.20\%$, P(1 of each color) $= 3/13 \approx 0.231 \approx 23.1\%$. Notes: There are $7 + 5 + 3 = 15$ balls initially. After each ball is selected, fewer balls remain in the bag. Use the conditional probability formulas. $P(B_1 \cap B_2 \cap B_3) = P(B_1)P(B_2|B_1)P(B_3|B_1 \cap B_2) = \left(\frac{7}{15}\right)\left(\frac{6}{14}\right)\left(\frac{5}{13}\right) = \frac{210}{2730} =$

$\frac{1}{13}$, $P(G_1 \cap G_2 \cap G_3) = P(G_1)P(G_2|G_1)P(G_3|G_1 \cap G_2) = \left(\frac{5}{15}\right)\left(\frac{4}{14}\right)\left(\frac{3}{13}\right) = \frac{60}{2730} = \frac{2}{91}$. B_1, B_2,

and B_3 **<u>don't</u>** refer to specific balls (unlike Chapter 4, where we did use subscripts to refer to specific balls); with the conditional probability formula, when the same color ball is to be selected in different events, we are using the subscripts to indicate that a ball of that color is being selected first, second, third, etc. $P(B \cap G \cap R) =$

$P(B)P(G|B)P(R|B \cap G) = \left(\frac{7}{15}\right)\left(\frac{5}{14}\right)\left(\frac{3}{13}\right) = \frac{105}{2730} = \frac{1}{26}$. Similarly, $P(B \cap R \cap G) =$

$P(G \cap B \cap R) = P(G \cap R \cap B) = P(R \cap B \cap G) = P(R \cap G \cap B) = \frac{1}{26}$, such that

$P(1 \text{ of each color}) = 6\left(\frac{1}{26}\right) = \frac{3}{13}$.

Alternate solution: There are $\binom{7}{3} = \frac{7!}{3!4!} = \frac{(7)(6)(5)}{(3)(2)(1)} = 35$ ways to choose 3 blue balls

from 7 blue balls, $\binom{5}{3} = \frac{5!}{3!2!} = \frac{(5)(4)(3)}{(3)(2)(1)} = 10$ ways to choose 3 green balls from 5 green

balls, and $\binom{15}{3} = \frac{15!}{3!12!} = \frac{(15)(14)(13)}{(3)(2)(1)} = 455$ ways to choose 3 balls out of 15. Divide 35

by 455 to get $P(3B) = \frac{35}{455} = \frac{1}{13}$ and divide 10 by 455 to get $P(3G) = \frac{10}{455} = \frac{2}{91}$. There

are $\binom{7}{1}\binom{5}{1}\binom{3}{1} = \frac{7!}{1!6!}\frac{5!}{1!4!}\frac{3!}{1!2!} = (7)(5)(3) = 105$ ways to choose one ball of each color.

Divide 105 by 455 to get $P(1 \text{ of each color}) = \frac{105}{455} = \frac{3}{13}$.

(13) (A) 4 (B) 18. Notes: If you select 3 socks, you could have one of each color; a 4th sock guarantees at least one matching pair. If you select 17 socks, in the worst-case scenario, you could have 1 black, 10 tan, and 6 white socks; an 18th sock guarantees at least one matching black pair.

(14) (A) 16 (B) 24. Notes: If you select 15 socks, in the worst-case scenario, you could have 1 black, 9 gray, and 5 white socks; a 16th sock guarantees at least one matching black pair. If you select 23 socks, in the worst-case scenario, you could have 13 black, 9 gray, and 1 white socks; a 24th sock guarantees at least one matching white pair.

(15) (A) 6 (B) 26. Notes: If you only select 5 socks, it's possible to only have one matching pair; for example, 3 pink socks, 1 orange sock, and 1 yellow sock, only has one matching pair. A 6th sock guarantees at least two matching pairs. If you select 25 socks, in the worst-case scenario, you could have 3 pink, 14 orange, and 8 yellow socks; a 26th sock guarantees at least two matching pink pairs.

(16) (A) 8 (B) 48. Notes: If you only select 7 socks, it's possible to only have two matching pairs; you could have 3 black socks, 3 gray socks, and 1 white sock. An 8th sock guarantees at least three matching pairs. If you select 47 socks, in the worst-case scenario, you could have 22 black, 1 gray, and 24 white socks. A 48th sock guarantees at least one matching pair in every color.

(17) $P(D) = 23/1000 = 0.023 = 2.3\%$, $P(A|D) = 15/23 \approx 0.652 \approx 65.2\%$. Notes: Use the formulas for the law of total probability and Baye's theorem. $P(D) = P(A)P(D|A) + P(B)P(D|B) + P(C)P(D|C) = (0.5)(0.03) + (0.3)(0.02) + (0.2)(0.01) = 0.015 + 0.006 + 0.002 = 0.023$ and $P(A|D) = \frac{P(A)P(D|A)}{P(D)} = \frac{(0.5)(0.03)}{0.023} = \frac{0.015}{0.023} = \frac{15}{23}$.

(18) P(D) = 19/1000 = 0.019 = 1.9%, P(A|D) = 2/19 ≈ 0.105 ≈ 10.5%. Notes: Use the formulas for the law of total probability and Baye's theorem. $P(D) = P(A)P(D|A) + P(B)P(D|B) + P(C)P(D|C) = (0.4)(0.005) + (0.35)(0.02) + (0.25)(0.04) = 0.002 + 0.007 + 0.01 = 0.019$ and $P(A|D) = \frac{P(A)P(D|A)}{P(D)} = \frac{(0.4)(0.005)}{0.019} = \frac{0.002}{0.019} = \frac{2}{19}$.

(Divide 0.5% by 100% to convert it to a decimal: $\frac{0.5}{100} = 0.005$.)

Chapter 6

(1) $P(2T) = 3/8 = 0.375 = 37.5\%$, $P(3H) = 1/4 = 0.25 = 25\%$, $P(\geq 3T) = 5/16 = 0.3125 = 31.25\%$, $P(4 \text{ of a kind}) = 1/8 = 0.125 = 12.5\%$. Notes: There are $2^4 = 16$ possible outcomes. There are $\frac{4!}{2!2!} = \frac{24}{(2)(2)} = 6$ permutations (Case 2) of TTHH (these are HHTT, HTHT, HTTH, THHT, THTH, TTHH), which is the same as $\binom{4}{2} = \frac{4!}{2!2!} = 6$ ways to choose 2 coins to be tails, such that $P(2T) = \frac{6}{16} = \frac{3}{8}$. There are $\frac{4!}{3!} = \frac{24}{6} = 4$ permutations of HHHT (these are HHHT, HHTH, HTHH, THHH), which is the same as $\binom{4}{3} = \frac{4!}{3!1!} = 4$ ways to choose 3 coins to be heads, such that $P(3H) = \frac{4}{16} = \frac{1}{4}$. Add 1 permutation of TTTT to 4 permutations of TTTH to get 5 ways to have at least 3 tails: $P(\geq 3T) = \frac{5}{16}$. There are 2 ways to make 4 of a kind (HHHH or TTTT): $P(4 \text{ of a kind}) = \frac{2}{16} = \frac{1}{8}$.

(2) $P(3H) = 5/16 = 0.3125 = 31.25\%$, $P(4T) = 15/64 = 0.234375 = 23.4375\%$, $P(\text{more H than T}) = 11/32 = 0.34375 = 34.375\%$. Notes: There are $2^6 = 64$ possible outcomes. There are $\frac{6!}{3!3!} = \frac{720}{(6)(6)} = 20$ permutations of HHHTTT, which is the same as $\binom{6}{3} = \frac{6!}{3!3!} = 20$ ways to choose 3 coins to be heads, such that $P(3H) = \frac{20}{64} = \frac{5}{16}$. There are $\frac{6!}{4!2!} = \frac{720}{(24)(2)} = 15$ permutations of TTTTHH, which is the same as $\binom{6}{4} = \frac{6!}{4!2!} = 15$ ways to choose 4 coins to be tails, such that $P(4T) = \frac{15}{64}$. There are $\frac{6!}{5!1!} = \frac{720}{(120)(1)} = 6$ permutations of HHHHHT and 1 permutation of HHHHHH, so there are $15 + 6 + 1 = 22$ ways to have 4, 5, or 6 coins be heads, such that $P(\text{more H than T}) = \frac{22}{64} = \frac{11}{32}$.

(3) $P(\text{doubles}) = 1/6 \approx 0.167 \approx 16.7\%$, $P(\text{sum}=7) = 1/6 \approx 0.167 \approx 16.7\%$, $P(\text{sum}\leq 4) = 1/6 \approx 0.167 \approx 16.7\%$. Notes: There are $6^2 = 36$ possible outcomes. There are 6 permutations with doubles (1+1, 2+2, 3+3, 4+4, 5+5, 6+6), 6 permutations with a sum of 7 (6+1, 5+2, 4+3, 3+4, 2+5, 1+6), and 6 permutations with a sum less than or equal to 4 (1+1, 1+2, 1+3, 2+1, 2+2, 3+1), such that $P(\text{doubles}) = P(\text{sum}=7) = P(\text{sum}\leq 4) = \frac{6}{36} = \frac{1}{6}$. (A sum of 7 is the most likely sum.)

(4) P(two 5's) = 2/27 ≈ 0.0741 ≈ 7.41%, P(1,2,3, any order) = 1/36 ≈ 0.0278 ≈ 2.78%, P(sum=15) = 5/108 ≈ 0.0463 ≈ 4.63%. Notes: There are $6^3 = 216$ possible outcomes. There are 16 permutations with at least two 5's (5+5+1, 5+5+2, 5+5+3, 5+5+4, 5+5+5, 5+5+6, 5+1+5, 5+2+5, 5+3+5, 5+4+5, 5+6+5, 1+5+5, 2+5+5, 3+5+5, 4+5+5, 6+5+5; be careful not to count 5+5+5 more than once), 6 permutations with 1, 2, 3 in any order (1+2+3, 1+3+2, 2+1+3, 2+3+1, 3+1+2, 3+2+1), and 10 permutations with a sum of 15 (3+6+6, 4+5+6, 4+6+5, 5+4+6, 5+5+5, 5+6+4, 6+3+6, 6+4+5, 6+5+4, 6+6+3), such that P(two 5's) = $\frac{16}{216} = \frac{2}{27}$, P(1,2,3, any order) = $\frac{6}{216} = \frac{1}{36}$, and P(sum=15) = $\frac{10}{216} = \frac{5}{108}$.

(5) P(H's=30 cents) = 23/128 ≈ 0.180 ≈ 18.0%, P(more H's on N's) = 163/256 ≈ 0.637 ≈ 63.7%. Notes: There are $2^8 = 256$ possible outcomes. (There are $2^5 = 32$ outcomes for the nickels and $2^3 = 8$ outcomes for the dimes, which makes $32 \times 8 = 256$ total outcomes.) A nickel is worth 5 cents and a dime is worth 10 cents. The total value of the coins that are heads can have a total value of 30 cents in the following ways:

- There is one permutation where the nickels are TTTTT and the dimes are HHH.
- There are $\frac{5!}{2!3!} = \frac{120}{(2)(6)} = 10$ permutations of HHTTT (for the nickels) and 3 permutations of HHT (for the dimes), which makes $(10)(3) = 30$ permutations where 2 nickels are heads and 2 dimes are heads.
- There are 5 permutations of HHHHT and 3 permutations of HTT, which makes $(5)(3) = 15$ permutations where 4 nickels are heads and 1 dime is heads.

Add these to get $1 + 30 + 15 = 46$ ways for the total value of the coins that are heads to equal 30 cents, which gives P(H's=30 cents) = $\frac{46}{256} = \frac{23}{128}$. There can be more heads on nickels than dimes the following ways:

- There are 6 ways for the nickels to have 4 or 5 heads (HHHHH, HHHHT, HHHTH, HHTHH, HTHHH, THHHH). All $2^3 = 8$ permutations of the dimes have fewer heads. This makes $(6)(8) = 48$ ways.
- There are $\frac{5!}{3!2!} = \frac{120}{(6)(2)} = 10$ ways for the nickels to have 3 heads. There are 7 permutations of the dimes with fewer than 3 heads (HHT, HTH, THH, HTT, THT, TTH, TTT). This makes $(10)(7) = 70$ ways.

- There are $\frac{5!}{2!3!} = \frac{120}{(2)(6)} = 10$ ways for the nickels to have 2 heads. There are 4 permutations of the dimes with fewer than 2 heads (HTT, THT, TTH, TTT). This makes $(10)(4) = 40$ ways.
  - There are 5 ways for the nickels to have 1 head. There is 1 way for the dimes to have fewer heads (TTT). This makes $(5)(1) = 5$ ways.

Add these to get $48 + 70 + 40 + 5 = 163$ ways for the nickels to show more heads than the dimes, which gives P(more H's on N's) $= \frac{163}{256}$.

(6) P(Q and D match) $= 1/2 = 0.5 = 50\%$, P(T's$\geq$30 cents) $= 3/8 = 0.375 = 37.5\%$. Notes: If the quarter shows heads, there is a 50% chance that the dime will also show heads because the dime has a 50% chance of showing heads. A similar argument applies if the quarter shows tails. (Between the quarter and dime, the possible outcomes are HH, HT, TH, and TT; 50% of these match. The nickel is irrelevant for the first question, though if you include the nickel, you will see that the quarter and dime match for 4 out of 8 outcomes.) There are $2^3 = 8$ possible outcomes for the 3 coins. A quarter is worth 25 cents, a dime is worth 10 cents, and a nickel is worth 5 cents. The quarter must be tails for the value of the tails to be 30 cents or more. If the quarter is tails, the only way the value of the tails would be less than 30 cents is if the nickel and dime are both heads. This leaves 3 outcomes where the value is at least 30 cents: Q=T, D=H, N=T; Q=T, D=T, N=H; Q=T, D=T, N=T. This gives P(T's$\geq$30 cents) $= \frac{3}{8}$.

(7) P(product=12) $= 1/9 \approx 0.111 \approx 11.1\%$, P(only 1's and/or 2's) $= 1/9 \approx 0.111 \approx 11.1\%$. Notes: There are $6^2 = 36$ possible outcomes. There are 4 permutations where the product is 12 (2×6, 3×4, 4×3, 6×2) and 4 permutations with only 1's and/or 2's (1+1, 1+2, 2+1, 2+2), such that P(product=12) = P(only 1's and/or 2's) $= \frac{4}{36} = \frac{1}{9}$.

(8) P(same number **not** on all 3 dice) $= 63/64 = 0.984375 = 98.4375\%$, P(3 different numbers) $= 21/32 = 0.65625 = 65.625\%$. Notes: There are $8^3 = 512$ possible outcomes. There are 8 ways for the same number to show on all 3 dice (111, 222, 333, 444, 555, 666, 777, 888), such that P(same number on all 3 dice) $= \frac{8}{512} = \frac{1}{64}$. Use the **complement rule** (Chapter 5): P(same number **not** on all 3 dice) $= 1 - \frac{1}{64} = \frac{63}{64}$. To get 3 different numbers, there are 8 choices for the first die (1 thru 8), there are

7 ways for the second die to be different from the first die, and there are 6 ways for the third die to be different from the first two dice. This makes $(8)(7)(6) = 336$ ways for all 3 dice to show different numbers, such that P(3 different numbers) $= \frac{336}{512} = \frac{21}{32}$.

Alternate solution: There are 8 ways to have triples (111, 222, 333, 444, 555, 666, 777, 888). There are 21 ways to have exactly two 1's (7 of the form 11x, 7 of the form 1x1, 7 of the form x11, where x is 2, 3, 4, 5, 6, 7, or 8). Similarly, there are 21 ways to have exactly two 2's, 3's, 4's, 5's, 6's, 7's, or 8's. This makes $(21)(8) = 168$ ways to have doubles. Add $168 + 8 = 176$ ways to have doubles or triples, such that P(doubles or triples) $= \frac{176}{512} = \frac{11}{32}$. Use the **complement rule**: P(3 different numbers) $= 1 - \frac{11}{32} = \frac{21}{32}$.

(9) $P(3T) = 1/4 = 0.25 = 25\%$, P(3T if it's known that blue is T) $= 3/8 = 0.375 = 37.5\%$, P(3T if it's known that blue is H) $= 1/8 = 0.125 = 12.5\%$. Notes: There are $2^4 = 16$ possible outcomes for the 4 coins. There are 4 outcomes with exactly 3 tails (HTTT, THTT, TTHT, TTTH), such that $P(3T) = \frac{4}{16} = \frac{1}{4}$. If the blue coin is tails, in order to have exactly 3 tails, 2 of the red coins must be tails. There are 3 ways for 2 red coins to be tails (HTT, THT, TTH) and there are $2^3 = 8$ possible outcomes for the 3 red coins, such that P(3T if it's known that blue is T) $= \frac{3}{8}$. If the blue coin is heads, in order to have 3 tails, all 3 red coins must be tails. There is 1 way for the 3 red coins to be tails (TTT), such that P(3T if it's known that blue is H) $= \frac{1}{8}$.

Alternate solution: Let A represent the event that the blue coin is tails and let B represent the event that exactly 3 of the 4 coins are tails. The **conditional probability** formula from Chapter 5 states that $P(A \cap B) = P(A)P(B|A)$. Here, $P(A \cap B)$ is the probability that the blue coin is tails **and** exactly 3 of the 4 coins are tails, while $P(B|A)$ is the probability that 3 coins are tails if the blue coin is known to be tails. There are 4 ways for 3 coins to be tails (HTTT, THTT, TTHT, TTTH); the blue coin is tails in 3 of these. Since there are $2^4 = 16$ possible outcomes for the 4 coins, $P(A \cap B) = \frac{3}{16}$. The blue coin is fair, so the probability that the blue coin is tails is $P(A) = \frac{1}{2}$. Plug $P(A \cap B) = \frac{3}{16}$ and $P(A) = \frac{1}{2}$ into the conditional probability formula $P(A \cap B) = P(A)P(B|A)$ to get $\frac{3}{16} = \frac{1}{2}P(B|A)$. Multiply by 2 on both sides: $\frac{3}{8} = P(B|A)$. You can similarly show that $P(C|A) = \frac{1}{8}$ where $P(C|A)$ is the probability that 3 coins are tails if the blue coin is known to be heads.

(10) P(3T) = 1/2 = 0.5 = 50%, P(3H) = 1/4 = 0.25 = 25%. Notes: The double-headed coin is always heads. The double-tailed coins are always tails. To get exactly 3 tails, exactly one of the two fair coins must be tails. The probability that exactly one of the fair coins is tails is P(3T) = $\frac{2}{4} = \frac{1}{2}$ (the 4 possible outcomes are HH, HT, TH, and TT; 2 of these have one T). To get 3 heads, both fair coins must be heads. The probability that both fair coins will be heads is P(3H) = $\frac{1}{4}$. (There are 4 possible outcomes for all 5 coins. The fair coins are listed first: HHHTT, HTHTT, THHTT, TTHTT.)

(11) P(sum=14) = 5/72 ≈ 0.0694 ≈ 6.94%, P(sum=15) = 1/18 ≈ 0.0556 ≈ 5.56%, P(12-sided die>6-sided die) = 51/72 ≈ 0.708 ≈ 70.8%. Notes: There are (6)(12) = 72 possible outcomes (since one die can be 1-6 and the other can be 1-12). There are 5 permutations with a sum of 14 (6+8, 5+9, 4+10, 3+11, 2+12), such that P(sum=14) = $\frac{5}{72}$. There are 4 permutations with a sum of 15 (6+9, 5+10, 4+11, 3+12), such that P(sum=15) = $\frac{4}{72} = \frac{1}{18}$. Following are the ways that the 12-sided die can show a larger number than the 6-sided die.

- If the 6-sided die shows 1, there are 11 ways for the 12-sided die to show a larger number (2, 3, 4, 5, 6, 7, 8, 9, 10, 11, and 12).
- If the 6-sided die shows 2, there are 10 ways for the 12-sided die to show a larger number (3, 4, 5, 6, 7, 8, 9, 10, 11, and 12).
- If the 6-sided die shows 3, there are 9 ways for the 12-sided die to show a larger number (4, 5, 6, 7, 8, 9, 10, 11, and 12).
- If the 6-sided die shows 4, there are 8 ways for the 12-sided die to show a larger number (5, 6, 7, 8, 9, 10, 11, and 12).
- If the 6-sided die shows 5, there are 7 ways for the 12-sided die to show a larger number (6, 7, 8, 9, 10, 11, and 12).
- If the 6-sided die shows 6, there are 6 ways for the 12-sided die to show a larger number (7, 8, 9, 10, 11, and 12).

Add 11 + 10 + 9 + 8 + 7 + 6 = 51 to find how many ways the 12-sided die can beat the 6-sided die, such that P(12-sided die>6-sided die) = $\frac{51}{72}$.

(12) P(2 vowels) = $1/6 \approx 0.167 \approx 16.7\%$, P(1 vowel and 1 consonant) = $1/2 = 0.5$ = 50%. Notes: There are $6^2 = 36$ possible outcomes. There are 2 ways for the first die to show a vowel (E$_1$, E$_2$) and 3 ways for the second die to show a vowel (A, I, U). This makes 6 ways for both dice to show vowels (E$_1$A, E$_1$I, E$_1$U, E$_2$A, E$_2$I, E$_2$U), such that P(2 vowels) = $\frac{6}{36} = \frac{1}{6}$. There are 2 ways for the first die to show a vowel (E$_1$, E$_2$) and 3 ways for the second die to show a consonant (R, D, S), while there are 4 ways for the first die to show a consonant (C, N, T, R) and 3 ways for the second die to show a vowel (A, I, U). This makes $(2)(3) + (4)(3) = 6 + 12 = 18$ ways to make one vowel and one consonant, such that P(1 vowel and 1 consonant) = $\frac{18}{36} = \frac{1}{2}$.

Alternate solution: The probability that the first die shows a vowel is $\frac{2}{6} = \frac{1}{3}$. The probability that the second die shows a vowel is $\frac{3}{6} = \frac{1}{2}$. Since the outcomes are independent, multiply to find the probability that both dice show vowels (recall Chapter 5): $P(V \cap V) = \left(\frac{1}{3}\right)\left(\frac{1}{2}\right) = \frac{1}{6}$. Similar arguments for one vowel and one consonant lead to $P(V \cap C) + P(C \cap V) = \left(\frac{1}{3}\right)\left(\frac{1}{2}\right) + \left(\frac{2}{3}\right)\left(\frac{1}{2}\right) = \frac{1}{6} + \frac{2}{6} = \frac{3}{6} = \frac{1}{2}$.

(13) P(sum=7) = $3/8 = 0.375 = 37.5\%$, P(2 coins match) = $1/2 = 0.5 = 50\%$. Notes: There are $2^3 = 8$ possible outcomes (1+2+3, 1+2+4, 1+3+3, 1+3+4, 2+2+3, 2+2+4, 2+3+3, 2+3+4). There are 3 outcomes with a sum of 7 (1+2+4, 1+3+3, 2+2+3), such that P(sum=7) = $\frac{3}{8}$. There are 4 outcomes where 2 coins match (1+3+3, 2+2+3, 2+2+4, 2+3+3), such that P(2 coins match) = $\frac{4}{8} = \frac{1}{2}$.

(14) P(same number of heads for each flip) = $5/16 = 0.3125 = 31.25\%$. Notes: There are $2^6 = 64$ possible outcomes. Break it down by the number of heads showing:

- There is one way for both flips to have 3 heads: HHH/HHH.
- There are 3 ways for a single flip to have 2 heads: HHT, HTH, THH. This makes $(3)(3) = 9$ ways for both flips to have 2 heads: HHT/HHT, HHT/HTH, HHT/THH, HTH/HHT, HTH/HTH, HTH/THH, THH/HHT, THH/HTH, THH/THH.
- There are 3 ways for a single flip to have 1 head: HTT, THT, TTH. This makes $(3)(3) = 9$ ways for both flips to have 1 head: HTT/HTT, HTT/THT, HTT/TTH, THT/HTT, THT/THT, THT/TTH, TTH/HTT, TTH/THT, TTH/TTH.
- There is one way for both flips to have 0 heads: TTT/TTT.

Add to get $1 + 9 + 9 + 1 = 20$ ways to get the same number of heads on both flips, such that P(same number of heads for each flip) $= \frac{20}{64} = \frac{5}{16}$.

(15) P(two 5's and one 4 in any order) $= 1/72 \approx 0.0139 \approx 1.39\%$, $P(10) = P(11) = 1/8 = 0.125 = 12.5\%$. Notes: There are $6^3 = 216$ possible outcomes. There are 3 permutations with two 5's and one 4 in any order (4+5+5, 5+4+5, 5+5+4), such that P(two 5's and one 4 in any order) $= \frac{3}{216} = \frac{1}{72}$. The two most likely sums are 10 and 11. Following are the best contenders.

- There are 21 permutations with a sum of 8: 1+1+6, 1+2+5, 1+3+4, 1+4+3, 1+5+2, 1+6+1, 2+1+5, 2+2+4, 2+3+3, 2+4+2, 2+5+1, 3+1+4, 3+2+3, 3+3+2, 3+4+1, 4+1+3, 4+2+2, 4+3+1, 5+1+2, 5+2+1, 6+1+1.
- There are 25 permutations with a sum of 9: 1+2+6, 1+3+5, 1+4+4, 1+5+3, 1+6+2, 2+1+6, 2+2+5, 2+3+4, 2+4+3, 2+5+2, 2+6+1, 3+1+5, 3+2+4, 3+3+3, 3+4+2, 3+5+1, 4+1+4, 4+2+3, 4+3+2, 4+4+1, 5+1+3, 5+2+2, 5+3+1, 6+1+2, 6+2+1.
- There are 27 permutations with a sum of 10: 1+3+6, 1+4+5, 1+5+4, 1+6+3, 2+2+6, 2+3+5, 2+4+4, 2+5+3, 2+6+2, 3+1+6, 3+2+5, 3+3+4, 3+4+3, 3+5+2, 3+6+1, 4+1+5, 4+2+4, 4+3+3, 4+4+2, 4+5+1, 5+1+4, 5+2+3, 5+3+2, 5+4+1, 6+1+3, 6+2+2, 6+3+1.
- There are 27 permutations with a sum of 11: 1+4+6, 1+5+5, 1+6+4, 2+3+6, 2+4+5, 2+5+4, 2+6+3, 3+2+6, 3+3+5, 3+4+4, 3+5+3, 3+6+2, 4+1+6, 4+2+5, 4+3+4, 4+4+3, 4+5+2, 4+6+1, 5+1+5, 5+2+4, 5+3+3, 5+4+2, 5+5+1, 6+1+4, 6+2+3, 6+3+2, 6+4+1.
- There are 25 permutations with a sum of 12: 1+5+6, 1+6+5, 2+4+6, 2+5+5, 2+6+4, 3+3+6, 3+4+5, 3+5+4, 3+6+3, 4+2+6, 4+3+5, 4+4+4, 4+5+3, 4+6+2, 5+1+6, 5+2+5, 5+3+4, 5+4+3, 5+5+2, 5+6+1, 6+1+5, 6+2+4, 6+3+3, 6+4+5, 6+5+1.
- There are 21 permutations with a sum of 13: 1+6+6, 2+5+6, 2+6+5, 3+4+6, 3+5+5, 3+6+4, 4+3+6, 4+4+5, 4+5+4, 4+6+3, 5+2+6, 5+3+5, 5+4+4, 5+5+3, 5+6+2, 6+1+6, 6+2+5, 6+3+4, 6+4+3, 6+5+2, 6+6+1.

There is a quicker way to determine that 10 and 11 are the two most likely sums.

Note that the average value of a single 6-sided die is 3.5. If two 6-sided dice are rolled, the most likely sum is $2(3.5) = 7$. If three 6-sided dice are rolled, $3(3.5) = 10.5$ is halfway between 10 and 11, which are the two most likely sums. The probabilities for the two most likely sums (which are the same) are therefore $P(10) = P(11) = \frac{27}{216} = \frac{1}{8}$.

(16) P(all 3 dice show 2-digit numbers) $= 1/64 = 0.015625 = 1.5625\%$, P(at least 1 die shows a 2-digit number) $= 37/64 = 0.578125 = 57.8125\%$. Notes: The probability that a single die doesn't show a 2-digit number is $\frac{9}{12} = \frac{3}{4}$ (since 10, 11, and 12 are the only 3 outcomes with 2 digits). The probability that all 3 numbers will have 1 digit is $\left(\frac{3}{4}\right)\left(\frac{3}{4}\right)\left(\frac{3}{4}\right) = \frac{27}{64}$. Use the **complement rule** (Chapter 5): P(at least 1 die shows a 2-digit number) $= 1 - \frac{27}{64} = \frac{37}{64}$. Similarly, P(all 3 dice show 2-digit numbers) $= \left(\frac{3}{12}\right)^3 = \frac{1}{64}$.

Alternate solution: There are $12^3 = 1728$ possible outcomes. There are $3^3 = 27$ permutations where all 3 dice show 10, 11, or 12: 10+10+10, 10+10+11, 10+10+12, 10+11+10, 10+11+11, 10+11+12, 10+12+10, 10+12+11, 10+12+12, 11+10+10, 11+10+11, 11+10+12, 11+11+10, 11+11+11, 11+11+12, 11+12+10, 11+12+11, 11+12+12, 12+10+10, 12+10+11, 12+10+12, 12+11+10, 12+11+11, 12+11+12, 12+12+10, 12+12+11, 12+12+12. This gives P(all 3 dice show 2-digit numbers) $= \frac{27}{1728} = \frac{1}{64}$. There are $9^3 = 729$ permutations where no dice show a 2-digit number. (In this case, each die can be 1, 2, 3, 4, 5, 6, 7, 8, or 9, which gives 9 outcomes for each die.) This gives P(all dice show 1-digit numbers) $= \frac{729}{1728} = \frac{27}{64}$. Use the **complement rule**: P(at least 1 die shows a 2-digit number) $= 1 - \frac{27}{64} = \frac{37}{64}$.

Another alternate solution: There are $(9)(9) = 81$ permutations of the form 10xy (where x and y can each be 1, 2, 3, 4, 5, 6, 7, 8, or 9). There are similarly 81 permutations of the form 11xy, 12xy, x10y, x11y, x12y, xy10, xy11, xy12. This makes $9(81) = 729$ permutations where exactly one die is 10, 11, or 12. There are 9 permutations of the form 1010x, 1011x, 1012x, 1110x, 1111x, 1112x, 1210x, 1211x, 1212x, which makes $(9)(9) = 81$ permutations where only the first two dice show 10, 11, or 12. There are similarly 81 permutations where only the first and third dice show 10, 11, or 12, and 81 permutations where only the second and third dice show

10, 11, or 12. This makes $81 + 81 + 81 = 243$ permutations where exactly two dice show 10, 11, or 12. Since 729 permutations have exactly one 2-digit number, 243 permutations have exactly two 2-digit numbers, and 27 permutations (see the original solution) have exactly three 2-digit numbers, there are $729 + 243 + 27 = 999$ permutations with at least one 2-digit number. This makes P(at least 1 die shows a 2-digit number) $= \frac{999}{1728} = \frac{37}{64}$. **Careful**: Be careful with the number 999. As shown in the alternate solution, 999 is the number of permutations where at least 1 die is 10, 11, or 12. It's easy to misinterpret the 999 if you're thinking about dice where each digit can be 1 thru 9, but 999 **isn't** the number of permutations where each digit is 1 thru 9. As shown in the original solution, 729 is the number of permutations where each digit is under 10. If you write out the numbers 1 thru 999, many of these will have **zeros**, like $900, 570$, or 202. That's why only 729 (much less than 999) permutations use only 1 thru 9. (Also, numbers 1-99 don't even have three digits. Of the numbers 100 thru 999, only 729 of them have no zeros.)

(17) $P(H) = 3/4 = 0.75 = 75\%$, $P(T) = 1/4 = 0.25 = 25\%$. Notes: According to the problem, $P(H) = 3\,P(T)$. We know that $P(H) + P(T) = 1$ since heads and tails are the only possible outcomes for a single flip. Plug $P(H) = 3\,P(T)$ into $P(H) + P(T) = 1$ to get $3\,P(T) + P(T) = 1$. This reduces to $4\,P(T) = 1$. Divide by 4 on both sides to get $P(T) = \frac{1}{4}$. It follows that $P(H) = 3\,P(T) = 3\left(\frac{1}{4}\right) = \frac{3}{4}$. Check: $P(H)$ is 3 times $P(T)$ since $3P(T) = 3\left(\frac{1}{4}\right) = \frac{3}{4} = P(H)$ and $P(H) + P(T) = \frac{3}{4} + \frac{1}{4} = 1$.

(18) $P(1H) = 36/125 = 0.288 = 28.8\%$, $P(2H) = 54/125 = 0.432 = 43.2\%$, $P(3H) = 27/125 = 0.216 = 21.6\%$, $P(\geq 2T) = 44/125 = 0.352 = 35.2\%$. Notes: The problem tells us that $P(H) = 0.6 = \frac{3}{5}$, such that $P(T) = 1 - P(H) = 1 - 0.6 = 0.4 = \frac{2}{5}$. Three permutations have one head: HTT, THT, TTH. Each of these permutations has a probability of $P(H)P(T)P(T) = \left(\frac{3}{5}\right)\left(\frac{2}{5}\right)\left(\frac{2}{5}\right) = \frac{12}{125}$. Multiply this by 3 to get $P(1H) = 3\left(\frac{12}{125}\right) = \frac{36}{125}$. Three permutations have two heads: HHT, HTH, THH. Each of these permutations has a probability of $P(H)P(H)P(T) = \left(\frac{3}{5}\right)\left(\frac{3}{5}\right)\left(\frac{2}{5}\right) = \frac{18}{125}$. Multiply this by 3 to get $P(2H) = 3\left(\frac{18}{125}\right) = \frac{54}{125}$. One permutation has three heads (HHH), such that $P(3H)$

$= P(H)P(H)P(H) = \left(\frac{3}{5}\right)\left(\frac{3}{5}\right)\left(\frac{3}{5}\right) = \frac{27}{125}$. The probability of exactly 2 tails is the same as

the probability of exactly 1 head (since both involve HTT, THT, TTH): $P(2T) = P(1H) =$

$\frac{36}{125}$. The probability of exactly 3 tails is $P(3T) = P(T)P(T)P(T) = \left(\frac{2}{5}\right)\left(\frac{2}{5}\right)\left(\frac{2}{5}\right) = \frac{8}{125}$. The

probability of at least 2 tails is $P(\geq 2T) = P(2T) + P(3T) = \frac{36}{125} + \frac{8}{125} = \frac{44}{125}$.

Check: $P(0H) + P(1H) + P(2H) + P(3H) = \frac{8}{125} + \frac{36}{125} + \frac{54}{125} + \frac{27}{125} = 1$.

(19) $P(2H) = 3/16 = 0.1875 = 18.75\%$, $P(2T) = 5/16 = 0.3125 = 31.25\%$, $P(1H) =$

$1/2 = 0.5 = 50\%$. Notes: $P_u(H) = \frac{3}{8}$ and $P_u(T) = \frac{5}{8}$ for the unfair coin. $P_f(H) = P_f(T) =$

$\frac{1}{2}$ for the fair coin. For 2 heads, $P(2H) = P_u(H)P_f(H) = \left(\frac{3}{8}\right)\left(\frac{1}{2}\right) = \frac{3}{16}$. For 2 tails, $P(2T)$

$= P_u(T)P_f(T) = \left(\frac{5}{8}\right)\left(\frac{1}{2}\right) = \frac{5}{16}$. For 1 head (and 1 tail), $P(1H) = P_u(H)P_f(T) +$

$P_u(T)P_f(H) = \left(\frac{3}{8}\right)\left(\frac{1}{2}\right) + \left(\frac{5}{8}\right)\left(\frac{1}{2}\right) = \frac{3}{16} + \frac{5}{16} = \frac{8}{16} = \frac{1}{2}$. The effect of the unfair coin is

that 2 tails is more likely than 2 heads. In contrast, 1 head and 1 tail is just as likely

as if both coins had been fair. When the unfair coin is heads, $P_u(H) = \frac{3}{8}$ is less likely

than for a fair coin, but when the unfair coin is tails, $P_u(T) = \frac{5}{8}$ is more likely than for

a fair coin, and these compensate one another in $P_u(H)P_f(T) + P_u(T)P_f(H)$.

Check: $P(0H) + P(1H) + P(2H) = \frac{5}{16} + \frac{1}{2} + \frac{3}{16} = \frac{8}{16} + \frac{1}{2} = \frac{1}{2} + \frac{1}{2} = 1$.

(20) $P(\text{three 5's}) = 1/36 \approx 0.0278 \approx 2.788\%$, $P(\text{sum}=12) = 1/6 \approx 0.167 \approx 16.7\%$,

$P(\text{3 different numbers}) = 5/9 \approx 0.556 \approx 55.6\%$. Notes: There are only $6^2 = 36$

possible outcomes since the loaded die is always a 5. We can just focus on the two

fair dice, knowing that the loaded die will be a 5. There is 1 permutation where both

of the fair dice show 5's, such that $P(\text{three 5's}) = \frac{1}{36}$. There are 6 permutations

where the two fair dice have a sum of 7 (1+6, 2+5, 3+4, 4+3, 5+2, 6+1), such that

the sum of all 3 dice is 12: $P(\text{sum}=12) = \frac{6}{36} = \frac{1}{6}$. To get 3 different numbers, the

loaded die will be 5, there are 5 choices for one fair die (1, 2, 3, 4, or 6), and there

are 4 choices for the second fair die to be different from the first fair die. This makes

(1)(5)(4) = 20 ways for all 3 dice to show different numbers, such that P(3 different

numbers) $= \frac{20}{36} = \frac{5}{9}$. If we list the fair dice first, the 20 ways are: 125, 135, 145, 165,

215, 235, 245, 265, 315, 325, 345, 365, 415, 425, 435, 465, 615, 625, 635 645.

(21) P(H and 2) = 1/12 ≈ 0.0833 ≈ 8.33%, P(H or 2) = 7/12 ≈ 0.583 ≈ 58.3%, P(T and ≥3) = 1/3 ≈ 0.333 ≈ 33.3%. Notes: The outcome of the coin flip doesn't impact the outcome of the die roll, and vice-versa. Therefore, the following events are **independent** (Chapter 5). $P(H) = \frac{1}{2}$, $P(2) = \frac{1}{6}$, $P(≥3) = \frac{2}{3}$ (since 3, 4, 5, and 6 make up 4 of the 6 possible outcomes of 1, 2, 3, 4, 5, and 6; note that the inequality includes the 3, so it's more than half of the possible outcomes). According to Chapter 5, if both events occur and are independent, we multiply: P(H and 2) = P(H)P(2) = $\left(\frac{1}{2}\right)\left(\frac{1}{6}\right)$ = $\frac{1}{12}$ and P(T and ≥3) = P(T)P(≥3) = $\left(\frac{1}{2}\right)\left(\frac{2}{3}\right)$ = $\frac{1}{3}$. Observe that P(H) and P(2) **aren't mutually exclusive** (Chapter 5) because both events can occur. We must therefore use the modified addition rule for unions from Chapter 5: P(H∪2) = P(H) + P(2) − P(H∩2) = $\frac{1}{2} + \frac{1}{6} - \frac{1}{12} = \frac{6}{12} + \frac{2}{12} - \frac{1}{12} = \frac{7}{12}$.

Alternate solution: For one coin and one die, it's easy to just list the 12 possible outcomes (but this method would be tedious for a large number of coins or dice): H1, H2, H3, H4, H5, H6, T1, T2, T3, T4, T5, T6. This makes it easy to see that P(H and 2) = $\frac{1}{12}$, P(H or 2) = $\frac{7}{12}$ (these are H1, H2, H3, H4, H5, H6, T2), and P(T and ≥3) = $\frac{4}{12} = \frac{1}{3}$ (these are T3, T4, T5, T6).

(22) P(1T) = 1/4 = 0.25 = 25%, P(2T) = 1/4 = 0.25 = 25%, P(3T) = 5/12 ≈ 0.417 ≈ 41.7%, P(0T) = 1/12 ≈ 0.0833 ≈ 8.33%, if 3T occurs, then P(coin is double-tailed) = 4/5 = 0.8 = 80%. Read carefully: Whichever coin is picked, that **same coin is flipped 3 times**. (It's **not** a problem where all 3 coins are flipped at once; only 1 coin will be flipped.) Notes: The 'trick' to this problem is to realize that you may apply the **law of total probability** (Chapter 5) because the events are **mutually exclusive** (either one coin or another coin is flipped). Let $1T$ be the event that exactly 1 flip results in tails. Let C_1 be the event that the first fair coin is flipped 3 times, C_2 be the event that the second fair coin is flipped 3 times, and let C_3 be the event that the double-tailed coin is flipped 3 times. According to the **law of total probability** (Chapter 5), $P(1T) = P(C_1)P(1T|C_1) + P(C_2)P(1T|C_2) + P(C_3)P(1T|C_3)$. Here, $P(C_1) = P(C_2) = P(C_3) = \frac{1}{3}$ because each coin has the same chance of being picked. Note that $P(1T|C_1) = P(1T|C_2) = \frac{3}{8}$ is the probability that tails will occur in exactly 1 of the 3 flips if the first

or second fair coin is picked (since in that case, 1T occurs if the coin flips are THH, HTH, or HHT, while there are 8 possible outcomes: HHH, HHT, HTH, THH, HTT, THT, TTH, TTT), and $P(1T|C_3) = 0$ because tails has to occur 3 times (not just once) if the double-tailed coin is picked. The law of total probability formula gives: $P(1T) =$ $\left(\frac{1}{3}\right)\left(\frac{3}{8}\right) + \left(\frac{1}{3}\right)\left(\frac{3}{8}\right) + \left(\frac{1}{3}\right)(0) = \frac{1}{8} + \frac{1}{8} + 0 = \frac{2}{8} = \frac{1}{4}$. Similarly, for 2T, for the fair coins, $P(2T|C_1) = P(2T|C_2) = \frac{3}{8}$ (since 2T occurs if the coin flips are TTH, THT, or HTT) and $P(2T|C_3) = 0$ (because tails occurs 3 times, not twice, if the double-tailed coin is picked). For 2T, we get $P(2T) = P(C_1)P(2T|C_1) + P(C_2)P(2T|C_2) + P(C_3)P(2T|C_3) =$ $\left(\frac{1}{3}\right)\left(\frac{3}{8}\right) + \left(\frac{1}{3}\right)\left(\frac{3}{8}\right) + \left(\frac{1}{3}\right)(0) = \frac{1}{8} + \frac{1}{8} + 0 = \frac{2}{8} = \frac{1}{4}$. Similarly, for 3T, for the fair coins, $P(2T|C_1) = P(2T|C_2) = \frac{1}{8}$ (since 3T occurs if the coin flips are TTT) and $P(3T|C_3) = 1$ (because TTT occurs 100% of the time for the double-tailed coin). For 3T, we get $P(3T) = P(C_1)P(3T|C_1) + P(C_2)P(3T|C_2) + P(C_3)P(3T|C_3) = \left(\frac{1}{3}\right)\left(\frac{1}{8}\right) + \left(\frac{1}{3}\right)\left(\frac{1}{8}\right) +$ $\left(\frac{1}{3}\right)(1) = \frac{1}{24} + \frac{1}{24} + \frac{1}{3} = \frac{2}{24} + \frac{4}{12} = \frac{1}{12} + \frac{4}{12} = \frac{5}{12}$. Similarly, for 0T, for the fair coins, $P(0T|C_1) = P(0T|C_2) = \frac{1}{8}$ (since 0T occurs if the coin flips are HHH) and $P(2T|C_3) = 0$ (because tails occurs 3 times, not zero, if the double-tailed coin is picked). For 0T, we get $P(0T) = P(C_1)P(0T|C_1) + P(C_2)P(0T|C_2) + P(C_3)P(0T|C_3) = \left(\frac{1}{3}\right)\left(\frac{1}{8}\right) + \left(\frac{1}{3}\right)\left(\frac{1}{8}\right) +$ $\left(\frac{1}{3}\right)(0) = \frac{1}{24} + \frac{1}{24} + 0 = \frac{2}{24} = \frac{1}{12}$. Observe that $\frac{1}{4} + \frac{1}{4} + \frac{5}{12} + \frac{1}{12} = \frac{1}{2} + \frac{1}{2} = 1$. For the last question, use **Baye's theorem** (Chapter 5):

$$P(3T|C_3) = \frac{P(C_3)P(3T|C_3)}{P(3T)} = \frac{\left(\frac{1}{3}\right)(1)}{5/12} = \frac{1}{3} \div \frac{5}{12} = \frac{1}{3} \times \frac{12}{5} = \frac{4}{5}$$

(23) P(4 occurs exactly 3 times) = 125/3888 ≈ 0.0322 ≈ 3.22%, P(4 occurs more than 2 occurs) = 223/648 ≈ 0.344 ≈ 34.4%. Notes: Each die has $P(4) = \frac{1}{6}$ and P(N) $= \frac{5}{6}$ where N stands for "not 4." If exactly three 4's occur, it happens with one of 10 structures: 444NN, 44N4N, 44NN4, 4N44N, 4N4N4, 4NN44, N444N, N44N4, N4N44, NN444. For the structure 444NN, the probability is P(444NN) = $P(4)P(4)P(4)P(N)P(N) = \left(\frac{1}{6}\right)\left(\frac{1}{6}\right)\left(\frac{1}{6}\right)\left(\frac{5}{6}\right)\left(\frac{5}{6}\right) = \frac{25}{7776}$. Since there are 10 such

structures, P(4 occurs exactly 3 times) $= 10 \left(\frac{25}{7776}\right) = \frac{250}{7776} = \frac{125}{3888}$. We will first find the probability that 2 and 4 occur the same number of times:

- There are $4^5 = 1024$ permutations with no 2's and no 4's, since each die has 4 possibilities (1, 3, 5, or 6).

- One 2 and one 4 can occur with one of 20 structures: 24NNN, 2N4NN, 2NN4N, 2NNN4, 42NNN, 4N2NN, 4NN2N, 4NNN2, N24NN, N2N4N, N2NN4, N42NN, N4N2N, N4NN2, NN24N, NN2N4, NN42N, NN4N2, NNN24, NNN42. For the structure 24NNN, there are $(4)(4)(4) = 64$ permutations (since each N can be 1, 3, 5, or 6). This makes $(20)(64) = 1280$ permutations.

- Two 2's and two 4's can occur with one of 30 structures: 2244N, 224N4, 22N44, 2424N, 242N4, 24N24, 2442N, 244N2, 24N42, 2N244, 2N424, 2N442, 4224N, 422N4, 42N24, 4242N, 424N2, 42N42, 4422N, 442N2, 44N22, 4N224, 4N242, 4N422, N2244, N2424, N2442, N4224, N4242, N4422. For the structure 2244N, there are 4 permutations (since N can be 1, 3, 5, or 6). This makes $(30)(4) = 120$ permutations.

Add $1024 + 1280 + 120 = 2424$ to get permutations with the same number of 2's as 4's. There are $6^5 = 7776$ possible outcomes for the 5 dice. The probability that there will be the same number of 2's and 4's is P(same number of 2's as 4's) $= \frac{2424}{7776} = \frac{101}{324}$.

Now observe that:

P(same number of 2's as 4's) + P(more 4's than 2's) + P(more 2's than 4's) = 1

Of the permutations where the number of 2's and 4's differ, it is just as likely for there to be more 2's as it is for there to be more 4's. Therefore, P(more 4's than 2's) = P(more 2's than 4's). The previous equation becomes:

$$P(\text{same number of 2's as 4's}) + 2\,P(\text{more 4's than 2's}) = 1$$

$$2\,P(\text{more 4's than 2's}) = 1 - P(\text{same number of 2's as 4's})$$

$$2\,P(\text{more 4's than 2's}) = 1 - \frac{101}{324} = \frac{223}{324} \text{ (now divide by 2 on both sides)}$$

$$P(\text{more 4's than 2's}) = \frac{1}{2}\left(\frac{223}{324}\right) = \frac{223}{648}$$

Alternate solution: There are $6^5 = 7776$ possible outcomes. If the first 3 dice are all 4's, there are 25 permutations of the form 444XY that have exactly three 4's. Here, X and Y can each be 1, 2, 3, 5, or 6 (and it's okay if X and Y are the same in this case because

44422, for example, meets the criteria), and $(5)(5) = 25$. There are 10 structures with exactly three 4's: 444XY, 44X4Y, 44XY4, 4X44Y, 4X4Y4, 4XY44, X444Y, X44Y4, X4Y44, XY444. (Note that 444YX would be the same as 444XY since X and Y are the same possible values.) There are $(25)(10)$ permutations with exactly three 4's. This gives P(4 occurs exactly 3 times) $= \frac{250}{7776} = \frac{125}{3888}$. For 4 to occur more than 2 occurs:

- One 4 and zero 2's can occur with one of the following 5 structures: 4NNNN, N4NNN, NN4NN, NNN4N, NNNN4. For the structure 4NNNN, there are $4^4 = 256$ permutations (since each N is a 1, 3, 5, or 6). This makes $(5)(256) = 1280$ permutations.

- Two 4's and zero 2's can occur with one of the following 10 structures: 44NNN, 4N4NN, 4NN4N, 4NNN4, N44NN, N4N4N, N4NN4, NN44N, NN4N4, NNN44. For the structure 44NNN, there are $4^3 = 64$ permutations (since each N is a 1, 3, 5, or 6). This makes $(10)(64) = 640$ permutations.

- Two 4's and one 2 can occur with one of the following 30 structures: 244NN, 24N4N, 24NN4, 2N44N, 2N4N4, 2NN44, 424NN, 42N4N, 42NN4, 442NN, 44N2N, 44NN2, 4N24N, 4N2N4, 4N42N, 4N4N2, 4NN24, 4NN42, N244N, N24N4, N2N44, N424N, N42N4, N442N, N44N2, N4N24, N4N42, NN244, NN424, NN442. For the structure 244NN, there are $4^2 = 16$ permutations (since each N is a 1, 3, 5, or 6). This makes $(30)(16) = 480$ permutations.

- Three 4's and zero 2's can occur with one of the following 10 structures: 444NN, 44N4N, 44NN4, 4N44N, 4N4N4, 4NN44, N444N, N44N4, N4NN4, NN444. For the structure 444NN, there are $4^2 = 16$ permutations (since each N is a 1, 3, 5, or 6). This makes $(10)(16) = 160$ permutations.

- Three 4's and one 2 can occur with one of the following 20 structures: 2444N, 244N4, 24N44, 2N444, 4244N, 424N4, 42N44, 4424N, 442N4, 4442N, 444N2, 44N24, 44N42, 4N244, 4N424, 4N442, N2444, N4244, N4424, N4442. For each structure, there are 4 permutations (since N can be 1, 3, 5, or 6). This makes $(20)(4) = 80$ permutations.

- There are 10 permutations with three 4's and two 2's: 22444, 24244, 24424, 24442, 42244, 42424, 42442, 44224, 44242, 44422.

- Four 4's and zero 2's can occur with one of the following 5 structures: 4444N,

444N4, 44N44, 4N444, N4444. For each structure, there are 4 permutations (since N can be 1, 3, 5, or 6). This makes $(5)(4) = 20$ permutations.

- There are 5 permutations with four 4's and one 2: 24444, 42444, 44244, 44424, 44442.
- There is 1 permutation with five 4's and zero 2's: 44444.

Add $1280 + 640 + 480 + 160 + 80 + 10 + 20 + 5 + 1 = 2676$ to find the number of ways there can be more 4's than 2's, such that P(more 4's than 2's) $= \frac{2676}{7776} = \frac{223}{648}$.

(24) P(only 2's and/or 5's) $= 1/8 = 0.125 = 12.5\%$, P(sum=12) $= 227/1728 \approx$ $0.131 \approx 13.1\%$. Notes: There are 8 permutations that only involve two's and fives: 222, 225, 252, 255, 522, 525, 552, 555. Since $P(2) = P(5) = 1/4$, each permutation has a probability of $\left(\frac{1}{4}\right)\left(\frac{1}{4}\right)\left(\frac{1}{4}\right) = \frac{1}{64}$. Multiply by 8 since there are 8 such permutations. This gives P(only 2's or 5's) $= \frac{8}{64} = \frac{1}{8}$. The sum can be 12 the following ways:

- $P(156) = P(165) = P(516) = P(561) = P(615) = P(651) = \left(\frac{1}{12}\right)\left(\frac{1}{4}\right)\left(\frac{1}{12}\right) = \frac{1}{576}$. Add these to get P(1,5,6, any order) $= \frac{6}{576} = \frac{1}{96}$.
- $P(246) = P(264) = P(426) = P(462) = P(624) = P(642) = \left(\frac{1}{4}\right)\left(\frac{1}{6}\right)\left(\frac{1}{12}\right) = \frac{1}{288}$. Add these to get P(2,4,6, any order) $= \frac{6}{288} = \frac{1}{48}$.
- $P(255) = P(525) = P(552) = \left(\frac{1}{4}\right)\left(\frac{1}{4}\right)\left(\frac{1}{4}\right) = \frac{1}{64}$. Add these to get P(2,5,5, any order) $= \frac{3}{64}$.
- $P(336) = P(363) = P(633) = \left(\frac{1}{6}\right)\left(\frac{1}{6}\right)\left(\frac{1}{12}\right) = \frac{1}{432}$. Add these to get P(3,3,6, any order) $= \frac{3}{432} = \frac{1}{144}$.
- $P(345) = P(354) = P(435) = P(453) = P(534) = P(543) = \left(\frac{1}{6}\right)\left(\frac{1}{6}\right)\left(\frac{1}{4}\right) = \frac{1}{144}$. Add these to get P(3,4,5, any order) $= \frac{6}{144} = \frac{1}{24}$.
- $P(444) = \left(\frac{1}{6}\right)\left(\frac{1}{6}\right)\left(\frac{1}{6}\right) = \frac{1}{216}$.

Add these to get P(sum=12) $= \frac{1}{96} + \frac{1}{48} + \frac{3}{64} + \frac{1}{144} + \frac{1}{24} + \frac{1}{216} = \frac{18+36+81+12+72+8}{1728} = \frac{227}{1728}$. (We found a common denominator of 1728. Note that $\frac{3}{64} = \frac{3(27)}{64(27)} = \frac{81}{1728}$.)

(25) $P(>3452) = 365/648 \approx 0.563 \approx 56.3\%$. Notes: A number greater than 3452 can arise the following ways:

- If the red die (thousands place) is 4 or higher, the number will definitely be larger than 3452. The probability that the red die will be 4 or higher is $P(\geq 4)$ $\frac{3}{6} = \frac{1}{2}$ (since 4, 5, and 6 are half of its possible outcomes).

- The number will be larger than 3452 if the red die (thousands place) is a 3 and the blue die (hundreds place) is a 5 or higher. The probability for this is $P(R = 3 \cap B \geq 5) = P(3)P(\geq 5) = \left(\frac{1}{6}\right)\left(\frac{2}{6}\right) = \left(\frac{1}{6}\right)\left(\frac{1}{3}\right) = \frac{1}{18}$ (since the 5 and 6 are one-third of the blue die's possible outcomes).

- The number will be larger than 3452 if the red die (thousands place) is a 3, the blue die (hundreds place) is a 4, and the yellow die (tens place) is a 6. The probability for this is $P(R = 3 \cap B = 4 \cap Y = 6) = P(3)P(4)P(6) = \left(\frac{1}{6}\right)\left(\frac{1}{6}\right)\left(\frac{1}{6}\right) = \frac{1}{216}$.

- The number will be larger than 3452 if the red die (thousands place) is a 3, the blue die (hundreds place) is a 4, the yellow die (tens place) is a 5, and the gray die (units place) is a 3 or higher. The probability for this is $P(R = 3 \cap B = 4 \cap Y = 5 \cap G \geq 3) = P(3)P(4)P(5)P(\geq 3) = \left(\frac{1}{6}\right)\left(\frac{1}{6}\right)\left(\frac{1}{6}\right)\left(\frac{2}{3}\right) = \frac{2}{648} = \frac{1}{324}$ (since 3, 4, 5, and 6 are two-thirds of the gray die's possible outcomes).

Add these to get $P(>3452) = \frac{1}{2} + \frac{1}{18} + \frac{1}{216} + \frac{1}{324} = \frac{324+36+3+2}{648} = \frac{365}{648}$.

Alternate solution: There are $6^4 = 1296$ possible outcomes. The following numbers are greater than 3452:

- All the outcomes in the 4000's. These start at 4111 and end at 6666 (and only include numbers with digits 1, 2, 3, 4, 5, 6). There are $(3)(6)(6)(6) = 648$ such outcomes (since the first digit is a 4, 5, or 6 and the other digits each have 6 choices).

- All the outcomes in the 3500's and 3600's. There are $(1)(2)(6)(6) = 72$ such outcomes (since the first digit has one choice, the second digit can be a 5 or 6, and the other digits each have 6 choices).

- All the outcomes in the 3460's. There are $(1)(1)(1)(6) = 6$ such choices: 3461, 3462, 3463, 3464, 3465, 3466.

- The 4 outcomes 3453, 3454, 3455, 3456.

Add these to get $648 + 72 + 6 + 4 = 730$. This gives $P(>3452) = \frac{730}{1296} = \frac{365}{648}$.

(26) $P(\text{B beats G}) = 7/12 \approx 0.583 \approx 58.3\%$, $P(\text{G beats R}) = 2/3 \approx 0.667 \approx 66.7\%$, $P(\text{R beats B}) = 5/9 \approx 0.556 \approx 55.6\%$, these are called **nontransitive** dice (see the note at the end). Notes: Following are ways that the blue die can beat the green die:

- If the blue die shows 3 and the green die shows 2, the blue die wins. The probability for this is $P(3 \cap 2) = \left(\frac{5}{6}\right)\left(\frac{3}{6}\right) = \frac{15}{36} = \frac{5}{12}$.

- If the blue die shows 6, the blue die wins. The probability for this is $P(6) = \frac{1}{6}$.

Since these events are **mutually exclusive** (Chapter 5), since that they can't both occur at the same time, $P(\text{B beats G}) = P(3 \cap 2) + P(6) = \frac{5}{12} + \frac{1}{6} = \frac{5}{12} + \frac{2}{12} = \frac{7}{12}$.

Following are ways that the green die can beat the red die:

- If the green die shows 2 and the red die shows 1, the green die wins. The probability for this is $P(2 \cap 1) = \left(\frac{3}{6}\right)\left(\frac{2}{6}\right) = \frac{6}{36} = \frac{1}{6}$.

- If the green die shows 5, the green die wins. The probability for this is $P(5) = \frac{3}{6} = \frac{1}{2}$.

Since these events are mutually exclusive, $P(\text{G beats R}) = P(2 \cap 1) + P(5) = \frac{1}{6} + \frac{1}{2} = \frac{1}{6} + \frac{3}{6} = \frac{4}{6} = \frac{2}{3}$. The only way that the red die can beat the blue die is if the red die shows 4 and the blue die shows 3. The probability for this is $P(\text{R beats B}) = \left(\frac{4}{6}\right)\left(\frac{5}{6}\right) = \frac{20}{36} = \frac{5}{9}$.

These dice don't obey the **transitive property**. You may recall the transitive property from algebra; if $x = y$ and $y = z$, it follows that $x = z$. The transitive property also applies to inequalities; if $a > b$ and $b > c$, it follows that $a > c$. Now consider these special dice. Here, blue beats green most of the time (about 58%) and green beats red most of the time (about 67%), yet it turns out the blue doesn't beat red most of the time (rather, red beats blue about 56% of the time). Since these dice don't obey the transitive property, they are called **nontransitive dice**. (These dice are similar in that regard to the game Rock, Paper, Scissors. In that game, rock beats scissors, scissors beats paper, and paper beats rock.) Nontransitive dice and many other cool math ideas can be found in a neat book entitled *Instant Mathematics: Key Thinkers,*

Theories, Discoveries, and Concepts Explained on a Single Page by Paul Parsons and Gail Dixon. (If you compare the nontransitive dice in that example to the problem in this book, note that the third die is different in this book, and therefore the numerical answers are not quite the same.)

Chapter 7

(1) $o = 2{:}1$. Note: $o = \dfrac{2/3}{1/3} = \dfrac{2}{3} \div \dfrac{1}{3} = \dfrac{2}{3} \times \dfrac{3}{1} = \dfrac{2}{1} = 2.$

(2) $o = 1{:}2$. Note: $o = \dfrac{1/3}{2/3} = \dfrac{1}{3} \div \dfrac{2}{3} = \dfrac{1}{3} \times \dfrac{3}{2} = \dfrac{1}{2}.$

(3) $o = 3{:}5$. Note: $o = \dfrac{3/8}{5/8} = \dfrac{3}{8} \div \dfrac{5}{8} = \dfrac{3}{8} \times \dfrac{8}{5} = \dfrac{3}{5}.$

(4) $o = 1{:}3$. Notes: $25\% = \dfrac{25}{100} = \dfrac{1}{4}$ and $o = \dfrac{1/4}{3/4} = \dfrac{1}{4} \div \dfrac{3}{4} = \dfrac{1}{4} \times \dfrac{4}{3} = \dfrac{1}{3}.$

(5) $o = 5{:}1$. Note: $o = \dfrac{5/6}{1/6} = \dfrac{5}{6} \div \dfrac{1}{6} = \dfrac{5}{6} \times \dfrac{6}{1} = \dfrac{5}{1} = 5.$

(6) $o = 4{:}5$. Note: $o = \dfrac{4/9}{5/9} = \dfrac{4}{9} \div \dfrac{5}{9} = \dfrac{4}{9} \times \dfrac{9}{5} = \dfrac{4}{5}.$

Shortcut: Since p and $1 - p$ have the same denominator, the denominators cancel out. So all you really need to do is divide the numerator of p by the numerator of $1 - p$. For example, in Exercise 6, $p = \dfrac{4}{9}$ and $1 - p = \dfrac{5}{9}$; dividing numerators gives $o = \dfrac{4}{5}$.

(7) $p = \dfrac{5}{7}$. Note: $p = \dfrac{5}{5+2} = \dfrac{5}{7}.$

(8) $p = \dfrac{1}{9}$. Note: $p = \dfrac{1}{1+8} = \dfrac{1}{9}.$

(9) $p = \dfrac{4}{15}$. Note: $p = \dfrac{4}{4+11} = \dfrac{4}{15}.$

(10) $p = \dfrac{5}{12}$. Note: $p = \dfrac{5}{5+7} = \dfrac{5}{12}.$

(11) $p = \dfrac{3}{7}$. Note: $p = \dfrac{3}{3+4} = \dfrac{3}{7}.$

(12) $p = \dfrac{7}{10}$. Note: $p = \dfrac{7}{7+3} = \dfrac{7}{10}.$

Chapter 8

(1) P(♦) = 1/4 = 0.25 = 25%, P(face card or ♠) = 11/26 ≈ 0.423 ≈ 42.3%, P(5-9) = 5/13 ≈ 0.385 ≈ 38.5%, P(black) = 1/2 = 0.5 = 50%. Notes: 13 out of 52 cards are diamonds, such that P(♦) = $\frac{13}{52}$ = $\frac{1}{4}$. Since P(face card) and P(♠) aren't mutually exclusive (Chapter 5), P(face card ∪ ♠) = P(face card) + P(♠) − P(face card ∩ ♠) = $\frac{12}{52} + \frac{13}{52} - \left(\frac{12}{52}\right)\left(\frac{13}{52}\right) = \frac{12}{52} + \frac{13}{52} - \left(\frac{3}{13}\right)\left(\frac{1}{4}\right) = \frac{12}{52} + \frac{13}{52} - \frac{3}{52} = \frac{22}{52} = \frac{11}{26}$. Alternatively, there are 13 spades and 9 face cards that aren't spades (3 hearts, 3 diamonds, and 3 clubs): 13 + 9 = 22. This gives P(face card ∪ ♠) = $\frac{22}{52} = \frac{11}{26}$. There are 5 values in the range 5-9 (recall Chapter 3): 5, 6, 7, 8, and 9. Each value comes in 4 suits. Multiply: (5)(4) = 20. This gives P(5-9) = $\frac{20}{52} = \frac{5}{13}$. One-half of the cards are ♠'s or ♣'s, such that P(black) = $\frac{26}{52} = \frac{1}{2}$.

(2) P(pair) = 1/17 ≈ 0.0588 ≈ 5.88%, P(both ♣'s) = 1/17 ≈ 0.0588 ≈ 5.88%, P(a ♥ and a ♣, any order) = 13/102 ≈ 0.127 ≈ 12.7%. Notes: There are $\binom{52}{2} = \frac{52!}{2!50!} = \frac{(52)(51)}{2} = 1326$ ways to choose 2 out of 52 cards. There are $\binom{13}{1}\binom{4}{2} = \frac{13!}{1!12!}\frac{4!}{2!2!} = (13)(6) = 78$ ways to make a pair of matching values (like two 6's or two Q's), there are $\binom{13}{2} = \frac{13!}{2!11!} = \frac{(13)(12)}{2} = 78$ ways to choose 2 out of 13 clubs, and there are $\binom{13}{1}\binom{13}{1} = (13)(13) = 169$ ways to choose 1 out of 13 hearts and 1 out of 13 clubs. This gives P(pair) = P(both ♣'s) = $\frac{78}{1326} = \frac{1}{17}$ and P(a ♥ and a ♣, any order) = $\frac{169}{1326} = \frac{13}{102}$. Note: If you're not confident with a result, sometimes it helps to work out a simpler case. For example, in this problem, some students are surprised that the probability of drawing one ♣ and one ♥ is more than double the probability of drawing two ♣'s. There are 13 ♣'s and 13 ♥'s to choose from when you get one of each; there are 13 ♣'s and then 12 ♣'s the second time to choose from when you get two ♣'s. Why are you more than twice as likely to get one ♣ and one ♥ as you are to get two ♣'s? If you're not seeing the 'why' here, try working out a simpler case. Let's use a deck with just 12 cards, where each suit just has the cards 2, 3, and 4. There are $\binom{12}{2} = \frac{12!}{2!10!} = \frac{(12)(11)}{2} = 66$

ways to choose 2 cards. There are $\binom{3}{2} = \frac{3!}{2!1!} = 3$ ways to choose 2 clubs. Here, it is easy to see that these are 1♣2♣, 1♣3♣, and 2♣3♣. There are $\binom{3}{1}\binom{3}{1} = (3)(3) = 9$ ways to choose 1 club and 1 heart. Here, it is easy to see that these are 1♣1♥, 1♣2♥, 1♣3♥, 2♣1♥, 2♣2♥, 2♣3♥, 3♣1♥, 3♣2♥, and 3♣3♥. Now it is easy to understand 'why' a club and heart is more than twice as likely as 2 clubs. First, 1♣2♥ and 2♣1♥ are different combinations because they involve different cards, whereas 1♣2♣ is the same combination as 2♣1♣ because they are the same two cards. Second, you can have the same value with two different suits, like 2♣2♥, but not in the same suit (because you'd have to draw the same card twice to make 2♣2♣). Back to the full deck, 13 ♣'s and 13 ♥'s have 26 cards to choose from, whereas 13 ♣'s and 12 ♣'s really involve only the same 13 cards.

Alternate solution: The probability that the second card will have the same value as the first card is $P(\text{pair}) = \frac{3}{51} = \frac{1}{17}$ (since there are 3 cards with the same value as the first card and 51 cards remain in the deck). The probability of drawing 2 clubs is $P(\text{both ♣'s}) = \frac{13}{52}\frac{12}{51} = \frac{156}{2652} = \frac{1}{17}$ (since 12 clubs remain after drawing the first club). The probability of drawing a ♥ first and then a ♣ is $\frac{13}{52}\frac{13}{51} = \frac{169}{2652} = \frac{13}{204}$ and the probability of drawing a ♣ first and then a ♥ is $\frac{13}{52}\frac{13}{51} = \frac{13}{204}$, such that $P(\text{a ♥ and a ♣, any order}) = \frac{13}{204} + \frac{13}{204} = \frac{13}{102}$.

(3) $P(\text{both black}) = 25/102 \approx 0.245 \approx 24.5\%$, $P(\text{both face cards}) = 11/221 \approx 0.0498 \approx 4.98\%$, $P(\text{red face card, black ace, any order}) = 2/221 \approx 0.00905 \approx 0.905\%$. Notes: There are $\binom{52}{2} = \frac{52!}{2!50!} = \frac{(52)(51)}{2} = 1326$ ways to choose 2 out of 52 cards. There are $\binom{26}{2} = \frac{26!}{2!24!} = \frac{(26)(25)}{2} = 325$ ways to choose 2 out of 26 black cards. There are 12 face cards (J, Q, and K of each suit); there are $\binom{12}{2} = \frac{12!}{2!10!} = \frac{(12)(11)}{2} = 66$ ways to choose 2 out of 12 face cards. There are 6 red face cards (J, Q, and K of hearts and diamonds) and 2 black aces (A♠ and A♣); there are $\binom{6}{1}\binom{2}{1} = (6)(2) = 12$ combinations with one of each. This gives $P(\text{both black}) = \frac{325}{1326} = \frac{25}{102}$, $P(\text{both face cards}) \frac{66}{1326} = \frac{11}{221}$, and $P(\text{red face card, black ace, any order}) = \frac{12}{1326} = \frac{2}{221}$.

Alternate solution: The probability that the first card is black is $\frac{26}{52} = \frac{1}{2}$; the probability that the second card is also black is $\frac{25}{51}$. The probability that the first card is a face card is $\frac{12}{52} = \frac{3}{13}$; the probability that the second card is also a face card is $\frac{11}{51}$. The probability that the first card is a red face card is $\frac{6}{52} = \frac{3}{26}$; the probability that the second card is a black ace is $\frac{2}{51}$. The probability that the first card is a black ace is $\frac{2}{52} = \frac{1}{26}$; the probability that the second card is a red face card is $\frac{6}{51} = \frac{2}{17}$. This gives P(both black) $= \left(\frac{1}{2}\right)\left(\frac{25}{51}\right) = \frac{25}{102}$, P(both face cards) $\left(\frac{3}{13}\right)\left(\frac{11}{51}\right) = \frac{11}{221}$, and P(red face card, black ace, any order) $= \left(\frac{3}{26}\right)\left(\frac{2}{51}\right) + \left(\frac{1}{26}\right)\left(\frac{2}{17}\right) = \frac{1}{221} + \frac{1}{221} = \frac{2}{221}$.

(4) P(pair) = 1/13 ≈ 0.0769 ≈ 7.69%, P(both ♣'s) = 1/16 = 0.0625 = 6.25%, P(a ♥ and a ♣, any order) = 1/8 = 0.125 = 12.5%. Notes: With **replacement**, there are 52 cards in the deck for each selection. In Chapter 4, we learned that we should work with permutations (not combinations) when the first card is placed back into the deck. There are (52)(52) = 2704 permutations with 2 cards. There are (4)(4) = 16 permutations with 2 aces. Since a pair can be made with any of 13 different values, there are (16)(13) = 208 permutations that make a pair. There are (13)(13) = 169 permutations with 2 clubs. There are (13)(13) = 169 permutations with a heart and then a club, and (13)(13) = 169 permutations with a club and then a heart; this makes 169 + 169 = 338 permutations with a heart and club in any order. This gives P(pair) $= \frac{208}{2704} = \frac{1}{13}$, P(both ♣'s) $= \frac{169}{2704} = \frac{1}{16}$, and P(a ♥ and a ♣, any order) $= \frac{338}{2704} = \frac{1}{8}$.

Alternate solution: Whatever the value of the first card is, since all 52 cards are still in the deck, the probability that the second card will have the same value as the first card is P(pair) $= \frac{1}{13}$. Since each card has a probability of $\frac{1}{4}$ of being a club, P(both ♣'s) $= \left(\frac{1}{4}\right)\left(\frac{1}{4}\right) = \frac{1}{16}$. Similarly, the probability of a heart first and then a club is $\frac{1}{16}$ and the probability of a club first and then a heart is $\frac{1}{16}$, such that P(a ♥ and a ♣, any order) $= \frac{1}{16} + \frac{1}{16} = \frac{1}{8}$. When the first card is placed back in the deck, **replacement** makes this form of the solution simpler.

(5) P(run of 3, same color) = 12/5525 ≈ 0.00217 ≈ 0.217%, P(set of 3) = 1/425 ≈ 0.00235 ≈ 0.235%. Notes: There are $\binom{52}{3} = \frac{52!}{3!49!} = \frac{(52)(51)(50)}{6} = 22{,}100$ ways to choose 3 out of 52 cards. There are $\binom{12}{1}\binom{4}{1} = \frac{12!}{1!11!}\frac{4!}{1!3!} = (12)(4) = 48$ ways to make a same-color run of 3 cards. (Why? In one suit, there are 12 runs: A-2-3, 2-3-4, 3-4-5, 4-5-6, 5-6-7, 6-7-8, 7-8-9, 8-9-10, 9-10-J, 10-J-Q, J-Q-K, Q-K-A. The note in the problem states that A-2-3 and Q-K-A are both acceptable for this problem. Multiply by 4 for the four different suits.) There are $\binom{13}{1}\binom{4}{3} = \frac{13!}{1!12!}\frac{4!}{3!1!} = (13)(4) = 52$ ways to make a set of 3. This gives P(run of 3, same color) $= \frac{48}{22{,}100} = \frac{12}{5525}$ and P(set of 3) $= \frac{52}{22{,}100} = \frac{1}{425}$.

Alternate solution: There are $\binom{52}{3} = \frac{52!}{3!49!} = \frac{(52)(51)(50)}{6} = 22{,}100$ ways to choose 3 out of 52 cards. In one suit, there are 12 runs: A-2-3, 2-3-4, 3-4-5, 4-5-6, 5-6-7, 6-7-8, 7-8-9, 8-9-10, 9-10-J, 10-J-Q, J-Q-K, Q-K-A. Multiply by 4 suits to get (12)(4) = 48 same-color runs of 3. This gives P(run of 3, same color) $= \frac{48}{22{,}100} = \frac{12}{5525}$. The probability that all 3 cards have the same value is P(set of 3) $= \frac{3}{51}\frac{2}{50} = \frac{6}{2550} = \frac{1}{425}$ (since 3 matching cards remain after the first selection and 2 remain after the second selection).

(6) P(all ♦'s) = 11/850 ≈ 0.0129 ≈ 1.29%, P(one pair plus one different card) = 72/425 ≈ 0.169 ≈ 16.9%. Notes: There are $\binom{52}{3} = \frac{52!}{3!49!} = \frac{(52)(51)(50)}{6} = 22{,}100$ ways to choose 3 out of 52 cards. There are $\binom{13}{3} = \frac{13!}{3!10!} = \frac{(13)(12)(11)}{6} = 286$ ways to choose 3 out of 13 diamonds. This gives P(all ♦'s) $= \frac{286}{22{,}100} = \frac{11}{850}$. To make one pair, be sure to account for the third card of a different value. There are $\binom{13}{1}\binom{4}{2}\binom{12}{1}\binom{4}{1} = \frac{13!}{1!12!}\frac{4!}{2!2!}\frac{12!}{1!11!}\frac{4!}{1!3!} = (13)(6)(12)(4) = 3744$ ways to choose one pair. (The first part, $\binom{13}{1}\binom{4}{2}$ chooses 2 of the 4 suits that for 1 of 13 values. The second part, $\binom{12}{1}\binom{4}{1}$, chooses 1 of the 4 suits that for 1 of 12 values different from the first pair.) This gives P(one pair plus one different card) $= \frac{3744}{22{,}100} = \frac{72}{425}$.

Alternate solution: The probability that all 3 cards are diamonds is P(all ♦'s) =

$\frac{13}{52}\frac{12}{51}\frac{11}{50} = \frac{1716}{132,600} = \frac{11}{850}$. The probability that the second card matches the first card

while the third card is different is $\frac{3}{51}\frac{48}{50} = \frac{144}{2550} = \frac{24}{425}$ (since 3 cards match the value of

the first card while 48 cards don't). Alternatively, the first and third cards could

match, or the second and third cards could match, such that P(one pair plus one

different card) $= \frac{24}{425} + \frac{24}{425} + \frac{24}{425} = \frac{72}{425}$.

(7) P(run of 4, same color) $= 44/270,725 \approx 0.000163 \approx 0.0163\%$, P(set of 4) $=$

$1/20,825 \approx 0.0000480 \approx 0.00480\%$. Notes: This is very similar to the solution to

Problem 5. There are $\binom{52}{4} = \frac{52!}{4!48!} = \frac{(52)(51)(50)(49)}{24} = 270,725$ ways to choose 4 out of

52 cards. There are $\binom{11}{1}\binom{4}{1} = \frac{11!}{1!11!}\frac{4!}{1!3!} = (11)(4) = 44$ ways to make a same-color run

of 4 cards. (Why? In one suit, there are 11 runs: A-2-3-4, 2-3-4-5, 3-4-5-6, 4-5-6-7, 5-6-

7-8, 6-7-8-9, 7-8-9-10, 8-9-10-J, 9-10-J-Q, 10-J-Q-K, J-Q-K-A. The note in the problem

states that A-2-3-4 and J-Q-K-A are both acceptable for this problem. Multiply by 4 for

the four different suits.) There are $\binom{13}{1}\binom{4}{4} = \frac{13!}{1!12!}\frac{4!}{4!0!} = (13)(1) = 13$ ways to make a

set of 4. This gives P(run of 4, same color) $= \frac{44}{270,725}$ and P(set of 4) $= \frac{13}{270,725} = \frac{1}{20,825}$.

(8) P(2 jokers) $= 1/1431 \approx 0.000699 \approx 0.0699\%$, P(1 joker) $= 104/1431 \approx$

$0.0727 \approx 7.27\%$, P(pair) $= 61/477 \approx 0.128 \approx 12.8\%$. Notes: There are $\binom{54}{2} =$

$\frac{54!}{2!52!} = \frac{(54)(53)}{2} = 1431$ ways to choose 2 out of 54 cards. There is $\binom{2}{2} = 1$ way to

choose 2 out of 2 jokers, such that P(2 jokers) $= \frac{1}{1431}$. There are $\binom{2}{1}\binom{52}{1} =$

$(2)(52) = 104$ ways to choose 1 out of 2 jokers and 1 out of 52 other cards, such

that P(1 joker) $= \frac{104}{1431}$. A pair could be made with or without jokers as follows:

- Without jokers, there are $\binom{13}{1}\binom{4}{2} = \frac{13!}{1!12!}\frac{4!}{2!2!} = (13)(6) = 78$ ways to choose

  2 cards of the same value.

- We already found that there are 104 ways to choose 1 out of 2 jokers. With

  the joker being a wildcard, this makes a pair.

- We already found that there is 1 way to choose both jokers. With the jokers

  being wild, this makes a pair.

Add to get $78 + 104 + 1 = 183$ ways to make a pair, such that P(pair) $= \frac{183}{1431} = \frac{61}{477}$.

Alternate solution: The probability that the first card is a joker is $\frac{2}{54}$ and the probability that the second card is also a joker is $\frac{1}{53}$, such that P(2 jokers) $= \left(\frac{2}{54}\right)\left(\frac{1}{53}\right) = \frac{1}{1431}$. The probability of first drawing a joker and then a different card is $\left(\frac{2}{54}\right)\left(\frac{52}{53}\right) = \frac{52}{1431}$ and the probability of drawing a regular card and then a joker is $\left(\frac{52}{54}\right)\left(\frac{2}{53}\right) = \frac{52}{1431}$, such that P(1 joker) $= \frac{52}{1431} + \frac{52}{1431} = \frac{104}{1431}$. The probability that the first card is an ace is $\frac{4}{54}$ and the probability that the second card is also an ace is $\frac{3}{53}$, such that the probability that both cards are aces is $\left(\frac{4}{54}\right)\left(\frac{3}{53}\right) = \frac{2}{477}$. Multiply by 13 since the pair could be made with any value: $(13)\left(\frac{2}{477}\right) = \frac{26}{477}$. Add this to the probabilities of getting one or two jokers to get P(pair) $= \frac{26}{477} + \frac{104}{1431} + \frac{1}{1431} = \frac{183}{1431} = \frac{61}{477}$.

(9) P(2 pairs, but not 4 of a kind) $= 216/20{,}825 \approx 0.0104 \approx 1.04\%$. Notes: There are $\binom{52}{4} = \frac{52!}{4!48!} = \frac{(52)(51)(50)(49)}{24} = 270{,}725$ ways to choose 4 out of 52 cards. There are $\binom{13}{2}\binom{4}{2}\binom{4}{2} = \frac{13!}{2!11!}\frac{4!}{2!2!}\frac{4!}{2!2!} = (78)(6)(6) = 2808$ ways to choose two different pairs. The $\binom{13}{2}$ chooses 2 out of 13 values; these are the values for the 2 pairs. Each $\binom{4}{2}$ chooses 2 out of 4 suits for each pair. This gives P(2 pairs, but not 4 of a kind) $= \frac{2808}{270{,}725} = \frac{216}{20{,}825}$.

Alternate solution: There are $\binom{52}{4} = \frac{52!}{4!48!} = \frac{(52)(51)(50)(49)}{24} = 270{,}725$ ways to choose 4 out of 52 cards. There are 6 ways to make a pair of aces: There are $\binom{4}{2} = \frac{4!}{2!2!} = 6$ ways to choose 2 out of 4 aces: A♥A♦, A♥A♠, A♥A♣, A♦A♠, A♦A♣, A♠A♣. Multiply by 13 to get $(6)(13) = 78$ ways to make the first pair. There are $\binom{4}{2} = \frac{4!}{2!2!} = 6$ ways to choose 2 out of 4 two's: 2♥2♦, 2♥2♠, 2♥2♣, 2♦2♠, 2♦2♣, 2♠2♣. Multiply by 12 (because we want a different value from the first pair) to get $(6)(12) = 72$ ways to make the second pair. Beware that multiplying 78 by 72 will give us **twice** as many answers as we want. (We encountered a similar issue in the alternate solution to Example 3.) Why? If the first pair is made with 9's and the second pair is made with 5's, this is a duplicate of when the first pair is made with 5's and the second pair is made with 9's. So we will divide by 2 after multiplying $(78)(72)$ to correct for double counting: There are $\frac{(78)(72)}{2} = 2808$ ways to make two pairs. This gives P(2 pairs, but not 4 of a kind) $= \frac{2808}{270,725} = \frac{216}{20,825}$.

(10) P(straight, but not a flush) $= 396/38,675 \approx 0.0102 \approx 1.02\%$. Notes: There are $\binom{52}{4} = \frac{52!}{4!48!} = \frac{(52)(51)(50)(49)}{24} = 270,725$ ways to choose 4 out of 52 cards. There are $\binom{11}{1}\binom{4}{1}\binom{4}{1}\binom{4}{1}\binom{4}{1} = (11)(4)^4 = 2816$ ways to make a straight with 4 cards, allowing the ace to be low or high (just as in Poker). The $\binom{11}{1}$ comes from the 11 ways to make a run of 4 cards: A-2-3-4, 2-3-4-5, 3-4-5-6, 4-5-6-7, 5-6-7-8, 6-7-8-9, 7-8-9-10, 8-9-10-J, 9-10-J-Q, 10-J-Q-K, J-Q-K-A. The four $\binom{4}{1}$'s choose one suit for each card. However, this includes straight flushes, and the problem asks for us to subtract out the straight flushes. There are $\binom{11}{1}\binom{4}{1} = (11)(4) = 44$ straight (and royal) flushes. Subtract to get $2816 - 44 = 2772$ flushes that aren't straight (or royal). This gives P(straight, but not a flush) $= \frac{2772}{270,725} = \frac{396}{38,675}$.

Alternate solution: There are $\binom{52}{4} = \frac{52!}{4!48!} = \frac{(52)(51)(50)(49)}{24} = 270,725$ ways to choose 4 out of 52 cards. There are 11 ways to make a run of 4 cards: A-2-3-4, 2-3-4-5, 3-4-5-6, 4-5-6-7, 5-6-7-8, 6-7-8-9, 7-8-9-10, 8-9-10-J, 9-10-J-Q, 10-J-Q-K, J-Q-K-A. For each run, each of the 4 cards can be one of 4 different suits, so that there are $(4)(4)(4)(4) = 256$ ways to make each run of 4 cards. Multiply $(11)(256) = 2816$ to get the total number of straights, including straight flushes. For each run, there are 4 straight (or royal) flushes (one for each suit), such that $(11)(4) = 44$ is the number of straight (or royal) flushes. Subtract to get $2816 - 44 = 2772$ flushes that aren't straight (or royal). This gives P(straight, but not a flush) $= \frac{2772}{270,725} = \frac{396}{38,675}$.

(11) P(set of 3) $= 1/253 \approx 0.00395 \approx 0.395\%$, P(sum=21) $= 37/2024 \approx 0.0183 \approx 1.83\%$, P($\blacktriangle$, $\blacksquare$, $\bullet$, any order) $= 64/253 \approx 0.253 \approx 25.3\%$. Notes: There are $\binom{24}{3} = \frac{24!}{3!21!} = \frac{(24)(23)(22)}{6} = 2024$ ways to choose 3 out of 24 cards. There are $\binom{8}{1}\binom{3}{3} =$

$\frac{8!}{1!7!}\frac{3!}{3!0!} = (8)(1) = 8$ ways to make a set of 3. This gives P(set of 3) $= \frac{8}{2024} = \frac{1}{253}$. A sum of 21 can be made the following ways:

- 7+7+7=21 has 1 combination: 7▲7■7●.
- 8+7+6=21 has 3 one-suit combinations (8▲7▲6▲, 8■7■6■, 8●7●6●), 6 ▲-■ combinations (8▲7▲6■, 8▲7■6▲, 8■7▲6▲, 8■7■6▲, 8■7▲6■, 8▲7■6■), 6 ▲-● combinations (8▲7▲6●, 8▲7●6▲, 8●7▲6▲, 8●7●6▲, 8●7▲6●, 8▲7●6●), 6 ●-■ combinations (8●7●6■, 8●7■6●, 8■7●6●, 8■7■6●, 8■7●6■, 8●7■6■), and 6 ▲-■-● combinations (8▲7■6●, 8▲7●6■, 8■7▲6●, 8■7●6▲, 8●7▲6■, 8●7■6▲).
- 8+8+5=21 has 9 combinations: 8▲8■5▲, 8▲8●5▲, 8■8●5▲, 8▲8■5■, 8▲8●5■, 8■8●5■, 8▲8■5●, 8▲8●5●, 8■8●5●.

Add to get $1 + 3 + 6 + 6 + 6 + 6 + 9 = 37$ combinations with a sum of 21, such that P(sum=21) $= \frac{37}{2024}$. There are $\binom{8}{1}\binom{8}{1}\binom{8}{1} = (8)(8)(8) = 512$ ways to choose one card from each suit, such that P(a ▲, a ■, a ●, any order) $= \frac{512}{2024} = \frac{64}{253}$.

Note: The easy way to find that there are 27 combinations with 8+7+6 is to realize that each card can be one of 3 suits, such that $(3)(3)(3) = 27$.

Alternate solution: The probability that each card is a 1 is $\left(\frac{3}{24}\right)\left(\frac{2}{23}\right)\left(\frac{1}{22}\right) = \frac{1}{2024}$. Multiply by 8 since each card could be a 2, 3, 4, etc.: P(set of 3) $= \frac{8}{2024} = \frac{1}{253}$. A sum of 21 can be made the following ways:

- The probability of 7+7+7=21 is $\left(\frac{3}{24}\right)\left(\frac{2}{23}\right)\left(\frac{1}{22}\right) = \frac{1}{2024}$.
- The probability that the first card is an 8, 7, or 6 is $\frac{9}{24}$ (since there are three 8's, three 7's, and three 6's). The probability that the second card is an 8, 7, or 6 but not the same as the first card is $\frac{6}{23}$ (there are 3 fewer options than the first card so that the second card doesn't match the first card; for example, if the first card is an 8, the second card can be one of three 7's or three 6's). The probability that the third card is an 8, 7, or 6 but not the same as either of the first two cards is $\frac{3}{22}$ (for example, if the first two cards are an 8 and 6, then the third card must be a 7). The probability of 8+7+6=21 in any order is $\left(\frac{9}{24}\right)\left(\frac{6}{23}\right)\left(\frac{3}{22}\right) = \frac{27}{2024}$.

- The probability of 8+8+5=21 in any order is $\left(\frac{3}{24}\right)\left(\frac{2}{23}\right)\left(\frac{3}{22}\right) + \left(\frac{3}{24}\right)\left(\frac{3}{23}\right)\left(\frac{2}{22}\right) +$

$\left(\frac{3}{24}\right)\left(\frac{3}{23}\right)\left(\frac{2}{22}\right) = \frac{18+18+18}{12,144} = \frac{9}{2024}$ (since there are three 8's and three 5's and

since the 5 could come third, second, or first; after one 8 is drawn, 2 remain).

Add to get $P(\text{sum}=21) = \frac{1}{2024} + \frac{27}{2024} + \frac{9}{2024} = \frac{37}{2024}$. The probability that the first card

has one of the 3 suits is $\frac{24}{24} = 100\%$, the probability that the second card has a

different suit than the first card is $\frac{16}{23}$ (since there are 16 cards that don't match the

suit of the first card), and the probability that the third card has a suit different from

both of the first two cards (if the first two cards have different suits) is $\frac{8}{22}$ (since the

last available suit has 8 cards). The probability of getting one card from each suit is

$P(\text{a ▲, a ■, a ●, any order}) = \left(\frac{24}{24}\right)\left(\frac{16}{23}\right)\left(\frac{8}{22}\right) = \frac{64}{253}$.

(12) $P(\text{3 of a kind, but not 4 of a kind}) = 32/165 \approx 0.194 \approx 19.4\%$, $P(\text{2 pairs, but not 4}$

of a kind$) = 12/55 \approx 0.218 \approx 21.8\%$, $P(\text{4 of a kind}) = 1/165 \approx 0.00606 \approx 0.606\%$.

Notes: The face cards include the jack (J), queen (Q), and king (K). There are 3 face

cards in each suit, for a total of $(3)(4) = 12$ face cards. There are $\binom{12}{4} = \frac{12!}{4!8!} =$

$\frac{(12)(11)(10)(9)}{24} = 495$ ways to choose 4 out of 12 cards. To make 3 of a kind, be sure to

account for the fourth card of a different value. There are $\binom{3}{1}\binom{4}{3}\binom{2}{1}\binom{4}{1} =$

$\frac{3!}{1!2!}\frac{4!}{3!1!}\frac{2!}{1!1!}\frac{4!}{1!3!} = (3)(4)(2)(4) = 96$ ways to choose 3 of a kind plus one different card.

(The first part, $\binom{3}{1}\binom{4}{3}$ chooses 3 of the 4 suits for one of the three face cards: J, Q, or K.

There are 12 choices for the first part since 3 face cards have 4 suits. The second part,

$\binom{2}{1}\binom{4}{1}$, chooses a suit for the 2 possible face cards that are different from the 3 of a

kind. For example, if 3 of a kind is made with queens, the two remaining face cards are J

and K; these 2 face cards come in 4 suits, making 8 choices for the second part.) This

gives $P(\text{3 of a kind, but not 4 of a kind}) = \frac{96}{495} = \frac{32}{165}$. There are $\binom{3}{2}\binom{4}{2}\binom{4}{2} =$

$\frac{3!}{2!1!}\frac{4!}{2!2!}\frac{4!}{2!2!} = (3)(6)(6) = 108$ ways to choose 2 different pairs. (The first part, $\binom{3}{2}$,

chooses 2 out of 3 values; these are the values for the 2 pairs. Each $\binom{4}{2}$ chooses 2 out of

4 suits for each pair.) This gives P(2 pairs, but not 4 of a kind) $= \frac{108}{495} = \frac{12}{55}$. There are $\binom{3}{1}\binom{4}{4} = (3)(1) = 3$ ways to make 4 of a kind: 4 J's, 4 Q's, or 4 K's. This gives P(4 of a kind) $= \frac{3}{495} = \frac{1}{165}$. (We'll check the answer by finding the probability of drawing a single pair at the end of the alternate solution.)

Alternate solution: The probability of drawing 3 jacks in a row and then a queen is $\frac{4}{12}\frac{3}{11}\frac{2}{10}\frac{4}{9} = \frac{96}{11,880} = \frac{4}{495}$. Since the queen could come first, second, third, or last, the probability of 3 jacks and a queen is $4\left(\frac{4}{495}\right) = \frac{16}{495}$. Three of a kind could have JJJ+Q, JJJ+K, QQQ+J, QQQ+K, KKK+J, or KKK+Q, such that P(3 of a kind, but not 4 of a kind) $= 6\left(\frac{16}{495}\right) = \frac{96}{495} = \frac{32}{165}$. The probability of drawing jack, jack, queen, and then queen is $\frac{4}{12}\frac{3}{11}\frac{4}{10}\frac{3}{9} = \frac{144}{11,880} = \frac{2}{165}$. Since there are $\binom{4}{2} = \frac{4!}{2!2!} = 6$ different orders for 2 jacks and 2 queens (these are JJQQ, JQJQ, JQQJ, QJJQ, QJQJ, QQJJ), the probability for two pairs with J's and Q's is $6\left(\frac{2}{165}\right) = \frac{4}{55}$. Since two pair can be made JJ+QQ, JJ+KK, or QQ+KK, P(2 pairs, but not 4 of a kind) $= 3\left(\frac{4}{55}\right) = \frac{12}{55}$. The probability that the second card matches the value of first card is $\frac{3}{11}$, the probability that the third card matches the first two cards is $\frac{2}{10}$, and the probability that the last card matches the first three cards is $\frac{1}{9}$, such that P(4 of a kind) $= \frac{3}{11}\frac{2}{10}\frac{1}{9} = \frac{6}{990} = \frac{1}{165}$.

Check: The probability of drawing two jacks first, then a queen, and then a king is $\frac{4}{12}\frac{3}{11}\frac{4}{10}\frac{4}{9} = \frac{192}{11,880} = \frac{8}{495}$. There are $\frac{4!}{2!} = 12$ ways to order JJQK, such that the probability of two jacks, a queen, and a king is $12\left(\frac{8}{495}\right) = \frac{96}{495} = \frac{32}{165}$. Since a single pair could also have QQ+JK or KK+JQ, the probability for a single pair is $3\left(\frac{32}{165}\right) = \frac{96}{165} = \frac{32}{55}$. Observe that $\frac{32}{165} + \frac{12}{55} + \frac{1}{165} + \frac{32}{55} = 1$.

(13) P(dealer has blackjack) $= 1/15 \approx 0.0667 \approx 6.67\%$, P(dealer<16) $= 14/45 \approx 0.311 \approx 31.1\%$. Notes: The dealer's J and the 6 other face-up cards make $1 + 6 = 7$ known cards. There are $52 - 7 = 45$ unknown cards. To make blackjack, the dealer needs an ace (A). There are $4 - 1 = 3$ aces remaining. This gives P(dealer has

blackjack) $= \frac{3}{45} = \frac{1}{15}$. To make less than 16, the dealer needs a 2, 3, 4, or 5. (Here, an ace would be counted as 11 points, not 1 point.) There are 3 two's, 4 three's, 4 four's, and 3 five's remaining (since one 2 and one 5 are visible). This makes $3 + 4 + 4 + 3 = 14$ ways to make 16 or less (since the J is worth 10 points). This gives P(dealer<16) $= \frac{14}{45}$ (without drawing any cards).

(14) P(21) $= 4/47 \approx 0.0851 \approx 8.51\%$, P($\leq$21) $= 22/47 \approx 0.468 \approx 46.8\%$, P(bust) $= 25/47 \approx 0.532 \approx 53.2\%$. Notes: There are $52 - 5 = 47$ unknown cards. The player currently has $8 + 7 = 15$ points. Since $21 - 15 = 6$, the player needs to draw a 6 to make 21. All four 6's remain unseen. This makes P(21) $= \frac{4}{47}$. To make a score less than or equal to 21, the player needs to draw an A, 2 ,3, 4, 5, or 6. (An ace may count as 1 point or as 11 points. In this case, it will be counted as 1 point so that the total won't exceed 21.) There are $(4)(6) - 2 = 24 - 2 = 22$ of these cards remaining (since an A and 5 are visible). This makes P($\leq$21) $= \frac{22}{47}$. From the complement rule (Chapter 5), P(bust) $= 1 - P(\leq 21) = 1 - \frac{22}{47} = \frac{25}{47}$.

(15) P(flush) $= 45/1081 \approx 0.0416 \approx 4.16\%$. Notes: There are $52 - 5 = 47$ unknown cards. (The 2 cards being discarded are part of the player's original hand.) The player is keeping 3 spades. To make a flush, the player needs to draw 2 more spades. There are $13 - 3 = 10$ spades remaining. The probability that the first card is a spade is $\frac{10}{47}$ and the probability that the second card is also a spade is $\frac{9}{46}$, such that the probability that both cards are spades is P(flush) $= \left(\frac{10}{47}\right)\left(\frac{9}{46}\right) = \frac{45}{1081}$.

(16) P(full house) $= 11/1081 \approx 0.0102 \approx 1.02\%$, P(3 of a kind, but not 4 of a kind or full house) $= 618/5405 \approx 0.114 \approx 11.4\%$. Notes: There are $52 - 5 = 47$ unknown cards. (The 3 cards being discarded are part of the player's original hand.) There are $\binom{47}{3} = \frac{47!}{3!44!} = \frac{(47)(46)(45)}{6} = 16{,}215$ ways to choose 3 out of 47 cards. A **full house** is 3 of one card plus one pair. Since the player is keeping 2 aces, there are two ways that the player can make a full house:

- The player could draw 3 matching cards that aren't aces. We have to treat 2's, 5's, and 10's differently from 3's, 4's, 6's, 7's, 8's, 9's, J's, Q's, and K's. (There are only three 2's, three 5's, and three 10's remaining, but there are four of each of the others.) There are $\binom{3}{1}\binom{3}{3} = (3)(1) = 3$ ways to choose all three 2's, 5's, or 10's. There are $\binom{9}{1}\binom{4}{3} = (9)(4) = 36$ ways to choose three of the four 3's, 4's, 6's, 7's, 8's, 9's, J's, Q's, or K's. Add to get $3 + 36 = 39$ ways to make a full house by drawing 3 of a kind.

- The player could draw 1 ace and a pair of cards that aren't aces. There are $\binom{2}{1}\binom{3}{1}\binom{3}{2} = (2)(3)(3) = 18$ ways to draw 1 of the 2 remaining aces and also draw a pair of 2's, 5's, or 10's (since each of these 3 cards has 3 remaining). There are $\binom{2}{1}\binom{9}{1}\binom{4}{2} = (2)(9)(6) = 108$ ways to draw 1 of the 2 remaining aces and also draw a pair of 3's, 4's, 6's, 7's, 8's, 9's, J's, Q's, or K's (since each of these 9 cards has all 4 remaining). Add to get $18 + 108 = 126$ ways to make a full house by drawing an ace and a pair of other cards.

Add to get $39 + 126 = 165$. This gives P(full house) $= \frac{165}{16,215} = \frac{11}{1081}$. To make 3 of a kind that isn't a full house or 4 of a kind, the player must draw one ace and two cards that aren't aces and aren't the same value. We will work out 3 cases separately:

- The cards drawn are A-2-5, A-2-10, or A-5-10 of any of the remaining suits of these cards. There are $\binom{2}{1}\binom{3}{2}\binom{3}{1}\binom{3}{1} = (2)(3)(3)(3) = 54$ ways to do this. The first $\binom{2}{1}$ chooses 1 out of the remaining 2 aces, the $\binom{3}{2}$ chooses 2 different cards out of 2, 5, or 10, and the $\binom{3}{1}\binom{3}{1}$ chooses the suits for those 2 cards.

- An ace is drawn along with one card that is a 2, 5, or 10 and another card that isn't an ace, 2, 5, or 10. There are $\binom{2}{1}\binom{3}{1}\binom{3}{1}\binom{9}{1}\binom{4}{1} = (2)(3^2)(9)(4) = 648$ ways to do this. The $\binom{2}{1}$ chooses 1 out of the remaining 2 aces, the $\binom{3}{1}\binom{3}{1}$ chooses a 2, 5, or 10 (first to pick one of these 3 cards and then to pick one of the 3 suits for that card), and the $\binom{9}{1}\binom{4}{1}$ chooses a 3, 4, 6, 7, 8, 9, J, Q, or K (first pick one of the 9 cards, then each card has all 4 suits available).

- An ace is drawn along with two non-matching cards that aren't an ace, 2, 5, or 10. There are $\binom{2}{1}\binom{9}{2}\binom{4}{1}\binom{4}{1} = (2)(36)(4)(4) = 1152$ ways to do this. The $\binom{2}{1}$ chooses 1 out of the remaining 2 aces, the $\binom{9}{2}\binom{4}{1}$ chooses 2 cards out of 3, 4, 6, 7, 8, 9, J, Q, or K, and the $\binom{4}{1}\binom{4}{1}$ chooses the suits for these 2 cards.

Add to get $54 + 648 + 1152 = 1854$. This gives P(3 of a kind, but not 4 of a kind or full house) $= \frac{1854}{16{,}215} = \frac{618}{5405}$.

Alternate solution: There are $\binom{47}{3} = \frac{47!}{3!44!} = \frac{(47)(46)(45)}{6} = 16{,}215$ ways to choose 3 out of 47 cards. The player could make full house the following ways:

- There is 1 way to draw three 2's: 2♥2♦2♣. There is 1 way to draw three 5's. There is 1 way to draw three 10's. There are 4 ways to draw three 3's: 3♥3♦3♠, 3♥3♦3♣, 3♥3♠3♣, 3♦3♠3♣. There are similarly 4 ways if the pair is made with 4's, 6's, 7's, 8's, 9's, J's, Q's, or K's. This makes a total of $1 + 1 + 1 + (4)(9) = 39$ ways to draw 3 of a kind.

- There are 6 ways to draw one ace and two 2's: A♦2♥2♦, A♦2♥2♠, A♦2♦2♠, A♣2♥2♦, A♣2♥2♠, A♣2♦2♠. (The A♥, A♠, and 2♣ are already visible.) There are similarly 6 ways to draw one ace and two 5's or to draw one ace and two 10's. There are 12 ways to draw one ace and two 3's: A♦3♥3♦, A♦3♥3♠, A♦3♥3♣, A♦3♦3♠, A♦3♦3♣, A♦3♠3♣, A♣3♥3♦, A♣3♥3♠, A♣3♥3♣, A♣3♦3♠, A♣3♦3♣, A♣3♠3♣. There are similarly 12 ways if the pair is made with 4's, 6's, 7's, 8's, 9's, J's, Q's, or K's. This makes a total of $(6)(3) + (12)(9) = 18 + 108 = 126$ ways to draw an ace and a pair of cards that aren't aces.

Add $39 + 126 = 165$. This gives P(full house) $= \frac{165}{16{,}215} = \frac{11}{1081}$. The player could make 3 of a kind (but not 4 of a kind or full house) the following ways:

- There are 18 ways to draw an ace, a 2, and a 5: A♦2♥5♥, A♦2♥5♠, A♦2♥5♣, A♦2♦5♥, A♦2♦5♠, A♦2♦5♣, A♦2♠5♥, A♦2♠5♠, A♦2♠5♣, A♣2♥5♥, A♣2♥5♠, A♣2♥5♣, A♣2♦5♥, A♣2♦5♠, A♣2♦5♣, A♣2♠5♥, A♣2♠5♠, A♣2♠5♣. There are similarly 18 ways to draw an ace, a 2, and 10, or to draw an ace, a 5, and 10. This makes

$(18)(3) = 54$ was to draw an ace and 2 non-matching cards that include a 2, 5, or 10.

- There are 24 ways to draw an ace, a 2, and a 3: A♦2♥3♥, A♦2♥3♦, A♦2♥3♠, A♦2♥3♣, A♦2♦3♥, A♦2♦3♦, A♦2♦3♠, A♦2♦3♣, A♦2♠3♥, A♦2♠3♦, A♦2♠3♠, A♦2♠3♣, A♣2♥3♥, A♣2♥3♦, A♣2♥3♠, A♣2♥3♣, A♣2♦3♥, A♣2♦3♦, A♣2♦3♠, A♣2♦3♣, A♣2♠3♥, A♣2♠3♦, A♣2♠3♠, A♣2♠3♣. There are similarly 24 ways if there is a 5 or a 10 instead of a 2, or if there is a 4, 6, 7, 8, 9, J, Q, or K instead of a 3. This makes $(24)(3)(9) = 648$ ways to draw an ace, a card that is a 2, 5, or 10, and a card that isn't an A, 2, 5, or 10.

- There are 32 ways to draw an ace, a 3, and a 4: A♦3♥4♥, A♦3♥4♦, A♦3♥4♠, A♦3♥4♣, A♦3♦4♥, A♦3♦4♦, A♦3♦4♠, A♦3♦4♣, A♦3♠4♥, A♦3♠4♦, A♦3♠4♠, A♦3♠4♣, A♦3♣4♥, A♦3♣4♦, A♦3♣4♠, A♦3♣4♣, A♣3♥4♥, A♣3♥4♦, A♣3♥4♠, A♣3♥4♣, A♣3♦4♥, A♣3♦4♦, A♣3♦4♠, A♣3♦4♣, A♣3♠4♥, A♣3♠4♦, A♣3♠4♠, A♣3♠4♣, A♣3♣4♥, A♣3♣4♦, A♣3♣4♠, A♣3♣4♣. There are $\binom{9}{2} = \frac{9!}{2!7!} = \frac{(9)(8)}{2} = 36$ ways to choose 2 cards from 3, 4, 6, 7, 8, 9, J, Q, or K; each of these 36 combinations has 32 ways to be drawn with an ace (like the ace, 3, and 4 we outlined). This makes $(32)(36) = 1152$ ways to draw an ace and 2 non-matching cards that are a 3, 4, 6, 7, 8, 9, J, Q, or K.

Add to get $54 + 648 + 1152 = 1854$. This gives P(3 of a kind, but not 4 of a kind or full house) $= \frac{1854}{16,215} = \frac{618}{5405}$.

(17) P(straight, but not flush) $= 5/1274 \approx 0.00392 \approx 0.392\%$, o(straight, but not flush) = 5:1269. Notes: There are $\binom{52}{5} = \frac{52!}{5!47!} = \frac{(52)(51)(50)(49)(48)}{(5)(4)(3)(2)(1)} = \frac{311,875,200}{120} = 2,598,960$ ways to choose 5 out of 52 cards. There are $\binom{10}{1}\binom{4}{1}\binom{4}{1}\binom{4}{1}\binom{4}{1}\binom{4}{1} = (10)(4)^5 = 10,240$ ways to make a straight with 5 cards, since the ace may be low or high. The $\binom{10}{1}$ comes from the 10 ways to make a run of 5 cards: A-2-3-4-5, 2-3-4-5-6, 3-4-5-6-7, 4-5-6-7-8, 5-6-7-8-9, 6-7-8-9-10, 7-8-9-10-J, 8-9-10-J-Q, 9-10-J-Q-K, 10-J-Q-K-A. The five $\binom{4}{1}$'s choose one suit for each card. However, this includes straight

flushes, and the problem asks for us to subtract out the straight flushes. There are $\binom{10}{1}\binom{4}{1} = (10)(4) = 40$ straight (and royal) flushes. Subtract to get $10,240 - 40 = 10,200$ flushes that aren't straight (or royal). This gives P(straight, but not a flush) $= \frac{10,200}{2,598,960} = \frac{5}{1274}$. From Chapter 7, $o = \frac{5/1274}{1269/1274} = \frac{5}{1269} = 5:1269$.

Alternate solution: There are $\binom{52}{5} = \frac{52!}{5!47!} = \frac{(52)(51)(50)(49)(48)}{(5)(4)(3)(2)(1)} = \frac{311,875,200}{120} = 2,598,960$ ways to choose 5 out of 52 cards. There are 10 ways to make a run of 5 cards: A-2-3-4-5, 2-3-4-5-6, 3-4-5-6-7, 4-5-6-7-8, 5-6-7-8-9, 6-7-8-9-10, 7-8-9-10-J, 8-9-10-J-Q, 9-10-J-Q-K, 10-J-Q-K-A. For each run, each of the 5 cards can be one of 4 different suits, so that there are $(4)(4)(4)(4)(4) = 1024$ ways to make each run of 5 cards. Multiply $(10)(1024) = 10,240$ to get the total number of straights, including straight flushes. For each run, there are 4 straight (or royal) flushes (one for each suit), such that $(10)(4) = 40$ is the number of straight (or royal) flushes. Subtract to get $10,240 - 40 = 10,200$ flushes that aren't straight (or royal). This gives P(straight, but not a flush) $= \frac{10,200}{2,598,960} = \frac{5}{1274}$.

(18) P(4 of a kind) $= 1/4165 \approx 0.000240 \approx 0.0240\%$, o(4 of a kind) = 1:4164. Notes: There are $\binom{52}{5} = \frac{52!}{5!47!} = \frac{(52)(51)(50)(49)(48)}{(5)(4)(3)(2)(1)} = \frac{311,875,200}{120} = 2,598,960$ ways to choose 5 out of 52 cards. Be sure to account for the fifth card of a different value. There are $\binom{13}{1}\binom{4}{4}\binom{12}{1}\binom{4}{1} = \frac{13!}{1!12!}\frac{4!}{4!0!}\frac{12!}{1!11!}\frac{4!}{1!3!} = (13)(1)(12)(4) = 624$ ways to choose 4 of a kind. (The first part, $\binom{13}{1}\binom{4}{4}$ chooses all 4 suits for 1 of 13 values. The second part, $\binom{12}{1}\binom{4}{1}$, chooses 1 of the 4 suits for 1 of 12 values different from the first 4 cards.) This gives P(4 of a kind) $= \frac{624}{2,598,960} = \frac{1}{4165}$. From Chapter 7, $o = \frac{1/4165}{4164/4165} = \frac{1}{4164} = 1:4164$.

Alternate solution: There are $\binom{52}{5} = \frac{52!}{5!47!} = \frac{(52)(51)(50)(49)(48)}{(5)(4)(3)(2)(1)} = \frac{311,875,200}{120} = 2,598,960$ ways to choose 5 out of 52 cards. There is 1 way to choose all 4 aces: A♥A♦A♠A♣. We need to choose 1 more card to go along with the aces; call it X. There are $52 - 4 = 48$ ways to choose X so that it isn't an ace. This makes 48 ways to choose 4 of a kind with aces along with a fifth card X. Multiply by 13 because 4 of a kind could be made with a card other than aces. This makes $(48)(13) = 624$ ways to make 4 of a kind. This gives $P(4 \text{ of a kind}) = \frac{624}{2,598,960} = \frac{1}{4165}$.

(19) $P(\text{full house}) = 6/4165 \approx 0.00144 \approx 0.144\%$, $o(\text{full house}) = 6{:}4159$. Notes:

There are $\binom{52}{5} = \frac{52!}{5!47!} = \frac{(52)(51)(50)(49)(48)}{(5)(4)(3)(2)(1)} = \frac{311,875,200}{120} = 2,598,960$ ways to choose 5

out of 52 cards. There are $\binom{13}{1}\binom{4}{3}\binom{12}{1}\binom{4}{2} = \frac{13!}{1!12!}\frac{4!}{3!1!}\frac{12!}{1!11!}\frac{4!}{2!2!} = (13)(4)(12)(6) =$

3744 ways to choose 3 of a kind plus a pair. (The first part, $\binom{13}{1}\binom{4}{3}$ chooses 3 of the 4

suits for 1 of the 13 values. The second part, $\binom{12}{1}\binom{4}{2}$, chooses 2 of the 4 suits for the

12 possible values that are different from the 3 of a kind.) This gives $P(\text{full house}) =$

$\frac{3744}{2,598,960} = \frac{6}{4165}$. From Chapter 7, $o = \frac{6/4165}{4159/4165} = \frac{6}{4159} = 6{:}4159$.

Alternate solution: There are $\binom{52}{5} = \frac{52!}{5!47!} = \frac{(52)(51)(50)(49)(48)}{(5)(4)(3)(2)(1)} = \frac{311,875,200}{120} = 2,598,960$

ways to choose 5 out of 52 cards. There are $\binom{4}{3} = \frac{4!}{3!1!} = 4$ ways to choose 3 out of 4

aces: A♥A♦A♠, A♥A♦A♣, A♥A♠A♣, A♦A♠A♣. Since they could be another card besides aces,

multiply by 13 to get $(4)(13) = 52$. There are $\binom{4}{2} = \frac{4!}{2!2!} = 6$ ways to choose 2 out of 4

jacks: J♥J♦, J♥J♠, J♥J♣, J♦J♠, J♦J♣, J♠J♣. Multiply by 12 to get $(6)(12) = 72$ ways to make the

second pair (since they don't have to be jacks; there are 12 values different from the 3

of a kind). Multiply to get $(52)(72) = 3744$ ways to make full house. This gives $P(\text{full}$

$\text{house}) = \frac{3744}{2,598,960} = \frac{6}{4165}$.

(20) $P(2 \text{ pairs, but not 4 of a kind or full house}) = 198/4165 \approx 0.0475 \approx 4.75\%$, $o(2$

pairs, but not 4 of a kind or full house$) = 198{:}3967$. Notes: There are $\binom{52}{5} = \frac{52!}{5!47!} =$

$\frac{(52)(51)(50)(49)(48)}{(5)(4)(3)(2)(1)} = \frac{311,875,200}{120} = 2,598,960$ ways to choose 5 out of 52 cards. Be sure to

account for the fifth card of a different value. There are $\binom{13}{2}\binom{4}{2}\binom{4}{2}\binom{11}{1}\binom{4}{1} =$

$\frac{13!}{2!11!}\frac{4!}{2!2!}\frac{4!}{2!2!}\frac{11!}{1!10!}\frac{4!}{1!3!} = (78)(6)(6)(11)(4) = 123,552$ ways to choose 2 different pairs.

(The $\binom{13}{2}$ chooses the two values for the two pairs. Each $\binom{4}{2}$ chooses 2 out of 4 suits for each pair. The last part, $\binom{11}{1}\binom{4}{1}$, chooses the value and suit for the card that is different from the two pairs.) This gives P(2 pairs, but not 4 of a kind) $= \frac{123{,}552}{2{,}598{,}960} = \frac{198}{4165}$. From Chapter 7, $o = \frac{198/4165}{3967/4165} = \frac{198}{3967} = 198{:}3967$.

Alternate solution: There are $\binom{52}{5} = \frac{52!}{5!47!} = \frac{(52)(51)(50)(49)(48)}{(5)(4)(3)(2)(1)} = \frac{311{,}875{,}200}{120} = 2{,}598{,}960$ ways to choose 5 out of 52 cards. There are 6 ways to make a pair of aces: There are $\binom{4}{2} = \frac{4!}{2!2!} = 6$ ways to choose 2 out of 4 aces: A♥A♦, A♥A♠, A♥A♣, A♦A♠, A♦A♣, A♠A♣. Multiply by 13 to get $(6)(13) = 78$ ways to make the first pair. There are $\binom{4}{2} = \frac{4!}{2!2!} = 6$ ways to choose 2 out of 4 two's: 2♥2♦, 2♥2♠, 2♥2♣, 2♦2♠, 2♦2♣, 2♠2♣. Multiply by 12 (because we want a different value from the first pair) to get $(6)(12) = 72$ ways to make the second pair. Beware that multiplying 78 by 72 will give us **twice** as many answers as we want. (We encountered a similar issue in the alternate solution to Example 3.) Why? If the first pair is made with 9's and the second pair is made with 5's, this is a duplicate of when the first pair is made with 5's and the second pair is made with 9's. So we will divide by 2 after multiplying $(78)(72)$ to correct for double counting: There are $\frac{(78)(72)}{2} = 2808$ ways to make two pairs. We still need to account for the fifth card; we will call it X. There are $52 - 8 = 44$ ways to choose X so that it isn't the same as a card from the two pairs. (For example, if one pair is made with J's and another pair is made with 7's, we subtract 4 jacks and 4 sevens from 52 to get 44 cards that aren't jacks or sevens.) Multiply to get $(2808)(44) = 123{,}552$ ways to make two pairs plus another card. This gives P(2 pairs, but not 4 of a kind) $= \frac{123{,}552}{2{,}598{,}960} = \frac{198}{4165}$.

(21) P(royal flush) $= 14/527{,}085 \approx 0.0000266 \approx 0.00266\%$. Notes: There are $\binom{54}{5} = \frac{54!}{5!49!} = \frac{(54)(53)(52)(51)(50)}{(5)(4)(3)(2)(1)} = \frac{379{,}501{,}200}{120} = 3{,}162{,}510$ ways to choose 5 cards out of 54. There are $\binom{7}{5}\binom{4}{1} = \frac{7!}{5!2!}\frac{4!}{1!3!} = \frac{(7)(6)}{2}\frac{4}{1} = (21)(4) = 84$ ways to make a royal flush using 2 jokers. The $\binom{7}{5}$ chooses 5 cards out of 10, J, Q, K, A, joker, joker while the $\binom{4}{1}$

chooses 1 out of 4 suits for the 10 thru A. This gives P(royal flush) $= \frac{84}{3,162,510} = \frac{14}{527,085}$.

Alternate solution: There are $\binom{54}{5} = \frac{54!}{5!49!} = \frac{(54)(53)(52)(51)(50)}{(5)(4)(3)(2)(1)} = \frac{379,501,200}{120} =$

3,162,510 ways to choose 5 cards out of 54. A royal flush could be made with zero, one, or two jokers:

- There are 4 ways to make a royal flush without jokers: 10-J-Q-K-A of each suit.
- Using 1 joker, the joker could replace the 10, J, Q, K, or A (for example, 10-J-Q-joker-A). For a single suit, there are $\binom{5}{1}\binom{2}{1} = \frac{5!}{1!4!}\frac{2!}{1!1!} = (5)(2) = 10$ ways to do this. (The $\binom{5}{1}$ chooses the 10, J, Q, K, or A for the joker to replace while the $\binom{2}{1}$ chooses one of the 2 jokers.) Since there are 4 suits, this makes $(10)(4) = 40$ ways to make a royal flush with 1 joker.
- Using 2 jokers, the jokers need to replace 2 of the 5 cards in 10-J-Q-K-A. For a single suit, there are $\binom{5}{2}\binom{2}{2} = \frac{5!}{2!3!}\frac{2!}{2!0!} = \frac{(5)(4)}{2}\frac{2}{2} = 10$ ways to do this: 10-J-Q-joker-joker, 10-J-joker-K-joker, 10-J-joker-joker-A, 10-joker-Q-K-joker, 10-joker-Q-joker-A, 10-joker-joker-K-A, joker-J-Q-K-joker, joker-J-Q-joker-A, joker-J-joker-K-A, joker-joker-Q-K-A. Since there are 4 suits, this makes $(10)(4) = 40$ ways to make a royal flush using 2 jokers.

Add $4 + 40 + 40 = 84$ ways to make a royal flush using 2 jokers. This gives P(royal flush) $= \frac{84}{3,162,510} = \frac{14}{527,085}$.

(22) P(royal flush) $= 1/30,940 \approx 0.0000323 \approx 0.00323\%$, o(royal flush) $= 1:30,939$.

Notes: There are $\binom{52}{7} = \frac{52!}{7!45!} = 133,784,560$ ways to choose 7 cards out of 52. We want to make a royal flush plus 2 other cards. There are 4 ways to make a royal flush: 10-J-Q-K-A for each suit. Now we need to include the 2 other cards; call these X and Y. Since 5 cards make the royal flush, there are $52 - 5 = 47$ other cards for X and Y. There are $\binom{47}{2} = \frac{47!}{2!45!} = \frac{(47)(46)}{2} = 1081$ ways to choose X and Y. This makes $(4)(1081) = 4324$ ways to make a royal flush, counting the best 5 out of 7 cards. This gives P(royal flush) $= \frac{4324}{133,784,560} = \frac{1}{30,940}$. From Chapter 7, $o = \frac{1/30,940}{30,939/30,940} = \frac{1}{30,939} =$ 1:30,939.

Chapter 9

(1) P(≥2 same birthday) ≈ 0.0405 ≈ 4.05%. Notes: Use the birthday formula with $N = 6$.

$$P(\geq 2 \text{ same birthday}) = 1 - \frac{6!}{365^6}\binom{365}{6} \approx 0.0405$$

If you prefer to write this out the long way, it is:

$$P(\geq 2 \text{ same birthday}) = 1 - \frac{(365)(364)(363)(362)(361)(360)}{365^6}$$

$$P(\geq 2 \text{ same birthday}) = 1 - \frac{(364)(363)(362)(361)(360)}{365^5}$$

since $365 - N + 1 = 365 - 6 + 1 = 360$ in this problem.

(2) P(≥2 same birthday) ≈ 0.315 ≈ 31.5%. Notes: Use the birthday formula with $N = 17$. To do this on a calculator, your calculator would ideally have a function (perhaps accessible from a menu) that uses the combination formula and would be able to handle relatively large numbers (since $\binom{365}{17}$ is on the order of 10^{28}). If you don't have a calculator that can handle this, you could try using a spreadsheet like Excel to do the calculation, or you could try using one of the formulas given for approximating the answer. (The way to do it on Excel is to multiply fractions. That is, multiply $\frac{364}{365}$ times $\frac{363}{365}$ times $\frac{362}{365}$ and so on, and then subtract from one.) Yet another option is to visit Mathematica's website (Wolfram).

$$P(\geq 2 \text{ same birthday}) = 1 - \frac{17!}{365^{17}}\binom{365}{17} \approx 0.315$$

(3) P(≥2 born on same day of the week) = 223/343 ≈ 0.650 ≈ 65.0%. Notes: There are 7 days in a week: Sunday, Monday, Tuesday, Wednesday, Thursday, Friday, Saturday. Any two people are much more likely to have been born on the same day of the week than on the same day of the year. (However, many people don't 'know' which day of the week they were born on. If you know the birthday, you could figure this out with a calendar app or try asking Alexa.) Use the birthday formula with $N = 4$ and with 7 in place of 365. (In this case, N is restricted to $N < 7$ people.)

$$P(\geq 2 \text{ born on same day of the week}) = 1 - \frac{4!}{7^4}\binom{7}{4} = 1 - \frac{120}{343} = \frac{223}{343} \approx 0.650$$

If you prefer to write this out the long way, it is:

$$P(\geq 2 \text{ born on same day of the week}) = 1 - \frac{(7)(6)(5)(4)}{7^4} = 1 - \frac{(6)(5)(4)}{7^3}$$

$$P(\geq 2 \text{ born on same day of the week}) = 1 - \frac{120}{343} = \frac{223}{343}$$

(4) $P(\geq 2 \text{ same number}) = 93{,}128{,}083/94{,}921{,}875 \approx 0.981 \approx 98.1\%$. Notes: Use the birthday formula with $N = 10$ and with 15 in place of 365.

$$P(\geq 2 \text{ same number}) = 1 - \frac{10!}{15^{10}}\binom{15}{10} = 1 - \frac{1{,}793{,}792}{94{,}921{,}875} = \frac{93{,}128{,}083}{94{,}921{,}875} \approx 0.981$$

It's important that each ball is **placed back** in the bag; this makes it possible for two people to select the same number. (If the balls are selected without replacement, the probability that two balls would have the same number would be zero.)

Chapter 10

(1) 720. Notes: $6! = 720$. This is like Part A of Example 1.

(2) 24. Notes: $(5 - 1)! = 4! = 24$. This is like Part B of Example 1.

(3) 40,320. Notes: $8! = 40,320$. This is like Part A of Example 1.

(4) 120. Notes: $(6 - 1)! = 5! = 120$. This is like Part B of Example 1.

(5) 5040. Notes: $\frac{10!}{(10-4)!} = \frac{10!}{6!} = 5040$. This is like Example 2.

(6) 20. Notes: If 3 members were sitting in a row, the answer would have been $\frac{5!}{(5-3)!} = \frac{5!}{2!} = 60$. Since they are instead sitting in a circle, divide by 3 to get $\frac{60}{3} = 20$. Why? Consider the problem of N people sitting in N chairs. If the chairs are in a row, there are $N!$ arrangements, but if the chairs are in a circle, there are $\frac{N!}{N} = (N - 1)!$ arrangements. (For example, if $N = 7$, there are $\frac{7!}{7} = 6!$ ways for 7 people to sit in 7 chairs in a circle). Another way to see this is given in the alternate solution.

Alternate solution: There are $\binom{5}{3} = \frac{5!}{3!2!} = \frac{(5)(4)}{2} = 10$ ways to choose 3 out of 5 members. For each set of 3 members, there are $(3 - 1)! = 2! = 2$ ways to arrange them in a circle. This makes a total of $(10)(2) = 20$ ways. These are shown below.

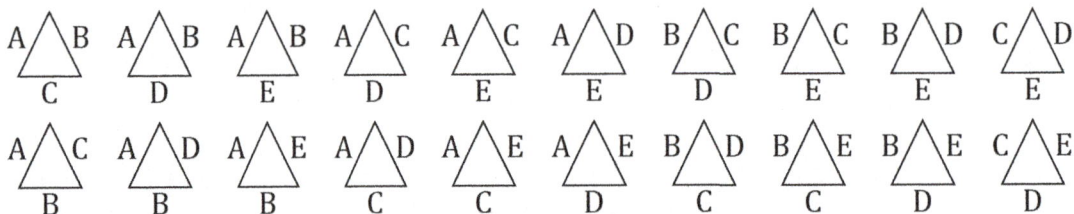

(7) 3600. Notes: There are $2 + 5 = 7$ people all together. Apply the principle of **complementary counting** (Chapter 3). There are a total of $7! = 5040$ permutations. If the sisters sit in the first 2 chairs, there are $2! = 2$ permutations of the sisters and $5! = 120$ permutations of the other people, for a total of $(2)(120) = 240$ permutations. We get 240 permutations if the sisters sit in chairs 1-2, 2-3, 3-4, 4-5, 5-6, or 6-7, so the total number of ways for the sisters to sit together is $(6)(240) = 1440$. From the principle of complementary counting, there are $5040 - 1440 = 3600$ ways for the sisters to not sit together.

Alternate solution: There are a total of $7! = 5040$ permutations. Think of the sisters as a single pair. There are $6! = 720$ permutations of the pair and 5 other people. There are $2! = 2$ permutations for the sisters in the pair. This makes $(720)(2) = 1440$ permutations where the sisters sit together. From the principle of complementary counting, there are $5040 - 1440 = 3600$ ways for the sisters to not sit together.

(8) 12. Notes: If girls don't sit next to each other, the arrangement will have boys and girls alternating: BGBGBG. There are $(3 - 1) = 2!$ ways to arrange the boys: clockwise (top row below) or counterclockwise (bottom row below). The girls may also be arranged clockwise or counterclockwise. In addition, the first girl may be placed between B1 and B2, between B2 and B3, or between B1 and B3. This makes a total of $(2)(2)(3) = 12$ arrangements. (Beware of rotational symmetry. If you don't put B1 at the top, the diagram will be equivalent to one of the diagrams shown below.)

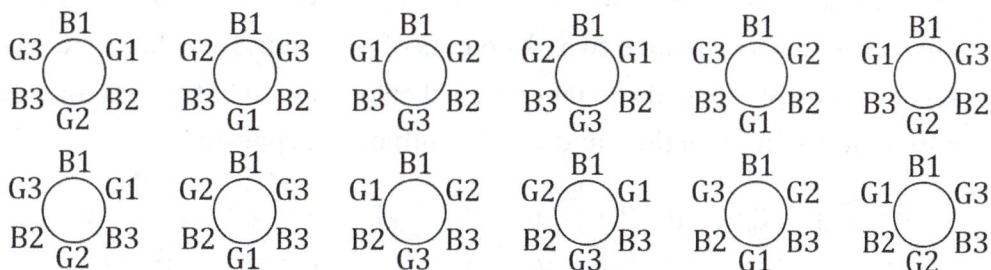

(9) 125. Notes: $5^3 = 125$. This is like Part A of Example 5. The formula is C^N, where the base C is the number of colors and the exponent N is the number of objects.

(10) 51. Notes: 5 placemats of 3 colors can be set in the following ways:

- There are 3 ways for all five placemats to be the same color.

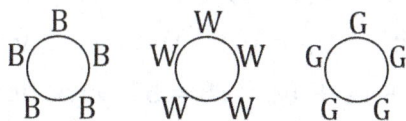

- There are 6 ways for four placemats to be the same color.

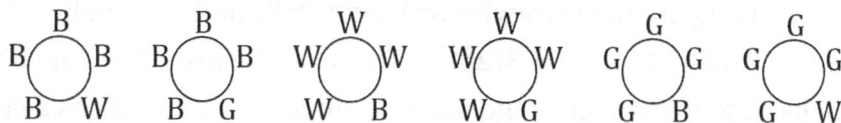

- There are 12 ways to have three placemats of one color and two placemats of another color (6 with the pair together and 6 with the pair separated).

```
    B             B             W             W             G             G
  B(   )B       B(   )B       W(   )W       W(   )W       G(   )G       G(   )G
    W   W         G   G         B   B         G   G         B   B         W   W

    B             B             W             W             G             G
  W(   )B       G(   )B       B(   )W       G(   )W       B(   )G       W(   )G
    B   W         B   G         W   B         W   G         G   B         G   W
```

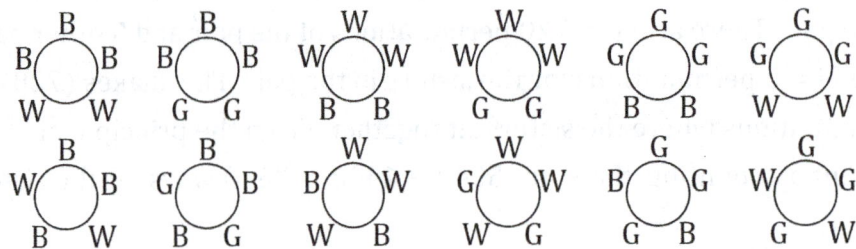

- There are 12 ways to have three placemats of one color and also have all three colors used (6 with the lone colors together and 6 with them separated).

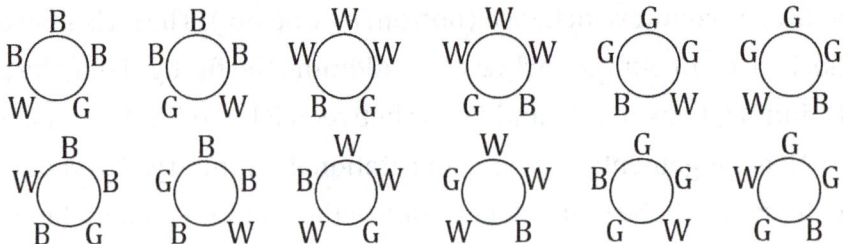

```
    B             B             W             W             G             G
  B(   )B       B(   )B       W(   )W       W(   )W       G(   )G       G(   )G
    W   G         G   W         B   G         G   B         B   W         W   B

    B             B             W             W             G             G
  W(   )B       G(   )B       B(   )W       G(   )W       B(   )G       W(   )G
    B   G         B   W         W   G         W   B         G   W         G   B
```

- There are 18 ways to have two placemats of one color, two placemats of a second color, and one placemat of a third color (6 with both pairs together, 6 with a single pair together, and 6 with both pairs separated).

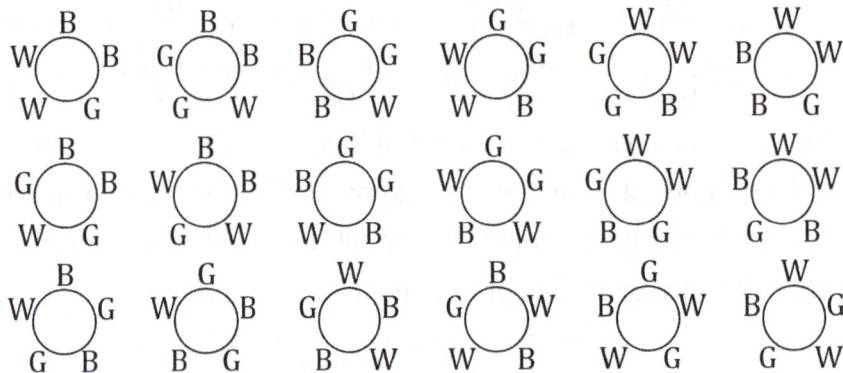

```
    B             B             G             G             W             W
  W(   )B       G(   )B       B(   )G       W(   )G       G(   )W       B(   )W
    W   G         G   W         B   W         W   B         G   B         B   G

    B             B             G             G             W             W
  G(   )B       W(   )B       B(   )G       W(   )G       G(   )W       B(   )W
    W   G         G   W         W   B         B   W         B   G         G   B

    B             G             W             B             G             W
  W(   )G       W(   )B       G(   )B       G(   )W       B(   )W       B(   )G
    G   B         B   G         B   W         W   B         W   G         G   W
```

This makes a total of $3 + 6 + 12 + 12 + 18 = 51$ ways. Beware of rotational symmetry. There are many ways to draw a diagram that is equivalent to one of the diagrams above. Compare the clockwise order carefully and thoroughly.

(11) 48. Notes: $(3)(2)(2)(2)(2) = 3(2^4) = 3(16) = 48$. This is like Part B of Example 5. The first unicorn has 3 choices. Each unicorn after that has 2 choices (since it can't be the same color as the previous unicorn).

(12) 8. Notes: All 3 colors must be different (otherwise, 2 chairs of the same color will be next to each other). There are $\binom{4}{3} = \frac{4!}{3!1!} = 4$ ways to choose 3 out of 4 colors.

Each case may be clockwise or counterclockwise, as shown in the diagram that follows.

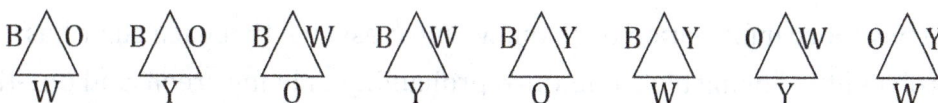

(13) P(first ball is 3 and last ball is 4) = 1/20 = 0.05 = 5%. Notes: There are a total of 5! = 120 permutations. If the first ball is 3 and the last ball is 4, there are 3! = 6 permutations for the remaining 3 balls. The probability is $\frac{6}{120} = \frac{1}{20}$.

Alternate solution: The probability that the first ball is a 3 is $\frac{1}{5}$. If the first ball is a 3, the probability that the last ball is a 4 is $\frac{1}{4}$ (since 4 balls remain). The combined probability is $\left(\frac{1}{5}\right)\left(\frac{1}{4}\right) = \frac{1}{20}$.

(14) P(father and son sit next to each other) = 1/3 ≈ 0.333 ≈ 33.3%. Notes: There are 7 people in total. There are $(7 - 1)! = 6! = 720$ clockwise permutations. If the people are A, B, C, D, E, F, S (where F is for father and S is for son), there are 5! = 120 permutations of the form FSvwxyz (where v thru z are the other 5 people in unknown order), 120 of the form FvSwxyz, 120 of the form FvwSxyz, 120 of the form FvwxSyz, 120 of the form FvwxySz, and 120 of the form FvwxyzS. (Note that these add up to 720. Let the father be the first to sit.) In FSvwxyz and also FvwxyzS the father and son sit together (since, on a circle, the first and last chairs are next to each other). The probability is $\frac{240}{720} = \frac{1}{3}$. The alternate solution is much simpler.

Alternate solution: Let the father sit. There are 6 chairs remaining. Two of the chairs are next to the father. The probability is $\frac{2}{6} = \frac{1}{3}$.

(15) P(only 2 of the colors are used) = 1/16 = 0.0625 = 6.25%. Notes: There are a total of (5)(4)(4)(4) = 320 arrangements. This is like Part B of Example 5. The first ring has 5 choices. Each ring after that has 4 choices (since it can't be the same color as the previous ring). There are $\binom{5}{2} = \frac{5!}{2!3!} = \frac{(5)(4)}{2} = 10$ ways to choose 2 out of 5 colors. For each pair of colors, there are (2)(1)(1)(1) = 2 ways to arrange the rings using only those 2 colors. For example, with black and silver these are BSBS or SBSB. This makes (10)(2) ways to arrange the rings using only 2 colors. The probability is $\frac{20}{320} = \frac{1}{16}$.

(16) P(1 chair of each color) = 2/9 ≈ 0.222 ≈ 22.2%. Notes: According to the instructions, we are to assume that the selection process is fair and random. Without any more information to go on, we must assume that each chair has a one-third probability of being blue, one-third probability of being green, and one-third probability of being red. (The same mechanism for determining color that is outlined in Exercise 17 would also work for this problem.) As discussed in Example 8, the **equally likely outcomes** may not be the same as the total number of unique outcomes. Since each chair has 3 color choices, there are (3)(3)(3) = 27 equally likely outcomes. These are shown below.

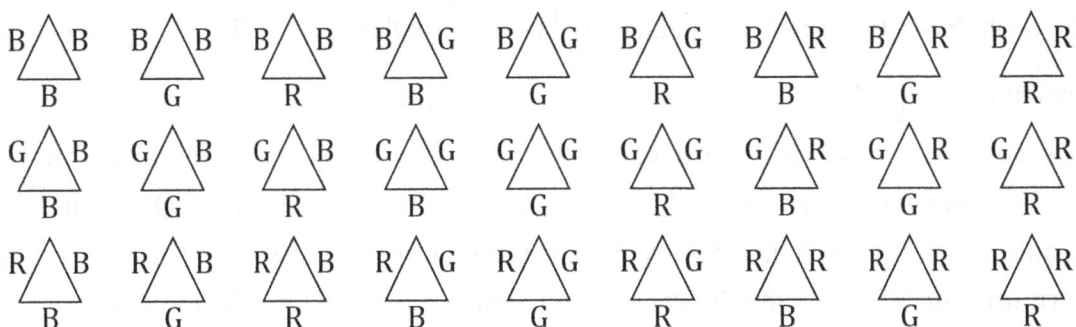

6 of these outcomes have one blue, one green, and one red. The probability is $\frac{6}{27} = \frac{2}{9}$. There are 11 unique outcomes shown below; 2 of these have 1 chair of each color. These are not equally likely outcomes, as discussed in Example 8. It would be **incorrect** to conclude that the answer is $\frac{2}{11}$. If you're not convinced, read the alternate solution.

Alternate solution: The probability that the second chair's color is different from the first chair is $\frac{2}{3}$. The probability that the third chair's color is different from the first two chairs (after the first two chairs already have different colors) is $\frac{1}{3}$. The probability that all three chairs have different colors is $\left(\frac{2}{3}\right)\left(\frac{1}{3}\right) = \frac{2}{9}$. Here we applied the concept of **conditional probability** (recall Chapter 5).

(17) P(no green balls) = 64/729 ≈ 0.0878 ≈ 8.78%. Notes: Each ball has 3 equally likely colors. The total number of permutations is $3^6 = 729$. This is like Part A of

Example 5. The formula is C^N, where the base C is the number of colors and the exponent N is the number of objects. If green isn't used, each ball has 2 color choices. This makes $2^6 = 64$ permutations without green. The probability is $\frac{64}{729}$.

Alternate solution: The probability that one ball isn't green is $\frac{2}{3}$. The probability that none of the 6 balls is green is $\left(\frac{2}{3}\right)^6 = \frac{64}{729}$.

(18) P(no green balls) $= 1/33 \approx 0.0303 \approx 3.03\%$. The answer is different from Problem 17 because in this problem, the probability of selecting each ball is affected by having fewer balls left in the bag, whereas in Problem 17 the probability of selecting each ball is the same because the die gives one-third probability for each color. The distinction has to do with the **replacement** issue discussed in Chapter 4. When selecting balls from a bag, if each ball is replaced back in the bag before the next selection, the probability is the same for each selection, but if balls aren't replaced back in the bag, the probability for each ball is affected by having fewer balls left in the bag. Notes: Initially, there are 8 balls that aren't green out of 12 balls. With each selection, there will be fewer balls. The probability that no ball is green is

$$\left(\frac{8}{12}\right)\left(\frac{7}{11}\right)\left(\frac{6}{10}\right)\left(\frac{5}{9}\right)\left(\frac{4}{8}\right)\left(\frac{3}{7}\right) = \frac{20{,}160}{665{,}280} = \frac{1}{33}.$$

Alternate solution: Using combinations, there are $\binom{12}{6} = \frac{12!}{6!6!} = 924$ ways to choose 6 balls out of 12 and $\binom{8}{6} = \frac{8!}{6!2!} = 28$ ways to choose 6 out of 8 balls that aren't green. The probability is $\frac{28}{924} = \frac{1}{33}$.

(19) P(exactly 3 heads, but not all next to each other) $= 5/32 = 0.15625 = 15.625\%$. Notes: As discussed in Example 8, the **equally likely outcomes** may not be the same as the total number of unique outcomes. Since each coin has 2 outcomes, there are $2^5 = 32$ equally likely outcomes. These are shown below.

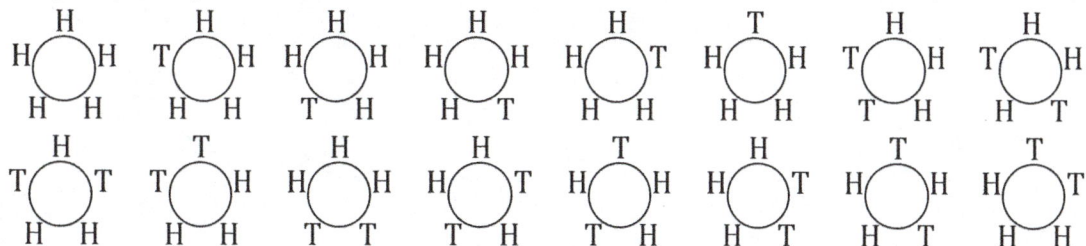

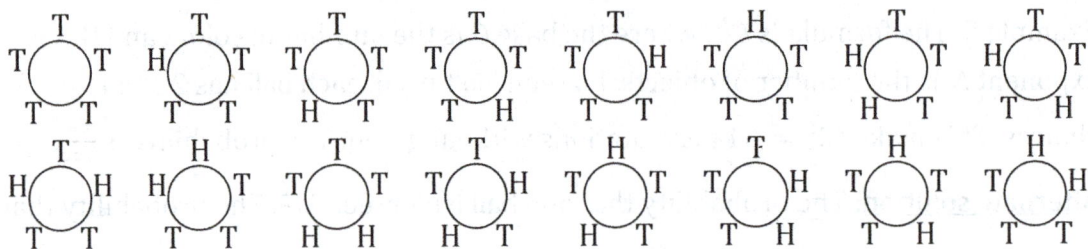

Of the outcomes shown above, those that have exactly 3 heads, but where all 3 heads aren't together, are shown below. There are 5 such outcomes.

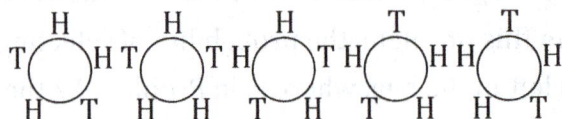

The probability is $\frac{5}{32}$. There are 8 unique outcomes shown below. These are not equally likely outcomes, as discussed in Example 8. It would be **incorrect** to conclude that the answer is $\frac{1}{8}$. If you're not convinced, read the alternate solution. **It may also help to review the solution to Problem 14 in Chapter 4.**

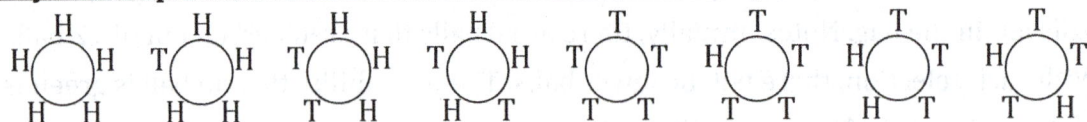

Alternate solution: There are $2^5 = 32$ total outcomes for flipping 5 coins. There are $\binom{5}{3} = \frac{5!}{3!2!} = 10$ ways to choose 3 heads out of 5 coins: HHHTT, HHTHT, HHTTH, HTHHT, HTHTH, HTTHH, THHHT, THHTH, THTHH, TTHHH. Of these, there are 5 ways for 3 heads not to be next to each other: HHTHT, HTHHT, HTHTH, THHTH, and THTHH. (Since it's a circle, 3 heads are actually next to each other in HHTTH and HTTHH. Why? Because the first H is next to the last H in a circle.) This probability is $\frac{5}{32}$.

Chapter 11

(1) P(the diagonal is horizontal) $= 1/10 = 0.1 = 10\%$. Notes: Following Example 1, there are $\binom{8}{2} - 8 = \frac{8!}{2!6!} - 8 = \frac{(8)(7)}{2} - 8 = 28 - 8 = 20$ diagonals. The diagram below shows a regular octagon with horizontal top and bottom edges. 2 diagonals are horizontal: BG and CF. The probability that a diagonal will be horizontal is $\frac{2}{20} = \frac{1}{10}$.

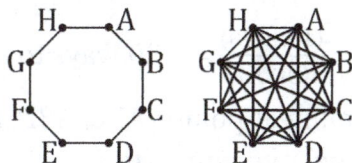

(2) P(the diagonals are parallel) $= 8/95 \approx 0.0842 \approx 8.42\%$. Notes: Following Example 1, there are $\binom{8}{2} - 8 = \frac{8!}{2!6!} - 8 = \frac{(8)(7)}{2} - 8 = 28 - 8 = 20$ diagonals. There are $\binom{20}{2} = \frac{20!}{2!18!} = \frac{(20)(19)}{2} = 190$ ways to choose 2 out of 20 diagonals. Out of these 190 pairs, the following pairs are parallel. Refer to the right diagram above.

- There are 2 horizontal or vertical pairs: AD&EH, BG&CF.
- There are 3 pairs like BH: BH&CG, BH&DF, CG&DF.
- There are 3 pairs like AC: AC&DH, AC&EG, DH&EG.
- There are 3 pairs like BD: AE&BD, AE&FH, BD&FH.
- There are 3 pairs like CE: AG&BF, AG&CE, BF&CE.
- 2 more pairs include: AF&BE, CH&DG.

This makes $2 + 3 + 3 + 3 + 3 + 2 = 16$ pairs of intersecting edges. The probability that 2 diagonals will be parallel is $\frac{16}{190} = \frac{8}{95}$.

(3) P(all 3 belong to one of those triangles) $= 13/120 \approx 0.108 \approx 10.8\%$. Notes:

- 3 triangles involve A: ABI, ACH, ADG.
- 3 triangles involve B but not A: BCP, BDF, BIP.
- 2 triangles involve C but not A-B: CDE, CEP.
- (All triangles involving D have already been counted.)
- 2 triangles involve E but not A-D: EFP, EGI.
- 2 triangles involve F but not A-E: FGH, FHP.

- (All triangles involving G have already been counted.)
- 1 triangle involves H but not A-G: HIP.
- (All triangles involving I and P have already been counted.)

There are $3 + 3 + 2 + 2 + 2 + 1 = 13$ triangles. There are 10 vertices: A, B, C, D, E, F, G, H, I, P. There are $\binom{10}{3} = \frac{10!}{3!7!} = \frac{(10)(9)(8)}{(3)(2)(1)} = 120$ ways to choose 3 out of 10 points.

The probability that 3 random vertices make one of the 13 triangles is $\frac{13}{120}$. Check:

- There are $\binom{10}{3} = \frac{10!}{3!7!} = \frac{(10)(9)(8)}{(3)(2)(1)} = 120$ ways to choose 3 out of 10 points.
- Subtract 15 sets of 3 collinear points: ABC, ABD, ACD, AGH, AGI, AHI, BCD, BFP, CHP, DEF, DEG, DFG, EFG, EIP, GHI.
- Subtract 8 sets that involve AE: ABE, ACE, ADE, AEF, AEG, AEH, AEI, AEP.
- Subtract 7 sets that involve AF: ABF, ACF, ADF, AFG, AFH, AFI, AFP. (Don't count AEF again. We counted it in the previous step.)
- Subtract 6 sets that involve AP: ABP, ACP, ADP, AGP, AHP, AIP. (Don't count AEP or AFP again. We counted those earlier.)
- Subtract 7 sets that involve BE: BCE, BDE, BEF, BEG, BEH, BEI, BEP. (Don't count ABE again. We counted it earlier.)
- Subtract 7 sets that involve BG: ABG, BCG, BDG, BFG, BGH, BGI, BGP. (Don't count BEG again. We counted it in the previous step.)
- Subtract 6 sets that involve BH: ABH, BCH, BDH, BFH, BHI, BHP. (Don't count BEH or BGH again. We counted those earlier.)
- Subtract 7 sets that involve CF: BCF, CDF, CEF, CFG, CFH, CFI, CFP. (Don't count ACF again. We counted it earlier.)
- Subtract 6 sets that involve CG: ACG, CDG, CEG, CGH, CGI, CGP. (Don't count BCG or CFG again. We counted those earlier.)
- Subtract 6 sets that involve CI: ACI, BCI, CDI, CEI, CHI, CIP. (Don't count CFI or CGI again. We counted those earlier.)
- Subtract 7 sets that involve DH: ADH, CDH, DEH, DFH, DGH, DHI, DHP. (Don't count BDH again. We counted it earlier.)
- Subtract 6 sets that involve DI: ADI, BDI, DEI, DFI, DGI, DIP. (Don't count CDI

or DHI again. We counted those earlier.)

- Subtract 5 sets that involve DP: BDP, CDP, DEP, DFP, DGP. (Don't count ADP, DHP, or DIP again. We counted those earlier.)

- Subtract 5 sets that involve EH: CEH, EFH, EGH, EHI, EHP. (Don't count AEH, BEH, or DEH again. We counted those earlier.)

- Subtract 5 sets that involve FI: BFI, EFI, FGI, FHI, FIP. (Don't count AFI, CFI, or DFI again. We counted those earlier.)

- Subtract 4 sets that involve GP: EGP, FGP, GHP, GIP. (Don't count AGP, BGP, CGP, or DGP again. We counted those earlier.)

Subtract: $120 - 15 - 8 - 7(5) - 6(5) - 5(3) - 4 = 120 - 23 - 35 - 30 - 15 - 4 = 120 - 58 - 49 = 120 - 107 = 13$.

(4) P(all 3 belong to one of those triangles) $= 9/28 \approx 0.321 \approx 32.1\%$. Notes:

- 6 triangles involve A: ABC, ABE, ABP, ACE, AEP, AFP.

- 2 triangles involve B but not A: BCE, BCP.

- 2 triangles involve C but not A-B: CDP, CEP.

- 5 triangles involve D but not A-C: DEF, DEI, DEP, DFP, DIP.

- 2 triangles involve E but not A-D: EFI, EFP.

- 1 triangle involves F but not A-E: FIP.

- (All triangles involving I and P have already been counted.)

There are $6 + 2 + 2 + 5 + 2 + 1 = 18$ triangles. There are 8 vertices: A, B, C, D, E, F, I, P. There are $\binom{8}{3} = \frac{8!}{3!5!} = \frac{(8)(7)(6)}{(3)(2)(1)} = 56$ ways to choose 3 out of 8 points. The

probability that 3 random vertices make one of the 18 triangles is $\frac{18}{56} = \frac{9}{28}$. Check:

- There are $\binom{8}{3} = \frac{8!}{3!5!} = \frac{(8)(7)(6)}{(3)(2)(1)} = 56$ ways to choose 3 out of 10 points.

- Subtract 8 sets of 3 collinear points: ACP, AEF, BEI, BEP, BIP, CDE, DFI, EIP.

- Subtract 6 sets that involve AD: ABD, ACD, ADE, ADF, ADI, ADP.

- Subtract 5 sets that involve AI: ABI, ACI, AEI, AFI, AIP. (Don't count ADI again. We counted it in the previous step.)

- Subtract 5 sets that involve BD: BCD, BDE, BDF, BDI, BDP. (Don't count ABD again. We counted it earlier.)

- Subtract 5 sets that involve BF: ABF, BCF, BEF, BFI, BFP. (Don't count BDF again. We counted it in the previous step.)
- Subtract 5 sets that involve CF: ACF, CDF, CEF, CFI, CFP. (Don't count BCF again. We counted it in the previous step.)
- Subtract 4 sets that involve CI: BCI, CDI, CEI, CIP. (Don't count ACI or CFI again. We counted those earlier.)

Subtract: $56 - 8 - 6 - 5(4) - 4 = 56 - 14 - 20 - 4 = 56 - 38 = 18$.

(5) P(form a square or rectangle with horizontal and vertical sides) $= 4/323 \approx$ $0.0124 \approx 1.24\%$. Notes: There are $(4)(5) = 20$ points in the grid. There are $\binom{20}{4} =$ $\frac{20!}{4!16!} = 4845$ ways to choose 4 of the 20 points. Four points can form a square or rectangle with horizontal and vertical sides in the following ways:

- There is 1 rectangle that is 4 units wide and 3 units tall (A1A5D5D1).
- There are 2 squares that are 3 units wide (like A1A4D4D1).
- There are 3 rectangles that are 2 units wide and 3 units tall (like A2A4D4D2).
- There are 4 rectangles that are 1 unit wide and 3 units tall (like A2A3D3D2).
- There are 2 rectangles that are 4 units wide and 2 units tall (like A1A5C5C1).
- There are 4 rectangles that are 3 units wide and 2 units tall (like A1A4C4C1).
- There are 6 squares that are 2 units wide (like B2B4D4D2).
- There are 8 rectangles that are 1 unit wide and 2 units tall (like A2A3C3C2).
- There are 3 rectangles that are 4 units wide and 1 unit tall (like B1B5C5C1).
- There are 6 rectangles that are 3 units wide and 1 unit tall (like C2C5D5D2).
- There are 9 rectangles that are 2 units wide and 1 unit tall (like A2A4B4B2).
- There are 12 squares that are 1 unit wide (like B3B4C4C3).
- (Although it would be geometrically possible to make a square with diagonal edges, the problem specifically asked us to use horizontal and vertical edges.)

There are a total of $1 + 2 + 3 + 4 + 2 + 4 + 6 + 8 + 3 + 6 + 9 + 12 = 60$ squares or rectangles with horizontal and vertical edges. The probability that all 4 randomly selected points will be the vertices of one of these squares or rectangles is $\frac{60}{4845} = \frac{4}{323}$.

(6) P(path passes through C3) = 18/35 ≈ 0.514 ≈ 51.4%. Notes: Each path involves 4 steps to the right and 3 steps down for a total of $4 + 3 = 7$ steps. Following Example 4, there are $\binom{7}{3} = \frac{7!}{3!4!} = \frac{(7)(6)(5)}{(3)(2)(1)} = 35$ such paths. There are $\binom{4}{2} = \frac{4!}{2!2!} = 6$ paths from A1 to C3 (since C3 is 2 units right + 2 units down from A1) and $\binom{3}{1} = 3$ paths from C3 to D5 (since D5 is 2 units right + 1 unit down from C3). These combine to make $(6)(3) = 18$ paths from A1 to D5 that pass through C3. (The 18 paths are: A1A3C3C5D5, A1A3C3C4D4D5, A1A3D3D5, A1A2B2B3C3C5D5, A1A2B2B3C3C4D4D5, A1A2B2B3D3D5, A1A2C2C5D5, A1A2C2C4D4D5, A1A2C2C3D3D5, A1B1B3C3C5D5, A1B1B3C3C4D4D5, A1B1B3D3D5, A1B1B2C2C5D5, A1B1B2C2C4D4D5, A1B1B2C2C3D3D5, A1C1C5D5, A1C1C4D4D5, A1C1C3D3D5.) If one of the 35 paths is randomly selected, the probability that it will pass through C3 is $\frac{18}{35}$.

(7) P(one edge of the triangle is AD) = 3/28 ≈ 0.107 ≈ 10.7%. Notes: There are 8 vertices (A-H). Since every vertex connects to every other vertex, this is the complete graph K_8. There are $\binom{8}{3} = \frac{8!}{3!5!} = \frac{(8)(7)(6)}{(3)(2)(1)} = 56$ ways to choose 3 out of 8 vertices (to form a triangle). 6 of those 56 triangles involve edge AD: ABD, ACD, ADE, ADF, ADG, ADH. The probability that one edge is AD is $\frac{6}{56} = \frac{3}{28}$.

(8) P(edges are parallel) = 11/105 ≈ 0.105 ≈ 10.5%. Notes: This is the complete bipartite graph (or bigraph) $K_{5,3}$. It has one set of 5 vertices (A, B, C, D, E) and one set of 3 vertices (F, G, H). Every vertex from one set is connected to every vertex of the other set (but no vertices within a set are connected). There are $(5)(3) = 15$ edges: AF, AG, AH, BF, BG, BH, CF, CG, CH, DF, DG, DH, EF, EG, EH). There are $\binom{15}{2} = \frac{15!}{2!13!} = \frac{(15)(14)}{2} = 105$ ways to choose 2 out of 15 edges. There are 11 pairs of parallel edges: AF&BG, AF&CH, AG&BH, BG&CH, BF&CG, BF&DH, CF&DG, CF&EH, CG&DH, DF&EG, DG&EH. The probability that 2 edges will be parallel is $\frac{11}{105}$.

Chapter 12

(1) P(point lies inside of the square) $= 2/\pi \approx 0.637 \approx 63.7\%$. Notes: (An alternative to saying that the square is inscribed in a circle is to say that the circle is circumscribed about the square.) As shown below, the diagonal of the square equals the diameter of the circle. Use the Pythagorean theorem to find the diagonal of the square: $L^2 + L^2 = D^2$ simplifies to $2L^2 = D^2$. Square root both sides: $L\sqrt{2} = D$. Since the diagonal of the square is the diameter of the circle and since the diameter is twice the radius, $L\sqrt{2} = 2R$. Divide by 2 on both sides: $\frac{L\sqrt{2}}{2} = R$.

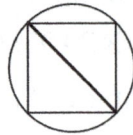

Divide the area of the square by the area of the circle. Plug in $R = \frac{L\sqrt{2}}{2}$. Note that

$$\left(\frac{L\sqrt{2}}{2}\right)^2 = \frac{L^2(\sqrt{2})^2}{2^2} = \frac{L^2(2)}{4} = \frac{L^2}{2} \text{ according to the rules } \left(\frac{ab}{c}\right)^d = \frac{a^d b^d}{c^d} \text{ and } \left(\sqrt{2}\right)^2 = 2.$$

$$\frac{\text{area of square}}{\text{area of circle}} = \frac{L^2}{\pi R^2} = \frac{L^2}{\pi\left(\frac{L\sqrt{2}}{2}\right)^2} = \frac{L^2}{\pi L^2/2} = \frac{1}{\pi/2} = 1 \div \frac{\pi}{2} = 1 \times \frac{2}{\pi} = \frac{2}{\pi}$$

(2) P(mark lies on the shortest piece) $= 1/6 \approx 0.167 \approx 16.7\%$. Notes: Let L be the length of the rod. The lengths of the pieces are $\frac{L}{6}, \frac{L}{3}$, and $\frac{L}{2}$. Observe that the ratio of the fractions $\frac{1}{6}:\frac{1}{3}:\frac{1}{2}$ is the same as the ratio 1:2:3. For example, $\left(\frac{1}{6}\right)(2) = \frac{2}{6} = \frac{1}{3}$ shows that 1/3 is double 1/6. Similarly, $\left(\frac{1}{6}\right)(3) = \frac{3}{6} = \frac{1}{2}$ shows that 1/2 is triple 1/6. (Alternatively, multiply 1/6, 1/3, and 1/2 each by 6 to make 1, 2, and 3, respectively.) The length of the shortest piece is $\frac{L}{6}$. Since this piece has one-sixth the length of the rod, the probability that the mark lies on the shortest piece is $\frac{1}{6}$.

(3) P(point lies inside of the triangle) $= \frac{48}{25\pi} \approx 0.611 \approx 61.1\%$. Notes: Since one side of the triangle is the diameter of the semicircle, Thales's theorem tells us that the triangle is a right triangle. The hypotenuse is the longest side; this side is the diameter. Since it is a right triangle, use the Pythagorean theorem. The square of the hypotenuse is $D^2 = 6^2 + 8^2 = 36 + 64 = 100$. Square root both sides to find that the diameter is $D = 10$. The radius of the circle is $R = \frac{D}{2} = \frac{10}{2} = 5$. The hard way to find the area of the triangle is to treat the base as 10 and try to figure out the height. The easy way is to turn the triangle around so that the base is 8. Since it is a right triangle, the height is 6. (The base and height are perpendicular.)

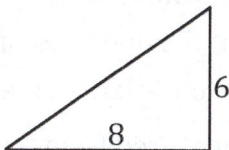

Divide the area of the triangle by the area of the semicircle. A semicircle has one-half the area of a circle. Note that the one-halves cancel. Since $25\pi \approx 78.5$, the answer works out to about 0.611. (Since probability can't be greater than 1, if a student gets an answer bigger than 1, it's a clear indication that a mistake was made.)

$$\frac{\text{area of triangle}}{\text{area of semicircle}} = \frac{bh/2}{\pi R^2/2} = \frac{bh}{\pi R^2} = \frac{(8)(6)}{\pi(5)^2} = \frac{48}{25\pi}$$

(4) P(point doesn't lie inside of the sphere) $= 1 - \frac{\pi}{6} = \frac{6-\pi}{6} \approx 0.476 \approx 47.6\%$. Notes: If a sphere is inscribed in a cube, the diameter of the sphere equals the length of the cube. This means that $L = 2R$ (like Example 1). Use the complement rule; first find the probability that the point lies inside of the sphere. Divide the volume of the sphere by the volume of the cube. The volume of the sphere is $\frac{4\pi R^3}{3}$.

$$P(\text{point lies in sphere}) = \frac{\text{volume of sphere}}{\text{volume of cube}} = \frac{4\pi R^3/3}{L^3} = \frac{4\pi R^3/3}{(2R)^3}$$

Note that $(2R)^3 = 2^3 R^3 = 8R^3$ according to the rule $(ab)^c = a^c b^c$.

$$P(\text{point lies in sphere}) = \frac{4\pi R^3/3}{8R^3} = \frac{4\pi}{3} \div 8 = \frac{4\pi}{3} \times \frac{1}{8} = \frac{4\pi}{(3)(8)} = \frac{\pi}{(3)(2)} = \frac{\pi}{6}$$

Since $\pi \approx 3.14$, $\frac{\pi}{6}$ represents about a 52.3% chance that the point lies inside of the sphere. But the question asked for the probability that the point **doesn't** lie inside of the sphere. Use the **complement rule** (Chapter 5). The probability that the point doesn't lie inside of the sphere is $1 - \frac{\pi}{6} = \frac{6}{6} - \frac{\pi}{6} = \frac{6-\pi}{6}$.

(5) P(point lies inside of the ¼-circle) $= \pi/4 \approx 0.785 \approx 78.5\%$. Notes: The radius of the quarter circle equals the length of the square: $L = R$. The area of a quarter circle is one-fourth of the area of a full circle. Divide the area of the quarter circle by the area of the square.

$$\frac{\text{area of ¼-circle}}{\text{area of square}} = \frac{\pi R^2/4}{L^2} = \frac{\pi R^2/4}{R^2} = \frac{\pi/4}{1} = \frac{\pi}{4}$$

(6) P(point lies on the shortest arc from A to B) $= 1/6 \approx 0.167 \approx 16.7\%$. Notes: The problem wants the probability that the point lies on the shorter of the two arcs between points A and B. This arc is one-sixth of the arc of the full circle (since a full circle makes an angle of 360° as measured from the center). The probability is $\frac{1}{6}$.

(7) P(point is closer to A than any of B-H) $= 1/8 = 0.125 = 12.5\%$. Notes: This is like Example 4, but for a cube. There are 8 corners. The cube can be divided into 8 octants. Any point in the octant that includes point A will be closer to A than any of the other points. Since an octant is one-eighth of a cube, the octant has one-eighth the volume of the cube. The probability is $\frac{1}{8}$.

(8) P(point lies inside of the sphere) $= 2/3 \approx 0.667 \approx 66.7\%$. Notes: Divide the volume of the sphere by the volume of the cylinder. The problem states that R is the same for the sphere (if they have the same diameter, they also have the same radius) and cylinder and that the height of the cylinder is $H = D = 2R$. (It should make sense that this answer is larger than the answer for Problem 4.)

$$\frac{\text{volume of sphere}}{\text{volume of cylinder}} = \frac{4\pi R^3/3}{\pi R^2 H} = \frac{4\pi R^3/3}{\pi R^2(2R)} = \frac{4\pi R^3/3}{2\pi R^3} = \frac{4\pi/3}{2\pi} = \frac{4\pi}{3} \div 2\pi = \frac{4\pi}{3} \times \frac{1}{2\pi} = \frac{2}{3}$$

(9) P(mark doesn't get cut out) $= 3/4 = 0.75 = 75\%$. Notes: If you divide the area of the hole by the area of the (original) disc, this will give the probability that the mark gets cut out. You will then need to use the complement rule. The disc is twice as wide as the hole: $R_d = 2R_h$. (This is equivalent to saying that the hole is half as wide as the disc.) Note that $(2R_h)^2 = 2^2 R_h^2 = 4R_h^2$ according to the rule $(ab)^2 = a^2 b^2$.

$$\frac{\text{area of hole}}{\text{area of disc}} = \frac{\pi R_h^2}{\pi R_d^2} = \frac{\pi R_h^2}{\pi(2R_h)^2} = \frac{\pi R_h^2}{4\pi R_h^2} = \frac{1}{4}$$

To find the probability that the mark doesn't get cut out, use the **complement rule** (Chapter 5): $1 - \frac{1}{4} = \frac{3}{4}$.

(10) P(point lies on either face that is 3 by 4) = 6/13 ≈ 0.462 ≈ 46.2%. Notes: The rectangular prism has 6 faces: two faces are 2 by 3, two faces are 2 by 4, and two faces are 3 by 4. Each face has the shape of a rectangle. The total surface area of the prism equals the sum of the areas of the six sides: A = (2)(3) + (2)(3) + (2)(4) + (2)(4) + (3)(4) + (3)(4) = 6 + 6 + 8 + 8 + 12 + 12 = 12 + 16 + 24 = 52. The area of one 3 by 4 face is (3)(4) = 12. The probability that the mark is on a particular 3 by 4 face is $\frac{12}{52} = \frac{3}{13}$. The probability that the mark is one 3 by 4 face or the other 3 by 4 face is (recall Chapter 5) $\frac{3}{13} + \frac{3}{13} = \frac{6}{13}$. Since the 3 by 4 faces have more surface area than the other faces, the probability is significantly higher for them.

(11) P(point lies inside of the triangle) = 2/π ≈ 0.637 ≈ 63.7%. Notes: Divide the area of the triangle by the area of the quarter circle. Note that $b = h = R$. That is, the base and height of the triangle are each the same as the radius of the quarter circle. The area of a quarter circle is one-fourth the area of a full circle.

$$\frac{\text{area of triangle}}{\text{area of ¼-circle}} = \frac{bh/2}{\pi R^2/4} = \frac{(R)(R)/2}{\pi R^2/4} = \frac{R^2/2}{\pi R^2/4} = \frac{1/2}{\pi/4} = \frac{1}{2} \div \frac{\pi}{4} = \frac{1}{2} \times \frac{4}{\pi} = \frac{2}{\pi}$$

(12) P(point lies inside of triangle DEF) = 1/4 = 0.25 = 25%. Notes: There are two ways to solve this problem. One way is to use the Pythagorean to find the missing side. BC = 12 + 12 = 24. The hypotenuse is AB = 13 + 13 = 26. The Pythagorean theorem is $AC^2 + BC^2 = AB^2$, which becomes $AC^2 + 24^2 = 26^2$. Simplify: $AC^2 = 676 - 576 = 100$. Square root both sides: AC = 10. Triangle ABC has a base of BC = 24 and a height of AC = 10. Similarly, triangle DEF has a base of DF = 12 and a height of DE = 5. An alternative way is to follow Example 3. First show that DEF and ABC are similar (all 4 of the small triangles are congruent), such that DE is one-half of AC and DF is one-half of BC. It follows that the area of DEF is one-fourth the area of ABC.

Chapter 13

(1) There are 11 values. The middle value is the 6th value when the data points are put in order. The median is the 6th value, which is 33.

Data Value	21	27	33	39	45
Frequency	1	4	3	2	1

$$\text{mean} = \frac{1(21) + 4(27) + 3(33) + 2(39) + 1(45)}{11} = \frac{21 + 108 + 99 + 78 + 45}{11}$$

$$\text{mean} = \frac{351}{11} \approx 31.909 \approx 31.9$$

To find the standard deviation, we will first put the 11 values in order.

21	27	27	27	27	33
33	33	39	39	45	

Subtract the mean (31.909) from each value.

-10.909	-4.909	-4.909	-4.909	-4.909	1.091
1.091	1.091	7.091	7.091	13.091	

Square each value.

119	24.1	24.1	24.1	24.1	1.2
1.2	1.2	50.3	50.3	171.4	

Add these values together.

$$119 + 4(24.1) + 3(1.2) + 2(50.3) + 171.4 = 491$$

Finally, divide by $N - 1$ and then take the square root.

$$\text{std. dev.} = \sqrt{\frac{491}{11 - 1}} = \sqrt{\frac{491}{10}} = \sqrt{49.1} \approx 7$$

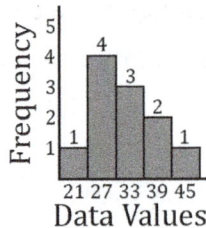

(2) There are 20 values. The two middle values are the 10th value (which is 80) and the 11th value (which is 85) when the data points are put in order. Therefore, the median is $\frac{80+85}{2} = \frac{165}{2} = 82.5$.

Data Value	70	75	80	85	90	95	100
Frequency	3	3	4	4	3	2	1

$$\text{mean} = \frac{3(70) + 3(75) + 4(80) + 4(85) + 3(90) + 2(95) + 1(100)}{20}$$

$$\text{mean} = \frac{210 + 225 + 320 + 340 + 270 + 190 + 100}{20} = \frac{1655}{20} = 82.75 \approx 82.8$$

To find the standard deviation, we will first put the 20 values in order.

70	70	70	75	75	75	80	80	80	80
85	85	85	85	90	90	90	95	95	100

Subtract the mean (82.75) from each value.

−12.75	−12.75	−12.75	−7.75	−7.75	−7.75	−2.75	−2.75	−2.75	−2.75
2.25	2.25	2.25	2.25	7.25	7.25	7.25	12.25	12.25	17.25

Square each value.

162.56	162.56	162.56	60.06	60.06	60.06	7.56	7.56	7.56	7.56
5.06	5.06	5.06	5.06	52.56	52.56	52.56	150.06	150.06	297.56

Add these values together: $3(162.56) + 3(60.06) + 4(7.56) + 4(5.06) + 3(52.56) + 2(150.06) + 1(297.56) = 1473.7$. Finally, divide by $N - 1$ and then take the square root.

$$\text{std. dev.} \approx \sqrt{\frac{1473.7}{20 - 1}} = \sqrt{\frac{1473.7}{19}} = \sqrt{77.6} \approx 8.8 \approx 9$$

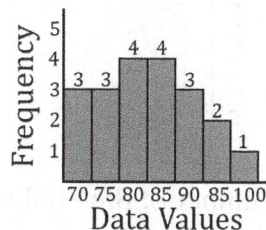

(3) First find the number of ways to select 2, 3, 4, 5, or 6 blue balls. Note that you can't choose 0 or 1 balls to be blue. Since only 4 balls are red, if you select 6 balls, you will get a minimum of 2 blue balls in the worst-case scenario. (It may help to review Chapter 4, especially the solution to Exercise 9.)

- There are $\binom{6}{2}\binom{4}{4} = \frac{6!}{2!4!}\frac{4!}{4!0!} = (15)(1) = 15$ ways to choose 2 blue balls (and 4 red balls).

- There are $\binom{6}{3}\binom{4}{3} = \frac{6!}{3!3!}\frac{4!}{3!1!} = (20)(4) = 80$ ways to choose 3 blue balls (and 3 red balls).

- There are $\binom{6}{4}\binom{4}{2} = \frac{6!}{4!2!}\frac{4!}{2!2!} = (15)(6) = 90$ ways to choose 4 blue balls (and 2 red balls).

- There are $\binom{6}{5}\binom{4}{1} = \frac{6!}{5!1!}\frac{4!}{1!3!} = (6)(4) = 24$ ways to choose 5 blue balls (and 1 red ball).

- There is $\binom{6}{6}\binom{4}{0} = \frac{6!}{6!0!}\frac{4!}{0!4!} = 1$ way to choose 6 blue balls (and zero red balls).

- Check: $15 + 80 + 90 + 24 + 1 = 210$. This agrees with $\binom{10}{6} = \frac{10!}{6!4!} = 210$ ways to choose 6 out of 10 balls.

Number of Blue Balls	2	3	4	5	6
Frequency	15	80	90	24	1

To find the corresponding probabilities, divide each frequency by $\binom{10}{6} = \frac{10!}{6!4!} = 210$:

$P(2B,4R) = \frac{15}{210} = \frac{1}{14}$, $P(3B,3R) = \frac{80}{210} = \frac{8}{21}$, $P(4B,2R) = \frac{90}{210} = \frac{3}{7}$, $P(5B,1R) = \frac{24}{210} = \frac{4}{35}$,

$P(6B,0R) = \frac{1}{210}$. Check: $\frac{1}{14} + \frac{8}{21} + \frac{3}{7} + \frac{4}{35} + \frac{1}{210} = \frac{15+80+90+24+1}{210} = \frac{210}{210} = 1$.

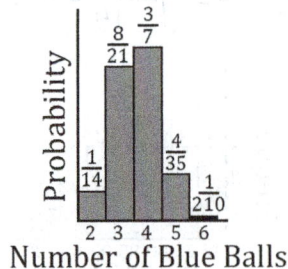

Number of Blue Balls

$$E = x_1 p_1 + x_2 p_2 + x_3 p_3 + \cdots + x_N p_N$$

$$E = 2\left(\frac{1}{14}\right) + 3\left(\frac{8}{21}\right) + 4\left(\frac{3}{7}\right) + 5\left(\frac{4}{35}\right) + 6\left(\frac{1}{210}\right)$$

$$E = \frac{1}{7} + \frac{8}{7} + \frac{12}{7} + \frac{4}{7} + \frac{1}{35} = \frac{5 + 40 + 60 + 20 + 1}{35} = \frac{126}{35} = \frac{18}{5} = 3.6$$

$$\text{Var.} = p_1(x_1 - E)^2 + p_2(x_2 - E)^2 + p_3(x_3 - E)^2 + \cdots + p_N(x_N - E)^2$$

$$\text{Var.} = \left(\frac{1}{14}\right)(2 - 3.6)^2 + \left(\frac{8}{21}\right)(3 - 3.6)^2 + \left(\frac{3}{7}\right)(4 - 3.6)^2 + \left(\frac{4}{35}\right)(5 - 3.6)^2 + \left(\frac{1}{210}\right)(6 - 3.6)^2$$

$$\text{Var.} = \left(\frac{1}{14}\right)\left(\frac{64}{25}\right) + \left(\frac{8}{21}\right)\left(\frac{9}{25}\right) + \left(\frac{3}{7}\right)\left(\frac{4}{25}\right) + \left(\frac{4}{35}\right)\left(\frac{49}{25}\right) + \left(\frac{1}{210}\right)\left(\frac{144}{25}\right)$$

$$\text{Var.} = \frac{32}{175} + \frac{24}{175} + \frac{12}{175} + \frac{28}{125} + \frac{24}{875} = \frac{160 + 120 + 60 + 196 + 24}{875} = \frac{560}{875} = \frac{16}{25} = 0.64$$

$$\text{std. dev.} = \sqrt{\text{Var.}} = \sqrt{\frac{16}{25}} = \frac{4}{5} = 0.8$$

The alternate method for the variance gives the same answer for the variance:

$$\text{Var.} = p_1 x_1^2 + p_2 x_2^2 + p_3 x_3^2 + \cdots + p_N x_N^2 - E^2$$

$$\text{Var.} = \left(\frac{1}{14}\right)2^2 + \left(\frac{8}{21}\right)3^2 + \left(\frac{3}{7}\right)4^2 + \left(\frac{4}{35}\right)5^2 + \left(\frac{1}{210}\right)6^2 - \left(\frac{18}{5}\right)^2$$

$$\text{Var.} = \frac{2}{7} + \frac{24}{7} + \frac{48}{7} + \frac{20}{7} + \frac{6}{35} - \frac{324}{25}$$

$$\text{Var.} = \frac{50 + 600 + 1200 + 500 + 30 - 2268}{175} = \frac{112}{175} = \frac{16}{25} = 0.64$$

(4) First find the number of ways to achieve each possible outcome. We will work with permutations. It may help to review Chapter 6.

- There is 1 way for the product to be 1: (1)(1).
- There are 2 ways for the product to be 2: (1)(2) and (2)(1).
- There are 2 ways for the product to be 3: (1)(3) and (3)(1).
- There are 3 ways for the product to be 4: (1)(4), (2)(2), and (4)(1).
- There are 2 ways for the product to be 6: (2)(3) and (3)(2).
- There are 2 ways for the product to be 8: (2)(4) and (4)(2).
- There is 1 way for the product to be 9: (3)(3).
- There are 2 ways for the product to be 12: (3)(4) and (4)(3).
- There is 1 way for the product to be 16: (4)(4).
- Check: These add to 16 and there are (4)(4) = 16 ways to roll two 4-sided dice.

Product	1	2	3	4	6	8	9	12	16
Frequency	1	2	2	3	2	2	1	2	1

To find the corresponding probabilities, divide each frequency by 16: $P(1) = \frac{1}{16}$,

$P(2) = \frac{2}{16} = \frac{1}{8}$, $P(3) = \frac{2}{16} = \frac{1}{8}$, $P(4) = \frac{3}{16}$, $P(6) = \frac{2}{16} = \frac{1}{8}$, $P(8) = \frac{2}{16} = \frac{1}{8}$, $P(9) = \frac{1}{16}$,

$P(12) = \frac{2}{16} = \frac{1}{8}$, $P(16) = \frac{1}{16}$. Check: $\frac{1}{16} + \frac{1}{8} + \frac{1}{8} + \frac{3}{16} + \frac{1}{8} + \frac{1}{8} + \frac{1}{16} + \frac{1}{8} + \frac{1}{16} =$

$$\frac{1+2+2+3+2+2+1+2+1}{16} = \frac{16}{16} = 1.$$

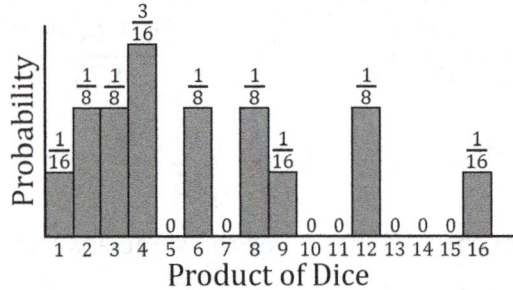

Product of Dice

$$E = x_1p_1 + x_2p_2 + x_3p_3 + \cdots + x_Np_N$$

$$E = 1\left(\frac{1}{16}\right) + 2\left(\frac{1}{8}\right) + 3\left(\frac{1}{8}\right) + 4\left(\frac{3}{16}\right) + 6\left(\frac{1}{8}\right) + 8\left(\frac{1}{8}\right) + 9\left(\frac{1}{16}\right) + 12\left(\frac{1}{8}\right) + 16\left(\frac{1}{16}\right)$$

$$E = \frac{1}{16} + \frac{1}{4} + \frac{3}{8} + \frac{3}{4} + \frac{3}{4} + 1 + \frac{9}{16} + \frac{3}{2} + 1$$

$$E = \frac{1+4+6+12+12+16+9+24+16}{16} = \frac{100}{16} = \frac{25}{4} = 6.25$$

$$\text{Var.} = p_1(x_1 - E)^2 + p_2(x_2 - E)^2 + p_3(x_3 - E)^2 + \cdots + p_N(x_N - E)^2$$

$$\text{Var.} = \left(\frac{1}{16}\right)(1 - 6.25)^2 + \left(\frac{1}{8}\right)(2 - 6.25)^2 + \left(\frac{1}{8}\right)(3 - 6.25)^2 + \left(\frac{3}{16}\right)(4 - 6.25)^2 + \left(\frac{1}{8}\right)(6 - 6.25)^2$$

$$+ \left(\frac{1}{8}\right)(8 - 6.25)^2 + \left(\frac{1}{16}\right)(9 - 6.25)^2 + \frac{1}{8}(12 - 6.25)^2 + \left(\frac{1}{16}\right)(16 - 6.25)^2$$

$$\text{Var.} = \left(\frac{1}{16}\right)\left(\frac{441}{16}\right) + \left(\frac{1}{8}\right)\left(\frac{289}{16}\right) + \left(\frac{1}{8}\right)\left(\frac{169}{16}\right) + \left(\frac{3}{16}\right)\left(\frac{81}{16}\right) + \left(\frac{1}{8}\right)\left(\frac{1}{16}\right) + \left(\frac{1}{8}\right)\left(\frac{49}{16}\right)$$

$$+ \left(\frac{1}{16}\right)\left(\frac{121}{16}\right) + \left(\frac{1}{8}\right)\left(\frac{529}{16}\right) + \left(\frac{1}{16}\right)\left(\frac{1521}{16}\right)$$

$$\text{Var.} = \frac{441 + 578 + 338 + 243 + 2 + 98 + 121 + 1058 + 1521}{256} = \frac{4400}{256} = \frac{275}{16} \approx 17.2$$

$$\text{std. dev.} = \sqrt{\text{Var.}} \approx \sqrt{15.867} \approx 4.1 \approx 4$$

The alternate method for the variance gives the same answer for the variance:

$$\text{Var.} = p_1x_1^2 + p_2x_2^2 + p_3x_3^2 + \cdots + p_Nx_N^2 - E^2$$

$$\text{Var.} = \left(\frac{1}{16}\right)1^2 + \left(\frac{1}{8}\right)2^2 + \left(\frac{1}{8}\right)3^2 + \left(\frac{3}{16}\right)4^2 + \left(\frac{1}{8}\right)6^2 + \left(\frac{1}{8}\right)8^2 + \left(\frac{1}{16}\right)9^2 + \left(\frac{1}{8}\right)12^2 + \left(\frac{1}{16}\right)16^2 - \left(\frac{25}{4}\right)^2$$

$$\text{Var.} = \frac{1}{16} + \frac{1}{2} + \frac{9}{8} + 3 + \frac{9}{2} + 8 + \frac{81}{16} + 18 + 16 - \frac{625}{16}$$

$$\text{Var.} = \frac{1 + 8 + 18 + 48 + 72 + 128 + 81 + 288 + 256 - 625}{16} = \frac{275}{16} \approx 17.2$$

Chapter 14

(1) $P(8H) = 495/4096 \approx 0.121 \approx 12.1\%$, $P(6H) = 231/1024 \approx 0.226 \approx 22.6\%$, $P(7T) = 99/512 \approx 0.193 \approx 19.3\%$. Notes: Use the binomial distribution with $n = 12$: $P(k) = \binom{n}{k} p^k q^{n-k}$. Since $p = q = \frac{1}{2}$, note that $p^k q^{n-k} = \left(\frac{1}{2}\right)^k \left(\frac{1}{2}\right)^{n-k} = \left(\frac{1}{2}\right)^{k+n-k} = \left(\frac{1}{2}\right)^n = \left(\frac{1}{2}\right)^{12} = \frac{1}{4096}$. Also, since $p = q = \frac{1}{2}$, in this problem $P(7T) = P(7H)$. That is, the probability of getting 7H and 5T is the same as the probability of getting 5H and 7T. You can see this by symmetry, or just note that swapping the roles of p and q leaves $P(k)$ unchanged in this problem. $P(8) = \binom{12}{8}\left(\frac{1}{2}\right)^{12} = \frac{495}{4096}$, $P(6) = \binom{12}{6}\left(\frac{1}{2}\right)^{12} = \frac{924}{4096} = \frac{231}{1024}$, $P(7) = \binom{12}{7}\left(\frac{1}{2}\right)^{12} = \frac{792}{4096} = \frac{99}{512}$.

(2) $P(\leq 3H) = 9/512 \approx 0.0176 \approx 1.76\%$, $P(\geq 11T) = 1941/32{,}768 \approx 0.0592 \approx 5.92\%$. Notes: Use the binomial distribution with $n = 15$: $P(k) = \binom{n}{k} p^k q^{n-k}$. Since $p = q = \frac{1}{2}$, note that $p^k q^{n-k} = \left(\frac{1}{2}\right)^k \left(\frac{1}{2}\right)^{n-k} = \left(\frac{1}{2}\right)^{k+n-k} = \left(\frac{1}{2}\right)^n = \left(\frac{1}{2}\right)^{15} = \frac{1}{32{,}768}$. $P(0) = \binom{15}{0}\left(\frac{1}{2}\right)^{15} = \frac{1}{32{,}768}$, $P(1) = \binom{15}{1}\left(\frac{1}{2}\right)^{15} = \frac{15}{32{,}768}$, $P(2) = \binom{15}{2}\left(\frac{1}{2}\right)^{15} = \frac{105}{32{,}768}$, $P(3) = \binom{15}{3}\left(\frac{1}{2}\right)^{15} = \frac{455}{32{,}768}$, $P(4) = \binom{15}{4}\left(\frac{1}{2}\right)^{15} = \frac{1365}{32{,}768}$. Use the cumulative probability distribution. $P(\leq 3H) = P(0) + P(1) + P(2) + P(3) = \frac{1+15+105+455}{32{,}768} = \frac{576}{32{,}768} = \frac{9}{512}$. If there are 11, 12, 13, 14, or 15 tails, this means that there are 4, 3, 2, 1, or 0 heads. $P(\geq 11T) = P(\leq 4H) = P(\leq 3H) + P(4) = \frac{1941}{32768} + \frac{1365}{32{,}768} = \frac{1941}{32{,}768}$.

(3) P(exactly 5 flips) $= 1/32 = 0.03125 = 3.125\%$, P($\leq$5 flips) $= 31/32 = 0.96875 = 96.875\%$. Notes: Use the geometric distribution with $k = 5$: $P(5) = pq^{5-1} = \left(\frac{1}{2}\right)\left(\frac{1}{2}\right)^{5-1} = \left(\frac{1}{2}\right)\left(\frac{1}{2}\right)^4 = \left(\frac{1}{2}\right)\left(\frac{1}{16}\right) = \frac{1}{32}$. Use the cumulative distribution: $P(\leq 5) = 1 - \left(\frac{1}{2}\right)^5 = 1 - \frac{1}{32} = \frac{31}{32}$.

(4) $P(4H) = 1120/6561 \approx 0.171 \approx 17.1\%$, $P(6H) = 1792/6561 \approx 0.273 \approx 27.3\%$. Notes: Use the binomial distribution with $n = 8$: $P(k) = \binom{n}{k} p^k q^{n-k}$. Use $p = \frac{2}{3}$,

$q = \frac{1}{3}$: $P(4) = \binom{8}{4}\left(\frac{2}{3}\right)^4\left(\frac{1}{3}\right)^{8-4} = (70)\left(\frac{2}{3}\right)^4\left(\frac{1}{3}\right)^4 = (70)\left(\frac{16}{81}\right)\left(\frac{1}{81}\right) = \frac{1120}{6561}$, $P(6) =$

$\binom{8}{6}\left(\frac{2}{3}\right)^6\left(\frac{1}{3}\right)^{8-6} = (28)\left(\frac{2}{3}\right)^6\left(\frac{1}{3}\right)^2 = (28)\left(\frac{64}{729}\right)\left(\frac{1}{9}\right) = \frac{1792}{6561}$.

(5) P(exactly 4 rolls) = 27/256 ≈ 0.105 ≈ 10.5%, P(≤4 rolls) = 175/256 ≈ 0.684 ≈ 68.4%, P(≥5 rolls) = 81/256 ≈ 0.316 ≈ 31.6%. Notes: Use the geometric distribution with $k = 4$, $p = \frac{1}{4}$ (since 1 out of 4 sides is a 3), $q = \frac{3}{4}$: $P(4) = pq^{4-1} = \left(\frac{1}{4}\right)\left(\frac{3}{4}\right)^{4-1} =$

$\left(\frac{1}{4}\right)\left(\frac{3}{4}\right)^3 = \left(\frac{1}{4}\right)\left(\frac{27}{64}\right) = \frac{27}{256}$. Use the cumulative distribution: $P(\leq 4) = 1 - q^4 =$

$1 - \left(\frac{3}{4}\right)^4 = 1 - \frac{81}{256} = \frac{175}{256}$. If a 3 doesn't occur in 4 or fewer rolls, it has to occur in 5 or

more rolls. Use the complement rule: $P(\geq 5) = 1 - P(\leq 4) = 1 - \frac{175}{256} = \frac{81}{256}$.

(6) P(6666222553, any order) = 175/839,808 ≈ 0.000208 ≈ 0.0208%, P(exactly 7 dice show less than 3) = 320/19,683 ≈ 0.0163 ≈ 1.63%. Notes: Use the multinomial distribution with $n = 10$, $k_1 = k_4 = 0$, $k_2 = 3$, $k_3 = 1$, $k_5 = 2$, $k_6 = 4$. Since the p's all equal $\frac{1}{6}$ and the k's add up to $n = 10$, note that $p_1^{k_1}p_2^{k_2}p_3^{k_3}p_4^{k_4}p_5^{k_5}p_6^{k_6}$

$= \left(\frac{1}{6}\right)^0\left(\frac{1}{6}\right)^3\left(\frac{1}{6}\right)^1\left(\frac{1}{6}\right)^0\left(\frac{1}{6}\right)^2\left(\frac{1}{6}\right)^4 = \left(\frac{1}{6}\right)^{10}$. Recall the rules $x^0 = 1$ and $x^a x^b = x^{a+b}$

from algebra. Also note that $0! = 1$ (Chapter 1).

$$\frac{n!}{k_1!\,k_2!\,k_3!\,k_4!\,k_5!\,k_6!}p_1^{k_1}p_2^{k_2}p_3^{k_3}p_4^{k_4}p_5^{k_5}p_6^{k_6} = \frac{10!}{0!\,3!\,1!\,0!\,2!\,4!}\left(\frac{1}{6}\right)^{10}$$

$$= \frac{3,628,800}{(1)(6)(1)(1)(2)(24)}\frac{1}{60,466,176} = \frac{12,600}{60,466,176} = \frac{175}{839,808}$$

Use the binomial distribution with $n = 10$: $P(k) = \binom{n}{k}p^k q^{n-k}$. Use $p = \frac{2}{6} = \frac{1}{3}$ (since

1 and 2 are 2 of the 6 possible outcomes), $q = \frac{2}{3}$: $P(7) = \binom{10}{7}\left(\frac{1}{3}\right)^7\left(\frac{2}{3}\right)^{10-7} =$

$(120)\left(\frac{1}{3}\right)^7\left(\frac{2}{3}\right)^3 = (120)\left(\frac{1}{2187}\right)\left(\frac{8}{27}\right) = \frac{960}{59,049} = \frac{320}{19,683}$.

(7) P(55522, any order) = 80/59,049 ≈ 0.00135 ≈ 0.135%, P(5 sixes) = 32/59,049 ≈ 0.000542 ≈ 0.0542%. Notes: Use the multinomial distribution with $n = 5$, $k_1 = k_3 = k_4 = k_6 = 0$, $k_2 = 2$, $k_5 = 3$, $p_1 = p_2 = p_3 = \frac{1}{9}$, $p_4 = p_5 = p_6 = \frac{2}{9}$. Recall the rules $x^0 = 1$ and $x^a x^b = x^{a+b}$ from algebra. Also note that $0! = 1$ (Chapter 1).

$$\frac{n!}{k_1!\,k_2!\,k_3!\,k_4!\,k_5!\,k_6!}p_1^{k_1}p_2^{k_2}p_3^{k_3}p_4^{k_4}p_5^{k_5}p_6^{k_6} = \frac{5!}{0!\,2!\,0!\,0!\,3!\,0!}\left(\frac{1}{9}\right)^0\left(\frac{1}{9}\right)^2\left(\frac{1}{9}\right)^0\left(\frac{2}{9}\right)^0\left(\frac{2}{9}\right)^3\left(\frac{2}{9}\right)^0$$

$$= \frac{120}{(1)(2)(1)(1)(6)(1)}(1)\left(\frac{1}{81}\right)(1)(1)\left(\frac{8}{729}\right)(1) = \frac{120}{12}\left(\frac{8}{59{,}049}\right) = \frac{80}{59{,}049}$$

Now let $k_1 = k_2 = k_3 = k_4 = k_5 = 0$, $k_6 = 5$.

$$\frac{5!}{0!\,0!\,0!\,0!\,0!\,5!}\left(\frac{1}{9}\right)^0\left(\frac{1}{9}\right)^0\left(\frac{1}{9}\right)^0\left(\frac{2}{9}\right)^0\left(\frac{2}{9}\right)^0\left(\frac{2}{9}\right)^5 = \frac{32}{59{,}049}$$

(8) P(exactly 3 rolls) $\approx 0.000129 \approx 0.0129\%$, P($\leq 1000$ rolls) $\approx 0.121 \approx 12.1\%$.

Notes: First use the multinomial distribution with $n = 5$, $k_1 = k_2 = k_3 = k_5 = k_6 = 0$, $k_4 = 5$ to find the probability that all 5 dice show 4's for a single roll. Recall the rules $x^0 = 1$ and $x^a x^b = x^{a+b}$ from algebra. Also note that $0! = 1$ (Chapter 1).

$$\frac{n!}{k_1!\,k_2!\,k_3!\,k_4!\,k_5!\,k_6!}p_1^{k_1}p_2^{k_2}p_3^{k_3}p_4^{k_4}p_5^{k_5}p_6^{k_6} = \frac{5!}{0!\,0!\,0!\,5!\,0!\,0!}\left(\frac{1}{6}\right)^5 = \frac{1}{6^5} = \frac{1}{7776}$$

Now use the geometric distribution with $k = 3$, $p = \frac{1}{7776}$, $q = \frac{7775}{7776}$: $P(3) = pq^{3-1} =$

$\left(\frac{1}{7776}\right)\left(\frac{7775}{7776}\right)^{3-1} = \left(\frac{1}{7776}\right)\left(\frac{7775}{7776}\right)^2 = \frac{7775^2}{7776^3} \approx 0.000129$. Use the cumulative

distribution: $P(\leq 1000) = 1 - q^{1000} = 1 - \left(\frac{7775}{7776}\right)^{1000} \approx 1 - 0.8793 \approx 0.121$.

This illustrates how unlikely it is to roll a Yahtzee or a Kismet in a single roll. However, if you see all 5 dice rolled 1000 different times, there is a good chance that you will see it happen at least once. (Remember, 12.1% is just for 4's. If you allow 5 of any number, you get $\frac{1}{1296}$ as the probability of rolling Yahtzee in a single roll and a $1 - \left(\frac{1295}{1296}\right)^{1000} \approx$

$1 - 0.4621 \approx 0.538 \approx 53.8\%$ chance of seeing it at least once.) But getting a Yahtzee in 3 rolls is easier than the first answer suggests; if you get 2 or more of a kind on the first roll, you would keep those dice and just roll the others (whereas in this problem, we rolled all 5 dice again no matter how many 4's or other number showed on the first roll).

(9) P(4B) $= 14/99 \approx 0.141 \approx 14.1\%$, P(2B) $= 56/165 \approx 0.339 \approx 33.9\%$, P(3R) $= 32/495 \approx 0.0646 \approx 6.46\%$. Notes: Since each selection is made **without replacement**, use the hypergeometric distribution with $n = 4$, $M = 8$, $N = 8 + 4 = 12$.

$$P(4B) = \frac{\binom{M}{k}\binom{N-M}{n-k}}{\binom{N}{n}} = \frac{\binom{8}{4}\binom{12-8}{4-4}}{\binom{12}{4}} = \frac{\binom{8}{4}\binom{4}{0}}{\binom{12}{4}} = \frac{(70)(1)}{495} = \frac{70}{495} = \frac{14}{99}$$

$$P(2B) = \frac{\binom{M}{k}\binom{N-M}{n-k}}{\binom{N}{n}} = \frac{\binom{8}{2}\binom{12-8}{4-2}}{\binom{12}{4}} = \frac{\binom{8}{2}\binom{4}{2}}{\binom{12}{4}} = \frac{(28)(6)}{495} = \frac{168}{495} = \frac{56}{165}$$

If 3 out of 4 balls are red, this means 1 out of 4 is blue. You could just find P(1B).

$$P(3R) = P(1B) = \frac{\binom{M}{k}\binom{N-M}{n-k}}{\binom{N}{n}} = \frac{\binom{8}{1}\binom{12-8}{4-1}}{\binom{12}{4}} = \frac{\binom{8}{1}\binom{4}{3}}{\binom{12}{4}} = \frac{(8)(4)}{495} = \frac{32}{495}$$

Alternatively, use $k = 3, n = 4, M = 4, N = 8 + 4 = 12$.

$$P(3R) = \frac{\binom{M}{k}\binom{N-M}{n-k}}{\binom{N}{n}} = \frac{\binom{4}{3}\binom{12-4}{4-3}}{\binom{12}{4}} = \frac{\binom{4}{3}\binom{8}{1}}{\binom{12}{4}} = \frac{(4)(8)}{495} = \frac{32}{495}$$

(10) $P(4B) = 16/81 \approx 0.198 \approx 19.8\%$, $P(2B) = 8/27 \approx 0.296 \approx 29.6\%$, $P(\leq 1B) = 1/9$ $\approx 0.111 \approx 11.1\%$. Notes: Unlike Problem 9, this time each ball is replaced before selecting a new ball. This is like Part B of Example 3. Use the binomial distribution with $n = 4$: $P(k) = \binom{n}{k}p^k q^{n-k}$. Use $p = \frac{2}{3}$ (since 8 out of 12 balls are blue), $q = \frac{1}{3}$: $P(4) =$

$\binom{4}{4}\left(\frac{2}{3}\right)^4\left(\frac{1}{3}\right)^{4-4} = (1)\left(\frac{2}{3}\right)^4\left(\frac{1}{3}\right)^0 = \left(\frac{16}{81}\right)(1) = \frac{16}{81}$, $P(2) = \binom{4}{2}\left(\frac{2}{3}\right)^2\left(\frac{1}{3}\right)^{4-2} = (6)\left(\frac{2}{3}\right)^2\left(\frac{1}{3}\right)^2$

$= (6)\left(\frac{4}{9}\right)\left(\frac{1}{9}\right) = \frac{24}{81} = \frac{8}{27}$. Use the cumulative probability distribution. $P(\leq 1) = P(0) +$

$P(1) = \binom{4}{0}\left(\frac{2}{3}\right)^0\left(\frac{1}{3}\right)^{4-0} + \binom{4}{1}\left(\frac{2}{3}\right)^1\left(\frac{1}{3}\right)^{4-1} = (1)(1)\left(\frac{1}{3}\right)^4 + (4)\left(\frac{2}{3}\right)\left(\frac{1}{3}\right)^3 = \frac{1}{81} + \frac{8}{81} = \frac{9}{81} =$

$\frac{1}{9}$. Recall from algebra that $x^0 = 1$.

Compare the answers to Problems 9-10: First look at the case of selecting 4 blue balls. Without replacement, $P(4B) \approx 14.1\%$ in Problem 9, whereas with replacement, $P(4B) \approx 19.8\%$. There is a much higher probability of selecting 4 blue balls in Problem 10 since there are always 4 blue balls in the bag with replacement. Now look at the case of selecting 2 blue balls and 2 red balls. In this case, without replacement, $P(2B) \approx$ 33.9% in Problem 9, whereas with replacement, $P(2B) \approx 29.6\%$ in Problem 10. It's backwards compared to the case of selecting 4 balls. Why? In Problem 10, with replacement, the chance of selecting a blue ball is always 2/3; since blue is much more likely, selecting the same number of balls (2B and 2R) is less likely with replacement. In contrast, in Problem 9, without replacement, once you select a ball of one color, the chance of selecting a ball of the opposite color increases compared to the previous selection. For example, the chance of the first ball being blue is 2/3, but if 2 blue balls have already been selected, the chance that the third ball will also be blue is 3/5 (that is, 60% instead of about 67%). To compare P(2B) another way, in Problem 9, without replacement, it is $\frac{8}{12}\frac{7}{11}\frac{4}{10}\frac{3}{9}(6) = \frac{56}{165} \approx 33.9\%$ (since there are 6 permutations of BBRR) where the number of balls decreases with each selection, whereas in Problem 10, with replacement, it is $\frac{8}{12}\frac{8}{12}\frac{4}{12}\frac{4}{12}(6) = \frac{8}{27} \approx 29.6\%$.

(11) P(4B) = 1/99 ≈ 0.0101 ≈ 1.01%, P(3B) = 14/99 ≈ 0.141 ≈ 14.1%, P(≤2G) = 14/15 ≈ 0.933 ≈ 93.3%. Notes: **Don't** use the multinomial distribution because the selections are made **without replacement**. Use the hypergeometric distribution with $n = 4, M = 5, N = 5 + 4 + 3 = 12$. (Note that each probability only concerns a single color. For P(3B), for example, a ball is either blue or non-blue.)

$$P(4B) = \frac{\binom{M}{k}\binom{N-M}{n-k}}{\binom{N}{n}} = \frac{\binom{5}{4}\binom{12-5}{4-4}}{\binom{12}{4}} = \frac{\binom{5}{4}\binom{7}{0}}{\binom{12}{4}} = \frac{(5)(1)}{495} = \frac{5}{495} = \frac{1}{99}$$

$$P(3B) = \frac{\binom{M}{k}\binom{N-M}{n-k}}{\binom{N}{n}} = \frac{\binom{5}{3}\binom{12-5}{4-3}}{\binom{12}{4}} = \frac{\binom{5}{3}\binom{7}{1}}{\binom{12}{4}} = \frac{(10)(7)}{495} = \frac{70}{495} = \frac{14}{99}$$

For green balls, now use $M = 4$. Use the cumulative distribution.

$$P(\leq 2G) = P(0G) + P(1G) + P(2G) = \frac{\binom{4}{0}\binom{12-4}{4-0}}{\binom{12}{4}} + \frac{\binom{4}{1}\binom{12-4}{4-1}}{\binom{12}{4}} + \frac{\binom{4}{2}\binom{12-4}{4-2}}{\binom{12}{4}}$$

$$P(\leq 2G) = \frac{\binom{4}{0}\binom{8}{4}}{\binom{12}{4}} + \frac{\binom{4}{1}\binom{8}{3}}{\binom{12}{4}} + \frac{\binom{4}{2}\binom{8}{2}}{\binom{12}{4}} = \frac{(1)(70) + (4)(56) + (6)(28)}{495}$$

$$P(\leq 2G) = \frac{70 + 224 + 168}{495} = \frac{462}{495} = \frac{14}{15}$$

(12) P(exactly 4 grabs) = 54/625 = 0.0864 = 8.64%, P($\leq$4 grabs) = 544/625 = 0.8704 = 87.04%. Notes: Since each ball is placed back in the back before the next selection, the probability for each selection is the same. This allows us to use the geometric distribution. $k = 4$, $p = \frac{4}{10} = \frac{2}{5}$ (since 4 out of 10 balls are red), $q = 1 - p = 1 - \frac{4}{10} = \frac{6}{10} = \frac{3}{5}$. $P(4) = pq^{4-1} = \left(\frac{2}{5}\right)\left(\frac{3}{5}\right)^{4-1} = \left(\frac{2}{5}\right)\left(\frac{3}{5}\right)^3 = \left(\frac{2}{5}\right)\left(\frac{27}{125}\right) = \frac{54}{625}$. Use the cumulative distribution: $P(\leq 4) = 1 - q^4 = 1 - \left(\frac{3}{5}\right)^4 = 1 - \frac{81}{625} = \frac{544}{625}$.

(13) P(all cards are clubs) = 33/66,640 $\approx$ 0.000495 $\approx$ 0.0495%. Notes: Since each card is dealt **without replacement**, use the hypergeometric distribution with $k = n = 5$, $M = 13$, $N = 52$. (Note that the question only concerns a single suit; a card is either clubs or not-clubs.)

$$P(\text{all clubs}) = \frac{\binom{M}{k}\binom{N-M}{n-k}}{\binom{N}{n}} = \frac{\binom{13}{5}\binom{52-13}{5-5}}{\binom{52}{5}} = \frac{\binom{13}{5}\binom{39}{0}}{\binom{52}{5}} = \frac{(1287)(1)}{2,598,960} = \frac{33}{66,640}$$

As we discussed in Example 2 in Chapter 8, if you want the probability of making a flush, you need to subtract out all of the flushes that are straight or royal (since the odds for a flush are figured separately from the odds of a straight or royal flush). So if you multiply the answer to this problem by 4, it **won't** be the probability of a flush.

(14) P(4 aces) = 1/54,145 $\approx$ 0.0000185 $\approx$ 0.00185%, P(4 of a kind) = 1/4165 $\approx$ 0.000240 $\approx$ 0.0240%. Notes: Since each card is dealt **without replacement**, use the hypergeometric distribution with $n = 5$, $k = M = 4$, $N = 52$. (Note that the question only concerns a single value; a card is either an ace or not-an-ace.)

$$P(\text{4 aces}) = \frac{\binom{M}{k}\binom{N-M}{n-k}}{\binom{N}{n}} = \frac{\binom{4}{4}\binom{52-4}{5-4}}{\binom{52}{5}} = \frac{\binom{4}{4}\binom{48}{1}}{\binom{52}{5}} = \frac{(1)(48)}{2,598,960} = \frac{1}{54,145}$$

For 4 of a kind, multiply by 13: $P(\text{4 of a kind}) = \frac{13}{54,145} = \frac{1}{4165}$.

(15) P(exactly 4 defects) $\approx$ 0.134 $\approx$ 13.4%, P($\geq$4 defects) $\approx$ 0.242 $\approx$ 24.2%. Notes: Use the Poisson approximation with $n = 500$, $p = \frac{0.5}{100} = 0.005$ (divide 0.5% by 100% to convert it to a decimal), $\lambda = np = (500)(0.005) = 2.5$, and $k = 4$: $P(4) \approx \frac{(np)^k e^{-np}}{k!} = $

$\frac{(2.5)^4 e^{-2.5}}{4!} \approx \frac{(39.06)(0.08208)}{24} \approx 0.134$. First use the cumulative distribution to find P(≤ 3) =

$P(0) + P(1) + P(2) + P(3) = \frac{(2.5)^0 e^{-2.5}}{0!} + \frac{(2.5)^1 e^{-2.5}}{1!} + \frac{(2.5)^2 e^{-2.5}}{2!} + \frac{(2.5)^3 e^{-2.5}}{3!} = \frac{(1)e^{-2.5}}{1} +$

$\frac{2.5e^{-2.5}}{1} + \frac{(6.25)e^{-2.5}}{2} + \frac{(15.625)e^{-2.5}}{6} \approx (1 + 2.5 + 3.125 + 2.604)e^{-2.5} \approx (9.229)(0.08208)$

≈ 0.758. Recall from Chapter 1 that $0! = 1$ and from algebra that $x^0 = 1$. If there aren't 3 or fewer defects, then there must be 4 or more defects. Use the complement rule: P(≥ 4) = $1 -$ P(≤ 3) $\approx 1 - 0.758 \approx 0.242$.

(16) P(exactly 12 won't get it) $\approx 0.0661 \approx 6.61\%$. Notes: Use the Poisson approximation with $n = 800, p = \frac{1}{50} = 0.02$ (since 1 out of 50 don't get it), $\lambda = np =$

$(800)(0.02) = 16$, and $k = 12$: $P(12) \approx \frac{(np)^k e^{-np}}{k!} = \frac{(16)^{12} e^{-16}}{12!} \approx 0.0661$.

Index

A

B

C

D

E

F

G

H

I

J

K

L

M

N

O

P

WAS THIS BOOK HELPFUL?

Much effort and thought were put into this book, such as:

- Introducing the main ideas at the beginning of each chapter. The goal was to be concise while also covering the pertinent information.
- Solving examples step by step to serve as a helpful guide.
- Including not just answers, but even the solutions to most of the problems.
- Adding alternate solutions to show that there are often multiple ways to solve a problem. (Solving a problem two different ways also helps to provide confidence in your solution.)

If you appreciate the effort that went into making this book possible, there is a simple way that you could show it:

<u>Please take a moment to post an honest review.</u>

For example, you can review this book at Amazon.com or Goodreads.com.

Even a short review can be helpful and will be much appreciated. If you are not sure what to write, following are a few ideas, though it is best to describe what is important to you.

- Was it helpful to have notes/solutions in addition to the answers at the back of the book?
- Were the examples useful?
- Were you able to understand the ideas at the beginning of the chapter?
- Did this book offer good practice for you?
- Would you recommend this book to others? If so, why?

Do you believe that you found a mistake? Please email the author, Chris McMullen, at greekphysics@yahoo.com to ask about it. One of two things will happen:

- You might discover that it wasn't a mistake after all and learn why.
- You might be right, in which case the author will be grateful and future readers will benefit from the correction. Everyone is human.

ABOUT THE AUTHOR

Dr. Chris McMullen has over 20 years of experience teaching university physics in California, Oklahoma, Pennsylvania, and Louisiana. Dr. McMullen is also an author of math and science workbooks. Whether in the classroom or as a writer, Dr. McMullen loves sharing knowledge and the art of motivating and engaging students.

The author earned his Ph.D. in phenomenological high-energy physics (particle physics) from Oklahoma State University in 2002. Originally from California, Chris McMullen earned his Master's degree from California State University, Northridge, where his thesis was in the field of electron spin resonance.

As a physics teacher, Dr. McMullen observed that many students lack fluency in essential math skills. In an effort to help students of all ages and levels become fluent in mathematics, he published a series of math workbooks on fractions, long division, word problems, algebra, geometry, trigonometry, logarithms, calculus, probability, differential equations, and more. Dr. McMullen has also published a variety of science books, including astronomy, chemistry, and physics workbooks.

Author, Chris McMullen, Ph.D.

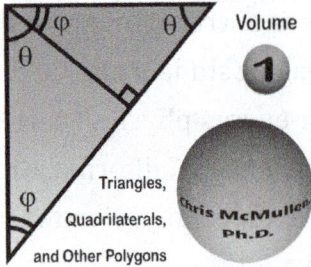

PLANE
GEOMETRY
Practice Workbook with Answers

Volume
1

Triangles,
Quadrilaterals,
and Other Polygons

Chris McMullen
Ph.D.

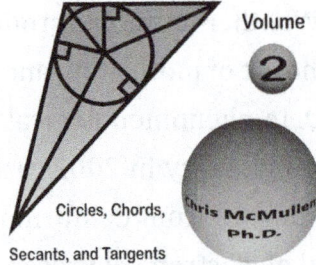

PLANE
GEOMETRY
Practice Workbook with Answers

Volume
2

Circles, Chords,
Secants, and Tangents

Chris McMullen
Ph.D.

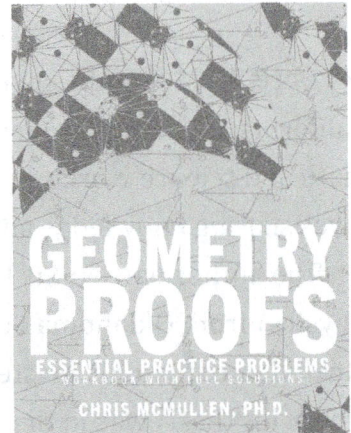

GEOMETRY
PROOFS
ESSENTIAL PRACTICE PROBLEMS
WORKBOOK WITH FULL SOLUTIONS

CHRIS MCMULLEN, PH.D.

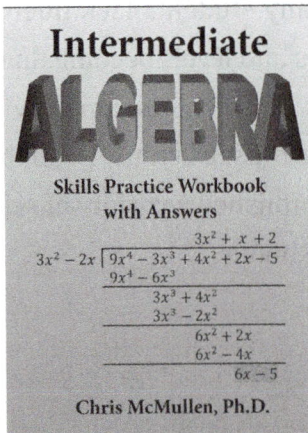

Intermediate
ALGEBRA

Skills Practice Workbook
with Answers

Chris McMullen, Ph.D.

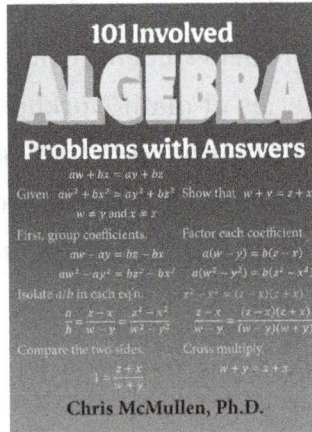

101 Involved
ALGEBRA
Problems with Answers

Chris McMullen, Ph.D.

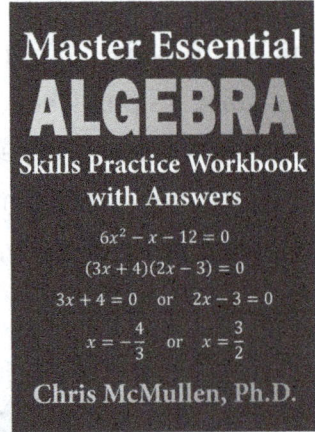

Master Essential
ALGEBRA

Skills Practice Workbook
with Answers

$$6x^2 - x - 12 = 0$$
$$(3x + 4)(2x - 3) = 0$$
$$3x + 4 = 0 \quad \text{or} \quad 2x - 3 = 0$$
$$x = -\frac{4}{3} \quad \text{or} \quad x = \frac{3}{2}$$

Chris McMullen, Ph.D.

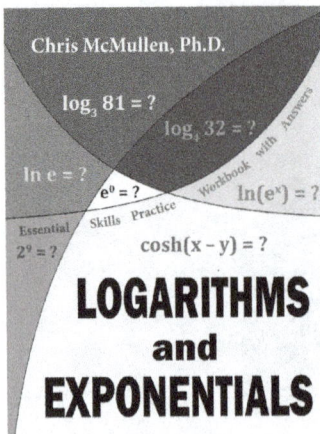

Chris McMullen, Ph.D.

$\log_3 81 = ?$

$\log_4 32 = ?$

$\ln e = ?$

$e^0 = ?$

$\ln(e^x) = ?$

Essential   Skills   Practice

$2^9 = ?$

$\cosh(x - y) = ?$

LOGARITHMS
and
EXPONENTIALS

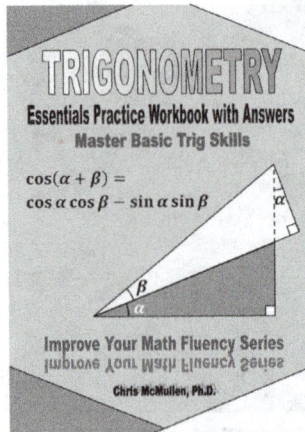

TRIGONOMETRY
Essentials Practice Workbook with Answers
Master Basic Trig Skills

$$\cos(\alpha + \beta) =$$
$$\cos \alpha \cos \beta - \sin \alpha \sin \beta$$

Improve Your Math Fluency Series

Chris McMullen, Ph.D.

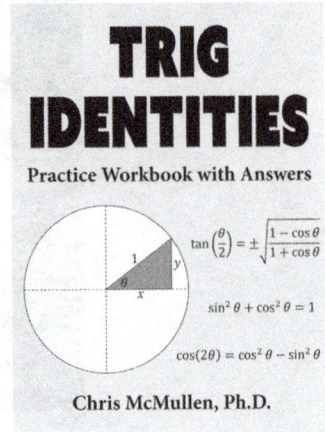

TRIG
IDENTITIES

Practice Workbook with Answers

$$\tan\left(\frac{\theta}{2}\right) = \pm\sqrt{\frac{1 - \cos\theta}{1 + \cos\theta}}$$

$$\sin^2\theta + \cos^2\theta = 1$$

$$\cos(2\theta) = \cos^2\theta - \sin^2\theta$$

Chris McMullen, Ph.D.

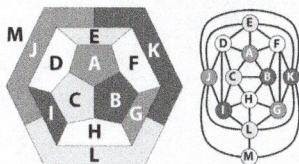

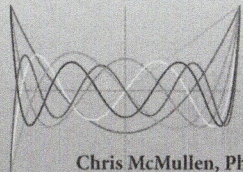

Made in the USA
Monee, IL
08 January 2025